Jon Holder

INTRODUCTION TO MECHANICS

PRENTICE-HALL INTERNATIONAL, INC., *London*
PRENTICE-HALL OF AUSTRALIA, PTY. LTD., *Sydney*
PRENTICE-HALL OF CANADA, LTD., *Toronto*
PRENTICE-HALL OF INDIA PRIVATE LTD., *New Delhi*
PRENTICE-HALL OF JAPAN, INC., *Tokyo*

2nd edition

INTRODUCTION TO MECHANICS

Irving J. Levinson

Dean of Faculty
Oakland Community College
Union Lake, Michigan

Prentice-Hall, Inc.
Englewood Cliffs, N.J.

Library of Congress Catalog Card Number: 68-20859
Printed in the United States of America

To my parents

PREFACE

Prior to the writing of the first edition of INTRODUCTION TO MECHANICS certain assumptions were listed as guidelines and boundaries to be carefully adhered to and referred to. These assumptions, based on more years of teaching experience than would want to be remembered, concerned the primary reasons for including a course in mechanics in the various technologies. It was assumed that mechanics was not taught for traditional reasons; not taught simply because it had been taught. The second assumption was that mechanics at the junior college level should not be solely an exercise in mathematics. The third assumption was that mechanics should deal with realistic and contemporary mechanical things since the technician will be a doer as well as a thinker and will be dealing with the down-to-earth hardware of his industry.

Six additional years of experience have reinforced the realism of the primary assumptions. This book is still not a mathematical treatise. It has not been made more difficult because the author thinks he is wiser. The book still offers reality rather than the abstract.

The author is indebted to Mrs. Marilyn Jantz and Mrs. Joyce Matthews for their invaluable help with this edition.

I. J. L.

CONTENTS

INTRODUCTION
TO MECHANICS

Chapter 1

INTRODUCTION

Perhaps no science is more basic to the understanding of nature than mechanics. In 350 B.C., Aristotle, an energetic Greek philosopher, attempted to explain the lever. This is when it all began.

The science of mechanics was developed by mathematicians and physicists. These men were mainly interested in a logical explanation of their observations. The lever and the pulley, free fall, and the movement of planets were studied at great length. Each investigator added to the store of knowledge, either with a new theory or with a correction in the theories of his predecessor. Isaac Newton climaxed the study in 1687 with his discovery of universal gravitation and his statement of three laws of motion. His discovery is the mechanics of today.

The importance of the science can be appraised by an accounting of its use. Today, not a building or a bridge or an automobile or an airplane is constructed without some prior analysis based on the principles of mechanics.

1-1 The Divisions of Mechanics: Statics and Dynamics

Statics is the study of bodies at rest—in a state of balance with their surroundings. A force analysis is the eventual goal in statics. Through the application of the principles of statics we answer questions such as: What load will the column have to support? What is the tension in the bridge cable? What is the mechanical advantage of the block and tackle?

Dynamics is, first, the study of the geometry of motion; and second, the study of the forces required to produce motion. The former is called *kinematics* and the latter, *kinetics*. The ultimate goal in dynamics is the determination of the forces required to produce motion and change in motion.

1-2 The Mathematics of Mechanics

Mechanics is an analytical subject; it makes extensive use of mathematics in all of its forms: algebra, geometry, and trigonometry. Although it is not the purpose of this book to dwell on mathematics for mathematics' sake, one phase, trigonometry, is used so frequently that it deserves some special attention.

Right triangles. A right triangle is a closed three-sided figure that has one right angle. The side of the triangle that is opposite the right angle is called the *hypotenuse*. The other two sides are named in relation to either of the two remaining angles. If θ (the Greek letter theta) is selected as the angle in question, then side BC in Fig. 1-1 is referred to as the *opposite side* and

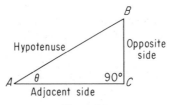

Figure 1-1

side AC, as the *adjacent side*. The six possible ratios of the sides are called the *trigonometric functions* and are given the following names:

$$\text{sine } \theta = \frac{\text{opposite side}}{\text{hypotenuse}} = \frac{O}{H}$$

$$\text{cosine } \theta = \frac{\text{adjacent side}}{\text{hypotenuse}} = \frac{A}{H}$$

$$\text{tangent } \theta = \frac{\text{opposite side}}{\text{adjacent side}} = \frac{O}{A}$$

$$\text{cotangent } \theta = \frac{\text{adjacent side}}{\text{opposite side}} = \frac{A}{O}$$

$$\text{secant } \theta = \frac{\text{hypotenuse}}{\text{adjacent side}} = \frac{H}{A}$$

$$\text{cosecant } \theta = \frac{\text{hypotenuse}}{\text{opposite side}} = \frac{H}{O}$$

These six *trigonometric functions* show that for a given angle θ, the ratios of the lengths of the sides of a right triangle are constant.

The functions, abbreviated *sin*, *cos*, and *tan*, of some of the most frequently used angles are given in Table 1-1. Table 1 of the Appendix lists the functions of all angles and their decimal parts.

Table 1-1

Angle	Sine	Cosine	Tangent
0°	0	1.000	0
30°	0.500	0.866	0.577
45°	0.707	0.707	1.000
60°	0.866	0.500	1.732
90°	1.000	0	infinity

There are five variables in a right triangle: three sides and two angles. If any two of these five quantities are known, the remaining three can easily be determined.

EXAMPLE 1: A 20-ft ladder leans against a wall, as shown in Fig. 1-2. Determine the distance d from the foot of the ladder to the wall.

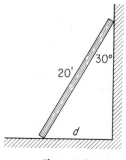

Figure 1-2

Solution: The sine of 30 deg defines the ratio of the desired length d, and the hypotenuse.

$$\sin 30° = \frac{d}{20}$$

therefore $\qquad\qquad d = 20 \sin 30° = 20(0.500) = 10 \text{ ft}$

The tangent functions are used extensively when accurate angles are to be drawn or measured. For example, to draw a line at 58.5 deg with some reference line, find the tangent of 58.5 deg in the table of trigonometric functions and construct a right triangle, Fig. 1-3, so that the ratio of the opposite side to the adjacent side is equal to this numerical value, in this case

$$\tan 58.5° = 1.632$$

The accuracy of the constructed angle depends upon the length of the sides drawn. Thus the legs of a triangle drawn in the ratio of 16.32 to 10 would give a far more precise angle than one drawn in the ratio of 1.632 to 1.

To measure rather than construct an angle, use a convenient adjacent length and measure the opposite side; then find the angle in the tables. This is one way surveyors measure angles.

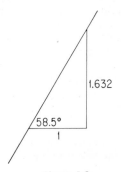

Figure 1-3

The cosine law. There are many applications in mechanics where two sides and an included angle of a triangle are known and the third side is to be computed. This calculation is carried out most conveniently by the *cosine law* which states: *the square of any side of a triangle is equal to the sum of the squares of the other two sides minus twice the product of those two sides and the cosine of the angle included by them.* For the triangle shown in Fig. 1-4, side c in terms of sides a and b, and the angle θ is

$$c^2 = a^2 + b^2 - 2ab \cos \theta$$
$$c = \sqrt{a^2 + b^2 - 2ab \cos \theta} \qquad\qquad (1\text{-}1)$$

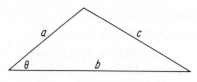

Figure 1-4

If the included angle θ is 90 deg, then the cosine law reduces to the well-known theorem of Pythagoras: *the square of the hypotenuse of a right triangle is the sum of the squares of the two remaining sides.*

$$c^2 = a^2 + b^2$$

and
$$c = \sqrt{a^2 + b^2}$$

The example that follows will demonstrate the use of the cosine law.

EXAMPLE 2: Determine the length of side c, of the triangle shown in Fig. 1-5.

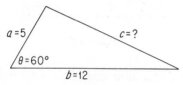

Figure 1-5

Solution: Direct substitution into the cosine law gives

$$c = \sqrt{a^2 + b^2 - 2ab \cos \theta}$$
$$= \sqrt{(5)^2 + (12)^2 - 2(5)12 \cos 60°}$$
$$= \sqrt{25 + 144 - 60} = \sqrt{109} = 10.4$$

EXAMPLE 3: Determine the length of side c of the triangle shown in Fig. 1-6.

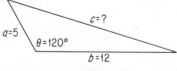

Figure 1-6

Solution: The cosine of any angle lying between 90 deg and 180 deg is negative and equal to

$$\cos \theta = - \cos (180° - \theta)$$

therefore
$$\cos 120° = - \cos 60°$$

substitution into the cosine law gives

$$c = \sqrt{a^2 + b^2 - 2ab \cos \theta}$$
$$= \sqrt{(5)^2 + (12)^2 + 2(5)12 \cos 60°}$$
$$= \sqrt{25 + 144 + 60} = \sqrt{229} = 15.1$$

The sine law. Another useful concept in trigonometry that has extensive use in mechanics states: *in any triangle the sides are proportional to the sines of the opposite angles.* For the triangle shown in Fig. 1-7 the statement of *the sine law* is

$$\frac{a}{\sin \beta} = \frac{b}{\sin \theta} = \frac{c}{\sin \alpha}$$

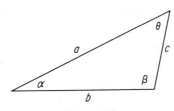

Figure 1-7

The sine law is used to find a third side of a triangle when two sides and an opposite angle are known or to find a side when one side and two angles are known.

EXAMPLE 4: Determine the lengths of sides a and c in the triangle shown in Fig. 1-8.

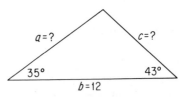

Figure 1-8

Solution: The sum of the three angles of a triangle equals 180 deg; therefore

$$\theta + 35° + 43° = 180°$$
$$\theta = 102°$$

Application of the sine law gives

$$\frac{a}{\sin 43°} = \frac{12}{\sin 102°}$$

The sine of an angle θ, lying between 90 deg and 180 deg is positive and equal to

$$\sin \theta = \sin (180° - \theta)$$

therefore

$$\sin 102° = \sin (180° - 102°) = \sin 78°$$

The sine functions are found in the tables and a is computed.

$$a = \frac{12 \sin 43°}{\sin 78°} = \frac{12(0.682)}{(0.978)} = 8.37$$

The process is repeated to find side c, thus

$$\frac{a}{\sin 43°} = \frac{c}{\sin 35°}$$

$$c = \frac{8.37 \sin 35°}{\sin 43°} = \frac{8.37(0.574)}{(0.682)} = 7.04$$

1-3 The Conversions of Units

Units are used to define the size of physical quantities. Feet, inches, and miles are units of length; seconds, minutes, and hours are units of time; ounces, pounds, and tons are units of weight, and so on. It is a familiar fact that there are 12 inches in a foot, 3 feet in a yard, 60 seconds in a minute, 2000 pounds in a ton; these and similar equalities are called *conversion factors*. These factors are used to convert from one system of measurement to another. For example, to change a measurement of 6 inches into units of feet requires that the measurement be multiplied by the ratio 1 ft/12 in. Since one foot is equal to 12 inches, the ratio changes merely the units of the given length and not the length itself.

$$6 \text{ in.} \times \frac{1 \text{ ft}}{12 \text{ in.}} = 0.5 \text{ ft}$$

The units are canceled, just as numbers would be canceled when a series of fractions is multiplied.

EXAMPLE 5: If a cubic inch of steel weighs 0.29 lb, what is the weight of a plate 3.5 ft long, 1.75 ft wide, and 1 in. thick?

Solution: The desired quantity, the weight, is the product of the volume and the weight per unit of volume. The latter is called the *density*.

$$W = 3.5 \text{ ft} \times 1.75 \text{ ft} \times 1 \text{ in.} \times \frac{12 \text{ in.}}{\text{ft}} \times \frac{12 \text{ in.}}{\text{ft}} \times \frac{0.29 \text{ lb}}{\text{in.}^3}$$

$$W = 3.5(1.75)\,12(12)(0.29) \text{ lb} = 256 \text{ lb}$$

EXAMPLE 6: Express a speed of 30 mph (miles per hour) in the units of fps (feet per second).

Solution:

$$30\frac{mi}{hr} = 30\frac{\cancel{mi}}{\cancel{hr}} \times \frac{5280\ ft}{\cancel{mi}} \times \frac{1\ \cancel{hr}}{60\ \cancel{min}} \times \frac{1\ \cancel{min}}{60\ sec}$$

$$= \frac{30(5280)}{60(60)}\frac{ft}{sec} = 44\ fps$$

PROBLEMS

1-1. The hypotenuse of a right triangle is 20 in. long, and one angle is 60 deg. Find the lengths of the sides that are opposite and adjacent to this angle.

1-2. Two sides of a right triangle are 6 in. and 4 in. Determine the angle between the hypotenuse and the shorter side.

1-3. Determine the length of the hypotenuse of a right triangle if the legs have equal lengths of 12 in.

1.4. A 30 ft ladder leans at an angle of 35 deg with the vertical against a wall. Determine the distance from the top of the ladder to the ground.

1.5. A ship sails 100 mi in a direction N20°E and then 50 mi N60°E as shown in Fig. P1-5. How far is the ship from its starting point?

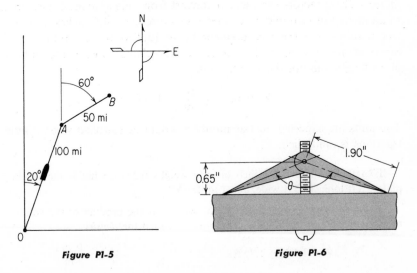

Figure P1-5   Figure P1-6

1-6. Find the angle between the wings of the toggle bolt shown in Fig. P1-6.

1-7. A roof truss has the dimensions shown in Fig. P1-7. Determine the angles *DBC* and *BCD*.

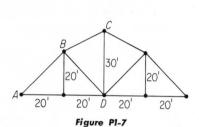

Figure P1-7

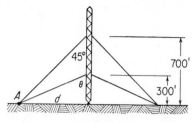

Figure P1-8

1-8. A television antenna that is 1000 ft high is secured by a double series of guy wires as shown in Fig. P1-8. Determine the distance from the anchor A to the antenna and the angle θ between the lower guy wires and the antenna.

1-9. A rectangle is 15 in. high and 35 in. long. Determine the length of the diagonal and the angle between it and the shorter side.

1-10. Find the lengths of the equal sides of an isosceles triangle and the base angles if the base is 10 in. long and the height is 20 in.

1-11. A clamping device for a jig is shown in Fig. P1-11. Find the difference in elevation between points A and B.

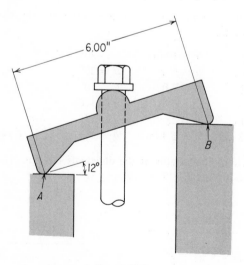

Figure P1-11

1-12. Determine the span L of the bridge shown in Fig. P1-12 if all six panels have equal widths.

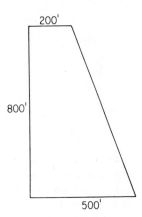

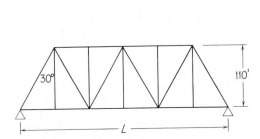

Figure P1-12

Figure P1-13

1-13. A parking lot has the shape shown in Fig. P1-13. Determine the number of square yards of paving material required.

1-14. Use the method of tangents to draw a line that forms an angle of 57.2 deg with a horizontal reference line.

1-15. Draw lines, by the method of tangents, at angles of 24.2, 69.7, and 11.7 deg with a horizontal reference line.

1-16. Determine the length of the third side c of the triangle shown in Fig. P1-16, if a, b, and θ are

a) $a = 5$ in., $b = 10$ in., $\theta = 30°$
b) $a = 6$ in., $b = 6$ in., $\theta = 20°$
c) $a = 14$ ft, $b = 7$ ft, $\theta = 70°$
d) $a = 2$ in., $b = 4$ in., $\theta = 120°$
e) $a = 15$ in., $b = 25$ in., $\theta = 135°$
f) $a = 10.3$ in., $b = 6.4$ in., $\theta = 127°$

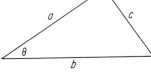

Figure P1-16

1-17–1-19. Determine the lengths of the diagonals BD and AC of the parallelogram shown in Figs. P1-17–P1-19.

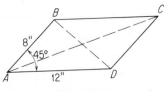

Figure P1-17

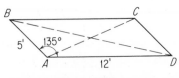

Figure P1-18

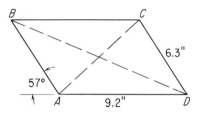

Figure P1-19

1-20. A fence is to extend along the long diagonal of a plot of land that has the shape of a parallelogram. The sides are 150 ft and 300 ft respectively and the acute angle between them is 55 deg. Determine the required length of fence, and the area of the field.

1-21. A man walks the zig-zag path from *A* to *F* shown in Fig. P1-21. How far is he from his starting point?

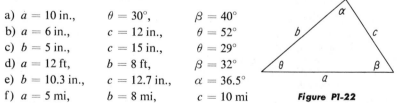

Figure P1-21

1-22. Determine in the triangle shown in Fig. P1-22, the missing sides and missing angles if

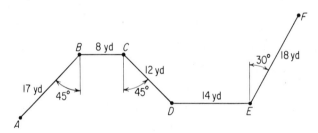

a) $a = 10$ in., $\theta = 30°$, $\beta = 40°$
b) $a = 6$ in., $c = 12$ in., $\theta = 52°$
c) $b = 5$ in., $c = 15$ in., $\theta = 29°$
d) $a = 12$ ft, $b = 8$ ft, $\beta = 32°$
e) $b = 10.3$ in., $c = 12.7$ in., $\alpha = 36.5°$
f) $a = 5$ mi, $b = 8$ mi, $c = 10$ mi

Figure P1-22

1-23. A ship, Fig. P1-23, must pass between the two buoys *A* and *B*. Radar indicates compass directions to the buoys and their respective distances from the point of observation. Find the distance *d*.

1-24. A weight is suspended from cables as shown in in Fig. P1-24. Determine the angle θ between cables *AC* and *BC*.

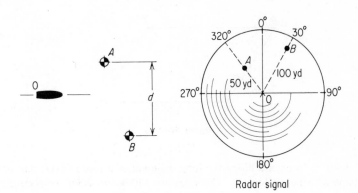

Radar signal

Figure P-23

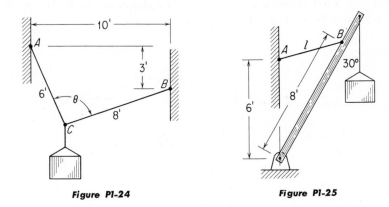

Figure P1-24   **Figure P1-25**

1-25. A rigging boom is supported by means of cable AB as shown in Fig. P1-25. Determine the length of the cable and the angle that it makes with the boom.

1.26. A crankshaft, connecting rod, and piston are shown in Fig. P1-26. Find the distance from the top of the piston to "top-dead-center," the highest point in the piston's path.

1-27. A rectangular bin 12 ft by 12 ft by 20 ft holds 170 tons of sand. How much does the sand weigh in units of pounds per cubic yard?

1-28. A pump discharges water at the rate of 100 gpm (gallons per minute). What rate does this represent in cubic feet per second? (1 gallon $= 231$ cubic inches.)

1-29. Sound travels at a speed of 1100 fps (feet per second) in air. Express this speed in units of miles per hour and yards per minute.

1-30. A "grain" is equal to 1/7000 of a pound. What is the weight in ounces of a 215 grain bullet?

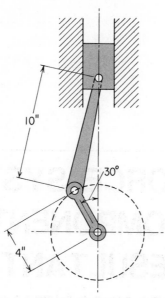

Figure P1-26

1-31. An acre is equivalent to 43,560 sq ft. How many gallons of water fall on a 100 acre farm for a rainfall of 0.2 in.?

Chapter 2

FORCE SYSTEMS: COMPONENTS, RESULTANTS, EQUIVALENCE

2-1 The Nature of a Force

A force is described by the effects that it produces. Objects stand still or move, rise or fall, spin or vibrate, because of the effect of forces.

Newton summarized the effect of forces in three laws. The first law states that a force is required to change the motion of a body. Thus, a body at rest will remain at rest and a body in motion will move uniformly in a straight line unless acted upon by a force.

The second law states that if a force acts on a body, the motion will change in speed or direction or both. This change in motion is proportional to the magnitude of the force and is in the direction of the force.

The third law states that if one body exerts a force on a second body, the second body must exert an equal but opposite force on the first. It is the principle of this law which completely discourages the manufacture of "sky hooks."

To summarize: a force is a directed action that tends to change the state of motion of a body; it is always accompanied by an opposing reaction of equal magnitude.

Since the "weight" of a body is the force of the earth's gravity, the units of force are defined in units of weight. In American engineering practice the standard *unit of force* is either the pound, the kip (kilopound = 1000 pounds), or the ton (2000 pounds).

2-2 Magnitude, Direction, and Line of Action

Forces can be described graphically, as in Fig. 2-1, by an arrow whose length represents the magnitude or quantity of the force. Point A, the tail of the arrow, indicates the point of application of the force, and the head of the arrow indicates the direction of the force's action. The line of action is indicated by the dashed line in the figure.

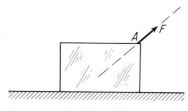

Figure 2-1

An important principle of statics, *the transmissibility of a force*, states that a force can be applied at any point on its line of action without a change in the external effects. Thus, a train of railroad cars would react equally in its motion to being pulled or pushed by a locomotive.

EXAMPLE 1: Locate, in Fig. 2-2, the point of intersection of the action line of the force and the base line of the rectangle, and then find the perpendicular distance from point O to the line of action of the force.

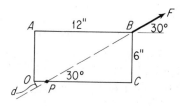

Figure 2-2

Solution: The line of action of the force cuts the base of the rectangle at an angle of 30 deg at P. Side PC can be found, since

$$\tan 30° = 6/\overline{PC}$$

$$\overline{PC} = \frac{6}{\tan 30°} = \frac{6}{0.577} = 10.4 \text{ in.}$$

The perpendicular distance d is computed in a similar manner.

$$\overline{OP} = 12 - \overline{PC} = 1.6 \text{ in.}$$

$$d = \overline{OP} \sin 30° = 1.6(0.5) = 0.8 \text{ in.}$$

2-3 Vectors

Many physical quantities, such as force, are *directed magnitudes*. These are called *vector quantities* or simply *vectors*. Some quantities, such as length and time, are specified by a single number; these are called *scalar quantities* or *scalars*.

"Two plus two equals three," is a realistic possibility when vectors are added. The reason is that magnitudes and directions are involved in the process of addition. To illustrate: Imagine two cities, A and C, three miles apart as shown in Fig. 2-3. One could travel from A to point B and then from B to the destination C. In this instance vector $\overrightarrow{AB}$ has been added to vector $\overrightarrow{BC}$; $\overrightarrow{AC}$ is the *resultant* of the addition. Symbolically, $\overrightarrow{AB}$ means "vector AB."

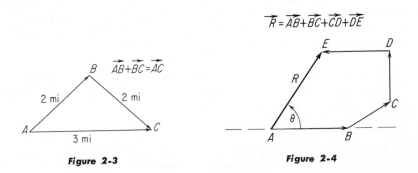

Figure 2-3   Figure 2-4

Figure 2-4 illustrates how four vectors are added to give the resultant vector R. This resultant represents the combined effects of the vector quantities and is completely defined by its magnitude and angular position θ; the latter is measured with respect to some known reference line.

The vector addition just described was performed by the *string polygon method*. The vectors are drawn joining one another, head to tail fashion; the resultant closes the string of vectors.

A *graphical solution* is obtained when the vectors are drawn accurately to some convenient scale, e.g., "Let 50 lb of force equal one inch." Angles are measured with a protractor or by the *method of tangents* described in Chapter 1. It is important to note that the order in which vectors are added does not in any way alter the direction or the magnitude of the resultant. Thus

$$\vec{R} = \vec{AB} + \vec{BC} = \vec{BC} + \vec{AB}$$

EXAMPLE 2: Find the magnitude and direction of the resultant R of the three forces shown in Fig. 2-5. Use the graphical method.

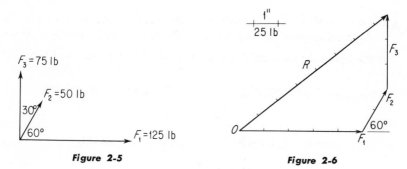

Figure 2-5   Figure 2-6

Solution: Select a force scale by allowing 1 in. = 25 lb and draw the vectors "head to tail" starting at a convenient origin O.

The resultant R and the angle θ, when measured, are found to be

$$R = 190 \text{ lb}$$

and

$$\theta = 38° \quad \angle$$

A second way of adding vectors is called the *parallelogram method*. In this procedure the vectors F_1 and F_2 are brought to a common origin O, and a parallelogram is constructed as shown in Fig. 2-7. The resultant R is the

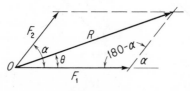

Figure 2-7

diagonal of this parallelogram. The cosine law is used to find the resultant.

$$R^2 = F_1^2 + F_2^2 - 2F_1F_2 \cos(180° - \alpha) = F_1^2 + F_2^2 + 2F_1F_2 \cos\alpha$$

$$R = \sqrt{F_1^2 + F_2^2 + 2F_1F_2 \cos\alpha} \qquad (2\text{-}1)$$

The directional angle θ, computed by the sine law, is

$$\sin\theta = \frac{F_2}{R}\sin(180° - \alpha) \qquad (2\text{-}2)$$

When more than two vectors are to be added by this method, a parallelogram is constructed between the third vector and the resultant of any two. The fourth vector is added in a similar manner to the resultant of the first three vectors, and so forth.

EXAMPLE 3: Determine the resultant of the forces F_1 and F_2, shown in Fig. 2-7, by the parallelogram method. Let $F_1 = 20$ lb, $F_2 = 40$ lb, and $\alpha = 30$ deg.

Solution: Find the resultant R and directional angle θ by means of Eqs. (2–1) and (2-2).

$$R = \sqrt{F_1^2 + F_2^2 + 2F_1F_2 \cos\alpha} = \sqrt{(20)^2 + (40)^2 + 2(20)40\cos 30°}$$

$$R = \sqrt{3386} = 58.2 \text{ lb}$$

$$\sin\theta = \frac{F_2}{R}\sin(180° - \alpha) = \frac{40}{58.2}\sin 30° = 0.344$$

$$\theta = 20.1°$$

2-4 The Addition of Vectors by the Method of Components

The previous section has shown how two vectors, A and B, can be combined to form a resultant R. The converse is also true: the resultant R can be replaced by two equivalent vectors A and B. These two vectors are termed the *components of the resultant* or simply *components*. Since each

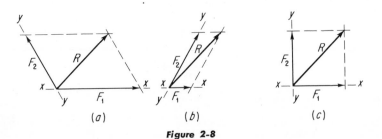

(a)   (b)   (c)

Figure 2-8

component is a vector in its own right, it too can be expressed in terms of other equivalent vectors. Thus, it is conceivable that the resultant R could be the sum of an infinite number of components. In each of the three cases shown in Fig. 2-8, the vector R has a *pair* or *set* of components, F_1 and F_2.

Figure 2-8(c) is a special case in that the lines of action x-x and y-y are at right angles to each other. As a consequence, F_1 and F_2 are referred to as *rectangular* or *orthogonal components*.

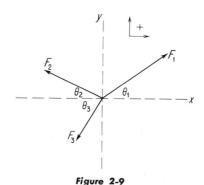

Figure 2-9

To add the forces F_1, F_2, and F_3 by the method of components, a rectangular coordinate system x-y is employed as shown in Fig. 2-9. Each force vector is resolved into its x- and y-components. The x-components are added algebraically and the y-components are added algebraically. The original force system of F_1, F_2, and F_3 is thereby reduced to a pair of forces, R_x along the x-axis, and R_y along the y-axis:

$$R_x = \Sigma\, F_x = (F_1)_x + (F_2)_x + (F_3)_x + \cdots$$
$$R_y = \Sigma\, F_y = (F_1)_y + (F_2)_y + (F_3)_y + \cdots \qquad (2\text{-}3)$$

The resultant, the vector sum of R_x and R_y, is found by the theorem of Pythagoras, thus

$$R = \sqrt{(R_x)^2 + (R_y)^2} \qquad (2\text{-}4)$$

where the tangent of the angle that the resultant R makes with the x-axis is

$$\tan \theta = \frac{R_y}{R_x} = \frac{\Sigma\, F_y}{\Sigma\, F_x} \qquad (2\text{-}5)$$

In Fig. 2-9, the positive directions are taken as "up" for y-components and to the "right" for x-components.

EXAMPLE 4: Find the resultant of the force system shown in Fig. 2-10.

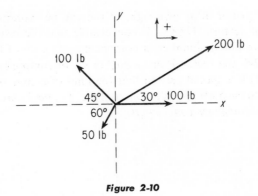

Figure 2-10

Solution: Find the components R_x and R_y of the resultant by an algebraic summation of the orthogonal components of the forces.

$$R_x = \Sigma \, F_x = 100 + 200 \cos 30° - 100 \cos 45° - 50 \cos 60°$$

$$R_x = 100 + 173.2 - 70.7 - 25 = +177.5 \text{ lb}$$

$$R_y = \Sigma \, F_y = 200 \sin 30° + 100 \sin 45° - 50 \sin 60°$$

$$R_y = 100 + 70.7 - 43.3 = +127.4 \text{ lb}$$

$$R = \sqrt{(R_x)^2 + (R_y)^2} = \sqrt{(177.5)^2 + (127.4)^2} = \sqrt{47,700}$$

$$R = 218 \text{ lb}$$

$$\theta = \text{arc tan} \frac{R_y}{R_x} = \text{arc tan} \frac{127.4}{177.5} = 35.7°$$

Expressed symbolically, the answer is

2-5 Subtraction of Vectors

By definition, the negative of a given vector is represented by an arrow whose direction has been changed by 180°. Thus, to subtract vector $\vec{F_2}$ from vector $\vec{F_1}$, reverse $\vec{F_2}$ and add it to $\vec{F_1}$ by any of the three methods described.

$$\vec{R} = \vec{F_1} - \vec{F_2} = \vec{F_1} + (-\vec{F_2}) \qquad (2\text{-}6)$$

2-6 Space Forces

The preceding discussion was concerned with components and resultants of groups of force vectors that occupied a single plane. In each instance, two rectangular components, R_x and R_y, completely identified the force. In contrast, a *three dimensional*, or *space force* is a vector that occupies

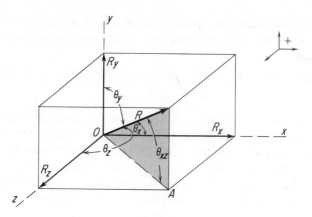

Figure 2-11

space, instead of lying in a plane, and it has three rectangular components.[1]

To aid in visualizing a three dimensional force, a rectangular box is drawn with the force R as the diagonal of this box. This is illustrated in Fig. 2-11. The far edges of the box lie on the three rectangular axes x, y, and z, and R_x, R_y, and R_z are the rectangular components of R. A study of the figure indicates that there are three right triangles, each having R as the hypotenuse and each lying in a different plane. The triangles are distorted by the perspective of the drawing. The angles θ_x, θ_y, and θ_z define the inclination of R with respect to the rectangular axis of each right triangle. The diagonal $\overline{OA}$ represents the component of R in the x-z plane.

$$(\overline{OA})^2 = R_x^2 + R_z^2$$

Since R is the resultant of OA and R_y, it follows that

$$R^2 = (\overline{OA})^2 + R_y^2 = R_x^2 + R_y^2 + R_z^2 \tag{2-7}$$

$$R = \sqrt{R_x^2 + R_y^2 + R_z^2} \tag{2-8}$$

The angle between the resultant and each rectangular component can be expressed as a cosine function; these are called *direction cosines*.

$$\cos \theta_x = \frac{R_x}{R}, \qquad R_x = R \cos \theta_x$$

$$\cos \theta_y = \frac{R_y}{R}, \qquad R_y = R \cos \theta_y \tag{2-9}$$

$$\cos \theta_z = \frac{R_z}{R}, \qquad R_z = R \cos \theta_z$$

---

[1] As an example of a space vector, imagine that to arrive at a given point, you have walked 2 blocks north, 3 blocks east, and then up 10 flights of stairs. The straight line drawn from where you were to where you are is a space vector.

When the components in terms of their direction cosines are substituted into Eq. (2-7), the sum of the squares of the direction cosines is found to equal unity.

$$R^2 = R_x^2 + R_y^2 + R_z^2 = R^2 \cos^2 \theta_x + R^2 \cos^2 \theta_y + R^2 \cos^2 \theta_z$$

$$\cos^2 \theta_x + \cos^2 \theta_y + \cos^2 \theta_z = 1$$

In some instances, the direction cosines are conveniently obtained by employing the coordinates of the force. For example, imagine that the force in Fig. 2-11 passes through the origin O and the coordinates (3, 4, 12); this means that if a rectangular box is drawn to a convenient scale, the x-component is 3 units long, the y-component 4 units long, and the z-component 12 units long. The resultant would have a scale length of

$$d = \sqrt{3^2 + 4^2 + 12^2} = 13$$

The direction cosines of the force are

$$\cos \theta_x = \tfrac{3}{13}$$

$$\cos \theta_y = \tfrac{4}{13}$$

$$\cos \theta_z = \tfrac{12}{13}$$

EXAMPLE 5: Determine the resultant of two space forces, $F_1 = 100$ lb and $F_2 = 200$ lb, having coordinates (2, 3, 4) and $(-3, 5, -2)$ respectively. Both forces pass through the origin of the coordinate system.

Solution: Set up a table and determine the x-, y-, and z-component of each force systematically, using the direction cosines.

Table 2.1

$F_1 = 100$ lb	$F_2 = 200$ lb
$d_1 = \sqrt{2^2 + 3^2 + 4^2} = 5.39$	$d_2 = \sqrt{(-3)^2 + (5)^2 + (-2)^2} = 6.16$
Direction Cosines	**Direction Cosines**
$\cos \theta_x = 2/5.39 = 0.371$	$\cos \theta_x = -3/6.16 = -0.487$
$\cos \theta_y = 3/5.39 = 0.557$	$\cos \theta_y = 5/6.16 = 0.812$
$\cos \theta_z = 4/5.39 = 0.742$	$\cos \theta_z = -2/6.16 = -0.325$
Force Components	**Force Components**
$(F_1)_x = 100(0.371) = 37.1$ lb	$(F_2)_x = 200(-0.487) = -97.4$
$(F_1)_y = 100(0.557) = 55.7$ lb	$(F_2)_y = 200(0.812) = 162.4$
$(F_1)_z = 100(0.742) = 74.2$ lb	$(F_2)_z = 200(-0.325) = -65.0$

Then add the components:

$$R_x = \Sigma F_x = 37.1 - 97.4 = -60.3 \text{ lb}$$

$$R_y = \Sigma F_y = 55.7 + 162.4 = 218.1 \text{ lb}$$

$$R_z = \Sigma F_z = 74.2 - 65.0 = 9.2 \text{ lb}$$

and find R from Eq. (2-8):

$$R = \sqrt{R_x^2 + R_y^2 + R_z^2} = \sqrt{(-60.3)^2 + (218.1)^2 + (9.2)^2}$$
$$= 226 \text{ lb}$$

The inclination of the resultant is specified by its direction cosines.

$$\cos \theta_x = \frac{-60.3}{226} = -0.267$$

$$\cos \theta_y = \frac{218.1}{226} = 0.965$$

$$\cos \theta_z = \frac{9.2}{226} = 0.041$$

2-7 The Resultant of Two Parallel Forces

Two forces having the same line of action are said to be *collinear*. The resultant of collinear forces that are equal in magnitude but opposite in direction is zero. Thus, by adding the collinear forces F to the parallel

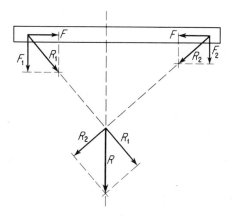

Figure 2-12

forces F_1 and F_2, in Fig. 2-12, the original force system is unchanged. The resultant R_1 of F_1 and F is added to the resultant R_2 of F_2 and F, giving the final resultant R. A problem of this type is best solved graphically.

2-8 Moment of a Force

A force has a moment about a given axis when it tends to produce rotation about that axis. The magnitude of the moment is defined as the product of the force and the perpendicular distance from the line of action of the force to the axis of rotation. In Fig. 2-13, the moment M is the product $F \cdot d$. Since a moment tends to produce rotation, the sign $(+)$ or $(-)$ is one of choice; clockwise or counterclockwise moments take opposite signs.

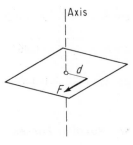

Figure 2-13

An important theorem of statics states that *the moment of a force is equal to the sum of the moments of the components*. The example that follows will demonstrate this theorem.

EXAMPLE 6: Determine the moment about point O of the 100 lb force that acts at point A on the bracket shown in Fig. 2-14 by: (a) finding the product of the force and its perpendicular distance from O; (b) taking moments of the rec-

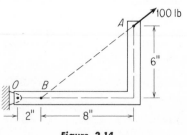
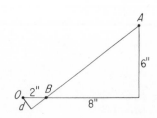

Figure 2-14

tangular components of the force at A; (c) taking moments of the rectangular components of the force at B.

Solution:

Part (a). First determine the distance $\overline{AB}$, the hypotenuse of the right triangle.

$$\overline{AB} = \sqrt{6^2 + 8^2} = 10 \text{ in.}$$

Next, find the distance d by using the ratio of the corresponding sides of the two similar triangles.

$$\frac{d}{2} = \frac{6}{10}$$

$$d = 1.2 \text{ in.}$$

The moment about point O of the 100 lb force is

$$M = F \cdot d = 100(1.2) = 120 \text{ lb in.}$$

Part (b). Since the slope of the force is given, the x- and y-components are

$$F_x = F \cos \theta = 100 \times \tfrac{4}{5} = 80 \text{ lb}$$

and

$$F_y = F \sin \theta = 100 \times \tfrac{3}{5} = 60 \text{ lb}$$

If a counterclockwise moment is positive, the algebraic sum of the moments about O is

$$M = 60(10) - 80(6) = 120 \text{ lb in.}$$

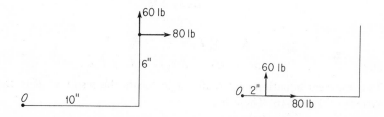

Part (c). The x- and y-components also act at point B, which is on the action line of the force. The 80 lb force has a moment equal to zero, since it passes through O. The moment of the 60 lb force is

$$M = 60(2) = 120 \text{ lb in.}$$

2-9 Resultants of Force Systems: The Use of the Principle of Moments

The resultant force that acts on a body has the same external effect as the forces it replaces. R_x represents the sum of the x-components of force; R_y, the sum of the y-components; R_z, the sum of the z-components. Symbolically, this is stated as

$$R_x = \Sigma \, F_x$$
$$R_y = \Sigma \, F_y \qquad \text{(2-10)}$$
$$R_z = \Sigma \, F_z$$

The moment of the resultant about all three rectangular axes must, in a similar fashion, be equal to the sum of the moments of the individual forces about each rectangular axis. In Fig. 2-15 a group of parallel forces, F_1, F_2, and F_3, act on the beam. The resultant R has the magnitude of $\Sigma \, F_y$, and its moment about any arbitrary point O must be equal to the sum of the moments of the individual forces about point O.

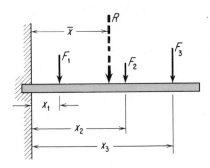

Figure 2-15

$$R = \Sigma \, F_y = F_1 + F_2 + F_3$$

and
$$M_0 = R\bar{x} = F_1 x_1 + F_2 x_2 + F_3 x_3 \qquad \text{(2-11)}$$

Two moment equations are required to locate the resultant R in the force system of Fig. 2-16. These are

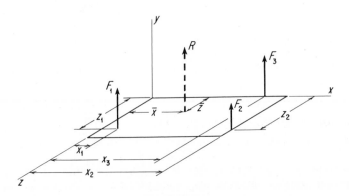

Figure 2-16

$$M_{0z} = R\bar{x} = F_1x_1 + F_2x_2 + F_3x_3$$

and $$M_{0x} = R\bar{z} = F_1z_1 + F_2z_2 + F_3z_3$$

The forces in this figure are parallel to the y-axis and therefore have a zero moment about this axis.

EXAMPLE 7: Determine the magnitude and location of the resultant of the parallel forces acting on the truss shown in Fig. 2-17.

Solution: The magnitude of the resultant is the algebraic sum of the parallel forces. Assume "down" to be the positive y-direction.

$$R_y = \Sigma F_y = 2 + 5 + 10 + 3 = 20 \text{ kips}$$

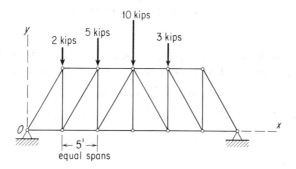

Figure 2-17

The moment of the resultant is equal to the sum of the moments of the individual forces. If clockwise moments are assumed to be positive, then

$$M_0 = R\bar{x} = \Sigma F{\cdot}x$$
$$20x = 2(5) + 5(10) + 10(15) + 3(20)$$
$$x = \frac{270}{20} = 13.5 \text{ ft to the right of } O$$

EXAMPLE 8: Find the resultant of the four forces that act on the bracket shown in Fig. 2-18.

Solution: The x-component and the y-component of the resultant are the sum of the force components in these two respective directions.

$$R_x = \Sigma F_x = 55 - 15 = 40 \text{ lb} \rightarrow$$
$$R_y = \Sigma F_y = 70 - 40 = 30 \text{ lb} \uparrow$$

The resultant R is the vector sum of R_x and R_y; thus

$$R = \sqrt{R_x^2 + R_y^2} = \sqrt{(40)^2 + (30)^2} = 50 \text{ lb}$$

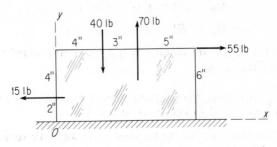

Figure 2-18

The inclination of the resultant is

$$\theta = \text{arc tan} \frac{\Sigma F_y}{\Sigma F_x} = \text{arc tan} \frac{30}{40}$$

$$\theta = 36.9° \quad \angle$$

The moment of the resultant must be equal to the sum of the moments of the forces acting on the bracket. Assume clockwise to be the positive direction.

$$R \cdot d = \Sigma \text{ Moments}_0$$

$$50 \cdot d = 55(6) - 70(7) + 40(4) - 15(2) = -30 \text{ lb in.}$$

$$d = -\frac{30}{50} = -0.6 \text{ in.}$$

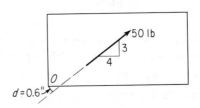

The negative sign indicates that the moment of the 50 lb resultant about O is counterclockwise or opposite to the assumed positive direction.

2-10 Couples

The force system shown in Fig. 2-19 consists of two equal but oppositely directed parallel forces separated by a distance d. This system, called a *couple*, has a resultant force equal to zero but a resultant moment equal to $F \cdot d$. Since the resultant of a couple is a *pure moment*, rotation of the couple in its plane does not alter its effect on the body. By computing the moment of the two forces about point O in Fig. 2-19 (assuming clockwise to be positive), it is also found that the moment of a couple does not depend upon its position in the plane of the body; thus

$$\Sigma\, M_0 = -\,Fx + F(x + d) = F \cdot d$$

The sum of two or more couples is simply the algebraic sum of their moments.

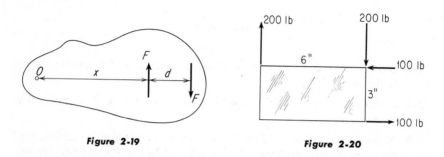

Figure 2-19   Figure 2-20

EXAMPLE 9: Compute the moment of the two couples that act on the body shown in Fig. 2-20.

Solution: Select clockwise as the positive direction. The resultant moment is the algebraic sum of the individual moments:

$$\Sigma\, M = 200(6) - 100(3) = 900 \text{ lb in.}$$

PROBLEMS

2-1. Draw each of the force vectors shown in Fig. P2-1 to scale. Allow 1 in. of length to equal 100 lb of force.

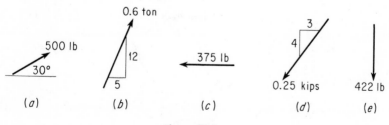

Figure P2-1

2-2. Two forces, F_1 and F_2, act on the beam as shown in Fig. P2-2. Determine the vertical distance above F_1 of the point of intersection of the action lines of these two forces.

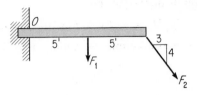

Figure P2-2

2-3. Determine the point of intersection of the action line of F_2 and the vertical wall in Prob. 2-2.

2-4. Find the perpendicular distance from the action line of F_2 to point O in Prob. 2-2.

2-5. A force acts as shown in Fig. P2-5 on the corner of the beam section. Find the perpendicular distance d from the action line of the force to the geometric center of the beam.

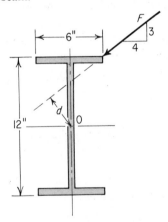

Figure P2-5

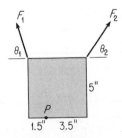

Figure P2-6

2-6. In Fig. P2-6, the lines of action of the two forces pass through point *P*. Determine the inclinations θ_1 and θ_2 of each force, measured from the horizontal reference line.

2-7–2-12. Determine the magnitudes and directions of the resultants in the Figs. P2-7–P2-12 by the string polygon method.

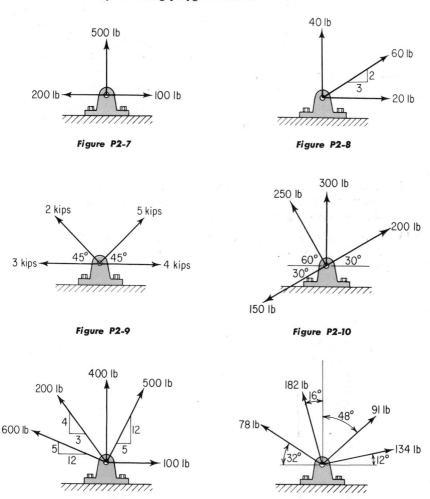

Figure P2-7

Figure P2-8

Figure P2-9

Figure P2-10

Figure P2-11

Figure P2-12

2-13. Three forces act on the tee crank as shown in Fig. P2-13. Find the magnitude and direction of the resultant by the string polygon method. Use a force scale of 100 lb = 1 in.

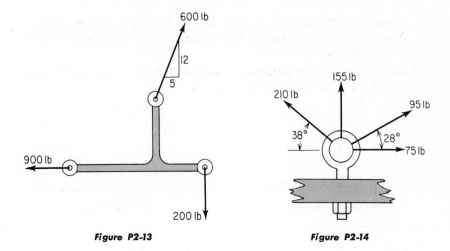

Figure P2-13   **Figure P2-14**

2-14. As shown in Fig. P2-14, four forces act on an "eye" hook. Select a convenient force scale and determine the magnitude and direction of the resultant by the string polygon method.

2-15. A system of maneuvering jets exerts forces on the rocket as shown in Fig. P2-15. Determine the magnitude and direction of the resultant by the string polygon method.

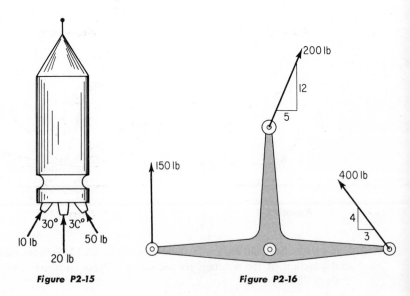

Figure P2-15   **Figure P2-16**

2-16. Three forces act on the tee crank as shown in Fig. P2-16. Find the resultant of these forces by the parallelogram method by first combining any two forces and then combining this resultant with the third force.

2-17. A rope that has been looped around a bracket supports the two loads indicated in Fig. 2-17. Find the resultant of these two forces.

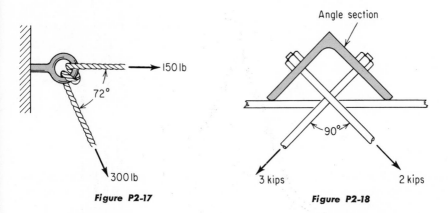

Angle section

Figure P2-17

Figure P2-18

2-18. A section of a tie rod brace is shown in Fig. P2-18. Find the resultant of the two tie rod forces and angle between the resultant and the vertical.

2-19. A section of a bucket elevator is shown in Fig. P2-19. Find the resultant of the two chain forces.

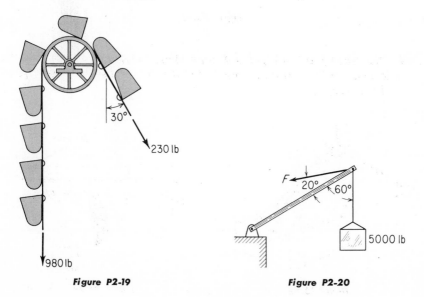

Figure P2-19

Figure P2-20

2-20. The resultant of the cable force F and the 5000 lb weight acts along the boom of the derrick shown in Fig. P2-20. Find the force F.

2-21. A uniform weight of 20 tons is lifted by the plate clamps and chains as shown in Fig. P2-21. Find the force in each chain.

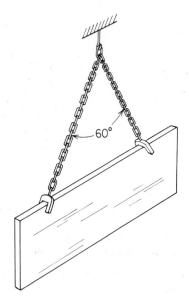

Figure P2-21

2-22. The "chain grab" in Fig. P2-22 has a lifting capacity of 3 tons. Find the force in the chain. Hint: the resultant of the two equal chain forces at point A is 3 tons.

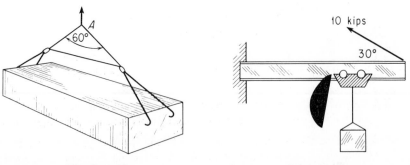

Figure P2-22   **Figure P2-23**

2-23. Determine the horizontal and vertical components of the 10 kip force acting on the jib crane shown in Fig. P2-23.

2-24. A reel is pulled up a ramp by a winch as shown in Fig. P2-24. The tensile force in the horizontal cable is 5 tons. Find the components of the force tangent to and normal to the ramp.

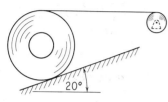

Figure P2-24

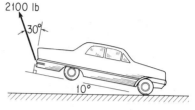

Figure P2-25

2-25. An automobile is being towed by a truck as shown in Fig. P2-25. Find the horizontal and vertical components of the 2100 lb force in the cable.

2-26. Determine the components, of a 220 lb force, that are perpendicular and parallel to a line making an angle of 28 deg with the force.

2-27. A uniform belt force of 325 lb is exerted throughout the entire tandem drive shown in Fig. P2-27. Find the direction and magnitude of the resultant force on each of the four pulleys *A*, *B*, *C*, and *D*.

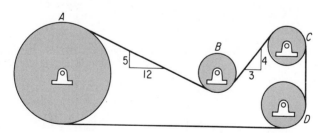

Figure P2-27

2-28. Show that the vector sum of the four resultant pulley forces in Prob. 2-27 is zero.

2-29. A vertical force of 20 lb can be resolved into two components, one of 40 lb and the other of 50 lb. Determine the angle each makes with the horizontal.

2-30–2-35. Use the method of components to determine the magnitude and direction of the resultant of the forces which act at a common point on a body as shown in the Figs. P2-30–P2-35.

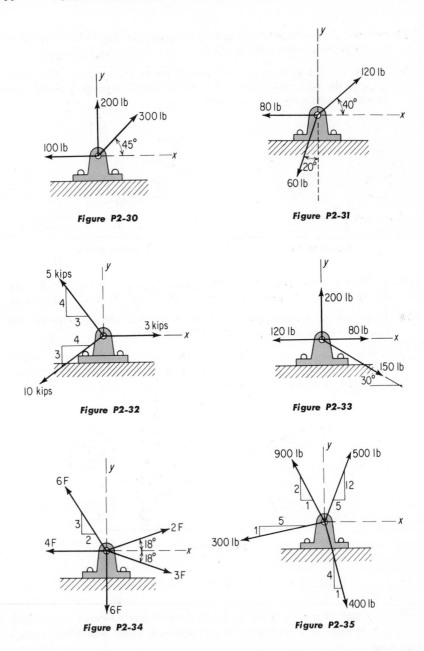

Figure P2-30

Figure P2-31

Figure P2-32

Figure P2-33

Figure P2-34

Figure P2-35

2-36. Plastics can be laminated by rolling several layers together. Small tensile forces keep the materials taut. Find the resultant of the three tensile forces. See Fig. P2-36.

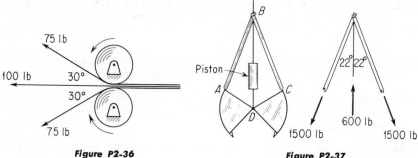

Figure P2-36   Figure P2-37

2-37. The clamshell bucket, used in earth excavations, is opened and closed by means of a piston. When it is in the position shown in Fig. P2-37, the forces in AB and BC are 1500 lb each, and in the piston BD, 600 lb. Determine the resultant of these three forces.

2-38. A 200 lb force pointing down and to the left makes an angle of 45 deg with the horizontal. A second 200 lb force points to the right at an angle of zero degrees with the horizontal. Determine the magnitude and direction of the resultant of these two forces.

2-39. Determine the resultant of the two forces that act on the truss in Fig. P2-39. Where does the resultant intersect member AB?

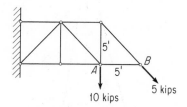

Figure P2-39

2-40. Two forces act as shown in Fig. P2-40. Find the force vector representing (a) $\vec{F_1} + \vec{F_2}$; (b) $\vec{F_1} - \vec{F_2}$; (c) $\vec{F_2} - \vec{F_1}$.

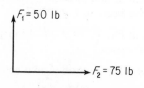   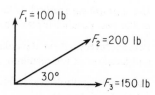

Figure P2-40   Figure P2-41

2-41. Three forces act at a point as shown in Fig. P2-41. Determine the force vector representing (a) $\vec{F_1} + \vec{F_2} + \vec{F_3}$; (b) $\vec{F_1} - \vec{F_2} + \vec{F_3}$; (c) $\vec{F_1} - \vec{F_2} - \vec{F_3}$; (d) $\vec{F_3} - \vec{F_2} - \vec{F_1}$.

2-42. With the aid of a three dimensional coordinate system, sketch a space force that passes through the origin and has coordinates of (2,2,2).

2-43. Make a perspective drawing of a space force having components $F_x = 10\,$lb, $F_y = 30\,$lb, $F_z = 50\,$lb. Determine the magnitude of the resultant and its direction cosines.

2-44. What are the direction cosines of a space force that passes through the origin and has coordinates of (2, 5, −3)?

2-45. Find the components of the resultant of two space forces: $F_1 = 200\,$lb, and $F_2 = 100\,$lb. Both forces pass through the origin. The coordinates of F_1 and F_2 are (1, 3, −2) and (2, 5, 1) respectively.

2-46. Find the magnitude and direction cosines of the resultant of the two space forces shown in Fig. P2-46.

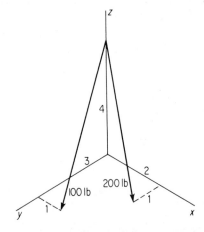

Figure P2-46

2-47. Use a graphical method to find the magnitude and location of the resultant of the two parallel forces which act on the beam in Fig. P2-47.

2-48. Parallel forces act on the column shown in Fig. P2-48. Find the magnitude and location of the resultant by graphical means.

2-49. Find the magnitude and location of the resultant in Prob. 2-48 if both forces act to the right.

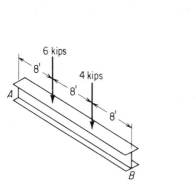

Figure P2-47

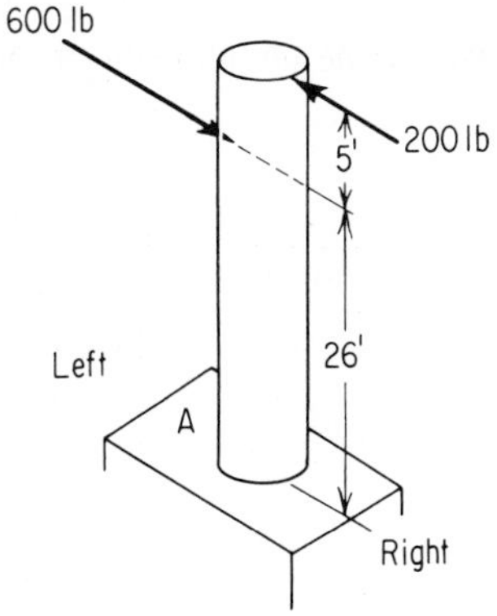

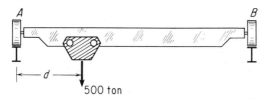

Figure P2-48

2-50. The overhead crane shown in Fig. P2-50 has a rated capacity of 500 tons. Find the moment of this load about end *A* if (a) $d = 3$ ft; (b) $d = 5$ ft; (c) $d = 12$ ft; (d) $d = 20$ ft.

Figure P2-50

2-51. The hairpin conveyor truck shown in Fig. P2-51 is used to move sheet steel coils to various places in a stamping plant. If the coil weighs 2 tons find the wheel reactions at *A* and *B* and the bending moment in the arm at *C*.

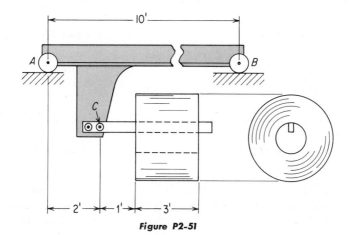

Figure P2-51

2-52. Determine the moment of the 3 kip load about point O in Fig. P2-52.

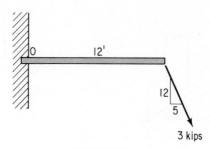

Figure P2-52

2-53–2-58. Find the magnitude, direction, and location of the resultant force which acts on the beam shown in the Figs. P2-53–P2-58.

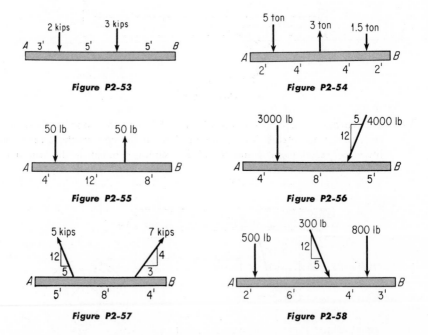

Figure P2-53

Figure P2-54

Figure P2-55

Figure P2-56

Figure P2-57

Figure P2-58

2-59–2-61. Find the magnitude and direction of the resultant force which acts on the plate shown in the Figs. P2-59–P2-61. Locate the resultant with respect to a point of intersection on a line collinear with AD.

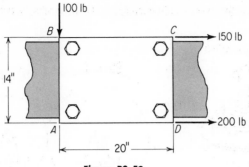

Figure P2-59

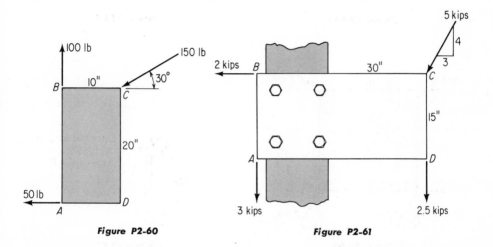

Figure P2-60

Figure P2-61

2-62–2-67. Determine the magnitude and the direction of the resultant couple which acts on the system shown in the Figs. P2-62–P2-67.

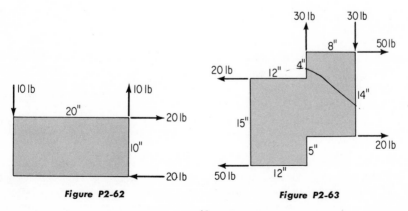

Figure P2-62

Figure P2-63

41

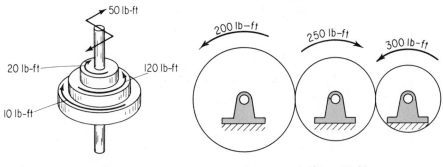

Figure P2-64

Figure P2-65

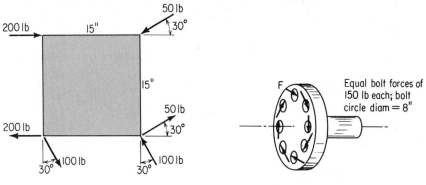

Figure P2-66

Figure P2-67

Chapter 3

CENTER OF GRAVITY

An infinite variety of man-made forces can act on a body; the magnitudes, directions, and locations of these forces can be changed at will by placing a cable here or by tightening a bolt there. One natural force, however, which is equally important, is *weight*—the earth's force of attraction for the body. In this instance, nature prescribes how much this is to be and through which point on the body it may be assumed to act. This point of action is called the *center of gravity*.

3-1 Experimental Determination of the Center of Gravity

The weight of a body is a resultant force that is equal to the sum of the weights of all the particles that comprise the body. The location of this resultant W may be determined experimentally by suspending the weight first from one point and then from another as shown in Fig. 3-1.

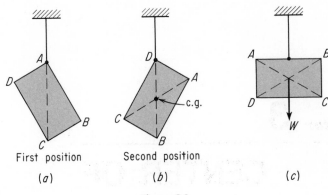

First position   Second position

(a)   (b)   (c)

Figure 3-1

Since the weight force acts downward, its line of action must be somewhere on line AC when suspended from point A. When the body is suspended from point D, the weight force acts somewhere on line DB. The
intersection of line AC with line DB is the center of gravity of the body.
The weight force always acts somewhere on a vertical line drawn downward
from the point of suspension.

In many instances it is not convenient to suspend the body and then
draw intersecting lines on it. Another method must be employed. Suppose,
for example, that it is important to know the location of the center of gravity
of a particular automobile. It can be determined by first weighing the front
axle with the car tipped upwards through some convenient angle θ as shown
in Fig. 3-2(a). The moment of the weight force W about the rear axle
must equal the moment of the scale force $(W_f)_1$, about that same point.

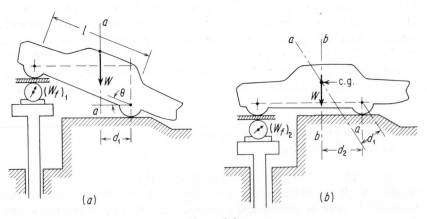

(a)   (b)

Figure 3-2

$$Wd_1 = (W_f)_1 l \cos \theta$$

and d_1 can be computed

$$d_1 = \frac{(W_f)_1 l \cos \theta}{W}$$

In a similar manner, with the car horizontal

$$d_2 = \frac{(W_f)_2 l}{W}$$

Lines a–a and b–b can be drawn on the car, or trigonometric calculations can be made and the center of gravity thus located.

EXAMPLE 1: Assume the car in Fig. 3-2 weighs 3000 lb and has a wheel base l of 10 ft. When the car is tipped at an angle of 30 deg, the recorded weight $(W_f)_1$ is 1200 lb; when it is horizontal, the recorded weight $(W_f)_2$ is 1500 lb. Locate the center of gravity of the car with respect to the rear axle.

Solution: The distances d_1 and d_2 are first computed:

$$d_1 = \frac{(W_f)_1 l \cos \theta}{W} = \frac{1200(10)(0.866)}{3000}$$

$$d_1 = 3.46 \text{ ft}$$

and
$$d_2 = \frac{(W_f)_2 l}{W} = \frac{1500(10)}{3000}$$

$$d_2 = 5 \text{ ft}$$

The location of the center of gravity above the rear axle is next computed. Trigonometric relationships are applied to the triangles that are drawn as shown in Fig. 3-3. The distance $\overline{BC}$ is given by

$$\overline{BC} = \frac{d_1}{\cos \theta} = \frac{3.46}{0.866}$$

where
$$\overline{BC} = 4 \text{ ft}$$

and
$$\overline{AB} = 5 - 4 = 1 \text{ ft}$$

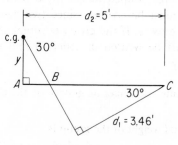

Figure 3-3

The quantity y is then computed

$$y = \frac{\overline{AB}}{\tan 30°} = \frac{1}{0.577} = 1.73 \text{ ft}$$

The center of gravity, therefore, is located 5 ft ahead of the rear axle and 1.7 ft above it.

3-2 Center of Gravity of Grouped Particles

A group of small particles with weights w_1, w_2, and w_3 is arranged in a straight line as shown in Fig. 3-4. The single resultant force W, which represents this system of particles, must: first, be equal to the sum of the individual weights

$$W = w_1 + w_2 + w_3$$

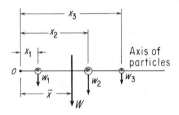

Figure 3-4

and second, have a moment about any arbitrary point equal to the sum of the moments of the individual weights. The lever arm $\bar{x}$ which locates the resultant, is the single *coordinate* of the center of gravity of this group.

$$W\bar{x} = w_1 x_1 + w_2 x_2 + w_3 x_3 \tag{3-1}$$

$$\bar{x} = \frac{w_1 x_1 + w_2 x_2 + w_3 x_3}{W}$$

When the particles are grouped to occupy a plane rather than a line, two moment equations must be written, since two coordinates are required to locate the center of gravity. If the group occupies space rather than a plane, three equations must be written in order to find the three coordinates of the center of gravity.

EXAMPLE 2: Locate the center of gravity of the grouped particles shown in Fig. 3-5.

Solution: The total weight of the group is

$$W = 6 + 2 + 5 + 3 = 16 \text{ lb}$$

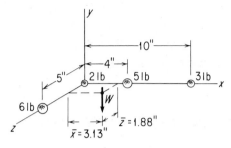

Figure 3-5

Since the system occupies a plane, two coordinates of the center of gravity must be found, one with respect to the x-axis and the other with respect to the z-axis. To find $\bar{x}$, moments are taken about the z-axis.

$$W\bar{x} = w_1x_1 + w_2x_2 + w_3x_3 + w_4x_4$$
$$16\bar{x} = 6(0) + 2(0) + 5(4) + 3(10)$$
$$\bar{x} = \frac{20 + 30}{16} = 3.13 \text{ in.}$$

Next, moments are summed with respect to the x-axis and $\bar{z}$ is computed

$$W\bar{z} = w_1z_1 + w_2z_2 + w_3z_3 + w_4z_4$$
$$16\bar{z} = 6(5) + 2(0) + 5(0) + 3(0)$$
$$\bar{z} = \frac{30}{16} = 1.88 \text{ in.}$$

EXAMPLE 3: Determine the center of gravity of two weights located in space as shown in Fig. 3-6.

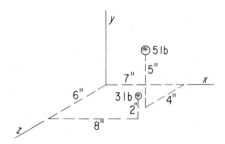

Figure 3-6

Solution: Since the system occupies space, three coordinates of the center of gravity must be found. The total weight of the system is

$$W = w_1 + w_2 = 3 + 5 = 8 \text{ lb}$$

Moments are taken with respect to the z-axis and $\bar{x}$ is found.

$$W\bar{x} = w_1 x_1 + w_2 x_2$$
$$8\bar{x} = 3(8) + 5(7)$$
$$\bar{x} = \frac{24 + 35}{8} = 7.38 \text{ in.}$$

In a similar manner, moments are taken with respect to the x-axis and $\bar{z}$ is computed.

$$W\bar{z} = w_1 z_1 + w_2 z_2$$
$$8\bar{z} = 3(6) + 5(4)$$
$$\bar{z} = \frac{18 + 20}{8} = 4.75 \text{ in.}$$

To find $\bar{y}$, it must be imagined that the entire system is turned about with the x–y axis horizontal. Moments are then taken with respect to the x-axis

$$W\bar{y} = w_1 y_1 + w_2 y_2$$
$$8\bar{y} = 3(2) + 5(5)$$
$$\bar{y} = \frac{6 + 25}{8} = 3.88 \text{ in.}$$

The center of gravity is located at

$$\bar{x} = 7.38 \text{ in.}, \qquad \bar{y} = 3.88 \text{ in.}, \qquad \bar{z} = 4.75 \text{ in.}$$

3-3 Centroids and Centers of Gravity of Two Dimensional Figures

The *centroid* of a geometrical figure corresponds to the *center of gravity* of a homogeneous body of the same form. The terms centroid and center of gravity are often used interchangeably; they differ in location, however, when the body is not homogeneous. For example, if a rod were made by joining a length of aluminum to an equal length of steel, the centroid would be located at the geometric center of the bar, while the center of gravity would be past the geometric center close to the heavy end.

Most irregularly shaped figures can be subdivided into shapes whose centroids are known. The plate shown in Fig. 3-7 consists of two rectangular areas A_1 and A_2. Since both of these areas are symmetrical, the centroid of each is located at the intersection of the diagonals as shown. By definition, the moment of the total area about any line must be equal to the sum of the moments of the portions of area about the same line. Thus, $\bar{x}$ is found by taking moments about the y-axis.

$$(A_1 + A_2)\bar{x} = A_1 x_1 + A_2 x_2$$

and
$$\bar{x} = \frac{A_1 x_1 + A_2 x_2}{(A_1 + A_2)} \tag{3-2}$$

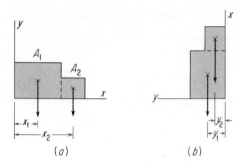

Figure 3-7

The second coordinate of the centroid is found by taking moments about the x-axis, thus

$$(A_1 + A_2)\bar{y} = A_1 y_1 + A_2 y_2$$

$$\bar{y} = \frac{A_1 y_1 + A_2 y_2}{A_1 + A_2} \tag{3-3}$$

Partial volumes are substituted for partial areas in Eqs. (3-2) and (3-3) when determining the centroids of solid geometric figures. In this case, three coordinates are needed to specify completely the position of the center of gravity.

$$\bar{x} = \frac{v_1 x_1 + v_2 x_2 + \cdots}{v_1 + v_2 + \cdots} \tag{3-4}$$

$$\bar{y} = \frac{v_1 y_1 + v_2 y_2 + \cdots}{v_1 + v_2 + \cdots} \tag{3-5}$$

$$\bar{z} = \frac{v_1 z_1 + v_2 z_2 + \cdots}{v_1 + v_2 + \cdots} \tag{3-6}$$

To aid in the computations that follow, centroids of several frequently encountered geometric figures are given in Table 3-1. The examples that follow will illustrate both the use of the table and the method of finding centroids.

EXAMPLE 4: Determine the x- and y-coordinates of the centroid of the figure shown in Fig. 3-8.

Solution: Three simple areas are represented in the composite figure: a rectangle of area A_1, a triangle of area A_2, and a circle of area A_3. Moments of these areas about the x-axis and the y-axis will locate the centroid. Since the circular area A_3 represents material that is "missing" from the figure, its moment is negative. Moments taken about the y-axis give

$$(A_1 + A_2 - A_3)\bar{x} = A_1 x_1 + A_2 x_2 - A_3 x_3$$

Table 3-1. Centroids

Rectangular area:		$\bar{x} = \dfrac{b}{2}, \quad \bar{y} = \dfrac{h}{2}$
Circular area:		$\bar{x} = \bar{y} = 0$
Triangular area:		$\bar{y} = \dfrac{h}{3}$
Semicircular area:		$\bar{y} = \dfrac{4r}{3\pi}$
Hemispherical volume:		$\bar{y} = \dfrac{3r}{8}$
Conic volume:		$\bar{y} = \dfrac{h}{4}$

Structural Shapes

	Size (in.)	Weight per ft (lb)	Area (in.²)	w (in.)	d (in.)	$\bar{x}$ (in.)	$\bar{y}$ (in.)
Wide Flange beam:	12 × 12	120	35.31	12.32	13.12	0	0
	10 × 10	100	29.43	10.35	11.12	0	0
Channel:	12 × 3	30	8.79	3.17	12.00	0.68	0
	6 × 2	13	3.81	2.16	6.00	0.52	0
Equal Leg angle:	6 × 6 × ½	19.6	5.75	6	66	1.68	1.68
	3 × 3 × ⅜	7.2	2.11	3	3	0.89	0.89

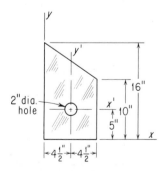

Figure 3-8

where

$$\bar{x} = \frac{[9(10)]\frac{9}{2} + [\frac{1}{2}(9)6]\frac{9}{3} - [\pi(1)^2]\frac{9}{2}}{9(10) + \frac{1}{2}(9)6 - \pi(1)^2}$$

$$= \frac{405 + 81 - 14.13}{90 + 27 - 3.14} = \frac{471.87}{113.86}$$

$$\bar{x} = 4.14 \text{ in. to the right of } y\text{-axis}$$

Moments taken about the x-axis give

$$(A_1 + A_2 - A_3)\bar{y} = A_1 y_1 + A_2 y_2 - A_3 y_3$$

where

$$\bar{y} = \frac{[9(10)]5 + [\frac{1}{2}(9)6][10 + \frac{6}{3}] - [\pi(1)^2]5}{113.86}$$

$$\bar{y} = \frac{450 + 324 - 15.7}{113.86} = \frac{758.3}{113.86}$$

$$\bar{y} = 6.66 \text{ in. above } x\text{-axis}$$

Alternate Solution: By selecting a set of rectangular axes x'-y' whose origin is at the centroid of the rectangle, the computations can be appreciably reduced, since the moment of both the rectangle and the circle would be zero:

$$\bar{x}' = \frac{A_1 x_1 + A_2 x_2 - A_3 x_3}{A_1 + A_2 - A_3}$$

$$= \frac{0 + \frac{1}{2}(9)6(1.5) - 0}{113.86} = 0.36 \text{ in. to the left of } y'\text{-axis}$$

Therefore $\bar{x} = 4.5 - 0.36 = 4.14$ in. to the right of y-axis

In a similar manner

$$\bar{y}' = \frac{\frac{1}{2}(9)(6)[5 + 2]}{113.86} = 1.66 \text{ in. above } x'\text{-axis}$$

Therefore $\bar{y} = 5 + 1.66 = 6.66$ in. above x-axis

EXAMPLE 5: Determine the center of gravity of the steel oven door shown in Fig. 3-9. A heat resistant glass insert 1 ft by 1 ft is located in the offset hole as illustrated. Assume that both the glass and the steel have a uniform thickness of $\frac{1}{4}$ in. Glass of this thickness weighs 3.5 lb per sq ft and steel this thick weighs 10 lb per sq ft.

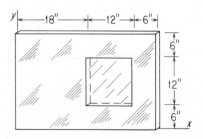

Figure 3-9

Solution: The body is symmetrical about a line 1 ft above the x-axis; therefore, by inspection, $\bar{y}$ is equal to 1 ft. Next take moments about the y-axis to locate the x-coordinate of the center of gravity.

The total weight of the door is

$$
\begin{aligned}
W &= \text{weight of steel} + \text{weight of glass} \\
&= (\text{volume} \times \text{density})_{\text{steel}} + (\text{volume} \times \text{density})_{\text{glass}} \\
&= [2(3) - 1(1)]10 + [1(1)]3.5 \\
&= 50 + 3.5 = 53.5 \text{ lb}
\end{aligned}
$$

Moments of the weights, summed about the y-axis, are

$$53.5\bar{x} = 2(3)10(1.5) - 1(1)10(2) + 1(1)3.5(2)$$

and

$$\bar{x} = \frac{90 - 20 + 7}{53.5} = \frac{77}{53.5}$$

$$\bar{x} = 1.44 \text{ ft to the right of } y\text{-axis}$$

Note: In the computation, subtract the moment of the missing steel from the moment of the entire steel plate and add the moment of the glass.

PROBLEMS

3-1. A frame is suspended first from corner A and then from corner B as shown in Fig. P3-1. Make a sketch of the part and graphically locate the center of gravity with respect to sides AB and BC.

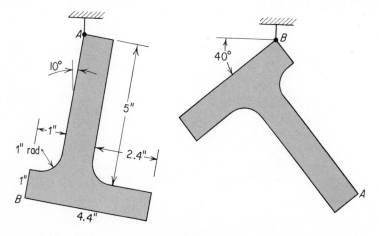

Figure P3-1

3-2. A scale indicates a weight of 2000 lb when it is placed under the two front wheels of an automobile. Placed under the rear wheels, the indicated weight is 1600 lb. Locate, with respect to the front wheels, the vertical action line that passes through the center of gravity. Assume the car to have a wheel base of 120 in. and to be horizontal during both weighings.

3-3. Locate the center of gravity with respect to corner A of the 5000 lb machine in Fig. P3-3 if a scale reading of 3500 lb is indicated when $\theta = 0°$ and 3000 lb when $\theta = 20°$.

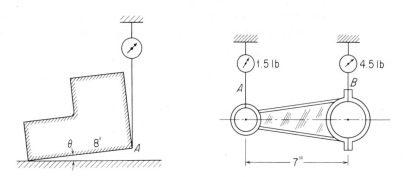

Figure P3-3   Figure P3-4

3-4. Two spring scales are used to weigh the connecting rod shown in Fig. P3-4. Determine the center of gravity of the rod if the left scale reads 1.5 lb and the right scale 4.5 lb.

3-5–3-9. Locate the coordinates of the center of gravity of the grouped weights in Figs. P3-5–P3-9.

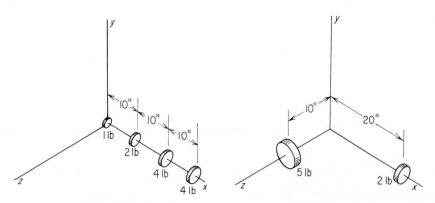

Figure P3-5   Figure P3-6

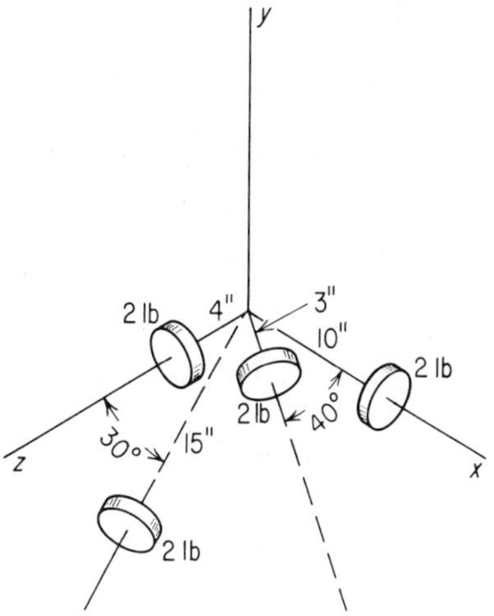

Figure P3-7

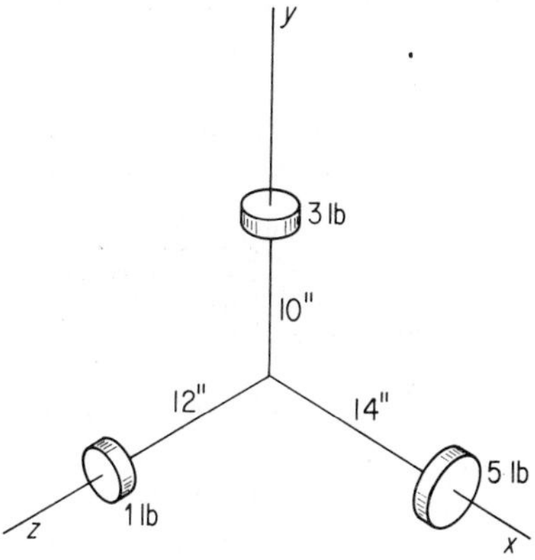

Figure P3-8

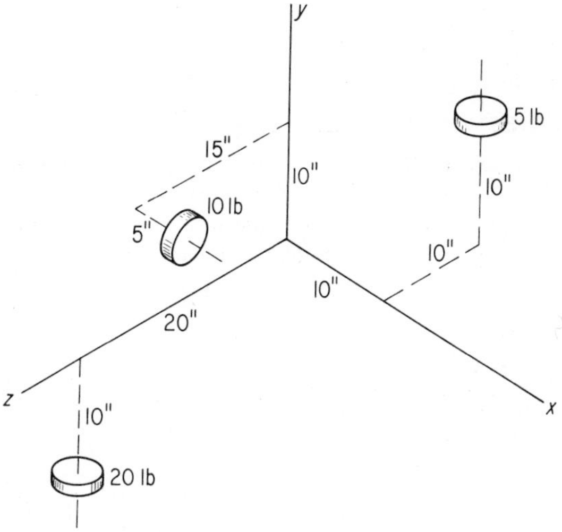

Figure P3-9

3-10–3-13. Determine the x- and y-coordinates of the centroid of the plane geometric forms shown in Figs. P3-10–P3-13.

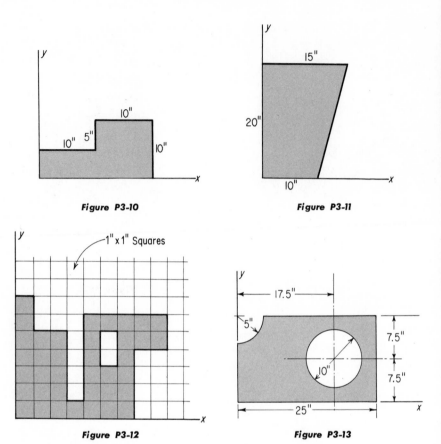

Figure P3-10

Figure P3-11

Figure P3-12

Figure P3-13

3-14. Determine the centroid of a beam fabricated by welding two 6 in. by 6 in. by $\frac{1}{2}$ in. angles to a flat plate as shown in Fig. P3-14.

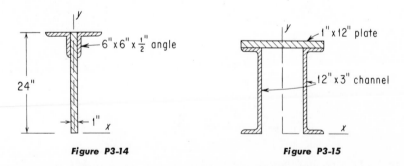

Figure P3-14

Figure P3-15

3-15. Two 12 in. by 3 in. by 30 lb per ft channels are welded to a plate as shown in Fig. P3-15. Determine the centroid of the composite section.

3-16. A 12 in. by 3 in. structural channel is welded to a 10 in. by 10 in. wide-flanged beam as shown in Fig. P3-16. Locate the centroid of the composite area.

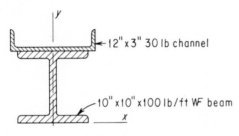

—12"x3" 30 lb channel

—10"x10"x100 lb/ft WF beam

Figure P3-16

3-17. A steel sphere with a diameter of 4 in. is fastened to the end of a square aluminum rod 1 in. by 1 in. by 18 in. long. Locate the center of gravity of the composite section. The densities of steel and aluminum are 0.28 lb per cu in. and 0.095 lb per cu in. respectively.

3-18. A steel shaft 3 ft long and weighing 25 lb has a 15 lb brass gear fastened to one end. A second brass gear weighing 30 lb is located at the other end. Find the center of gravity of the assembly.

3-19. A steel block has a 5 in. diameter hole drilled through it as shown in Fig. P3-19. Locate the center of gravity of the block.

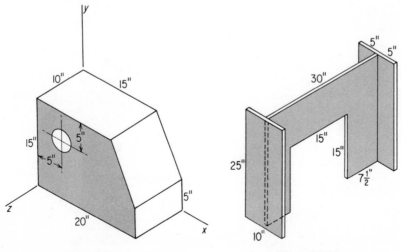

Figure P3-19   **Figure P3-20**

3-20. A welded machine frame has the shape shown in Fig. P3-20. Find the center of gravity of the frame if the steel has a uniform thickness throughout.

3-21. A thin rectangular plate is bent to form the bracket shown in Fig. P3-21. Locate the center of gravity of the bracket.

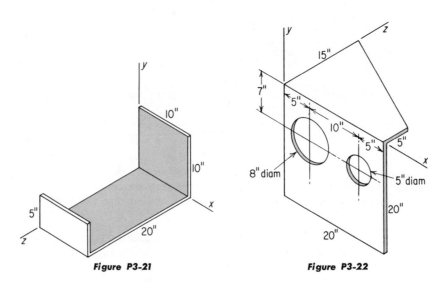

Figure P3-21   Figure P3-22

3-22. A piece of thin sheet metal is stamped to form the bracket shown in Fig. P3-22. Locate the center of gravity of the stamping.

Chapter 4

EQUILIBRIUM

A body at rest is a body in equilibrium. The forces and moments that act are completely balanced by counteracting forces and counteracting moments. The mathematical conditions for equilibrium are very simply stated:

$$\Sigma \, F = 0$$

$$\Sigma \, M = 0 \tag{4-1}$$

This chapter will show how the problem of equilibrium is approached and how the forces and moments required to maintain equilibrium are determined for two-dimensional systems and for space systems.

4-1 The Free-Body Diagram

It would be a hopeless task to assemble a complicated piece of machinery without a blueprint showing what part goes where and in what order. A similar situation exists in mechanics; an analysis of forces and moments cannot be made unless there is a pictorial representation of where and how these forces and moments act on the body. This pictorial representation is called the *free-body diagram*. Its construction is perhaps the most important single step in the solution of statics as well as dynamics problems.

In sketching the free-body diagram, the primary thing to remember is that forces are exerted on bodies either because they are in *contact* with other bodies or because the bodies are acted upon by a *remote* force of attraction like that of gravity or magnetism. To illustrate: a weight W is suspended from a group of cables as shown in Fig. 4-1(a). What are the forces in the cables? The answer lies hidden in the original figure, but it is apparent in Fig. 4-1(b) and Fig. 4-1(c). Each of the cables is cut and the junction B removed and isolated. The three forces T_{AB}, T_{BC}, T_{BD} are in equilibrium; their resultant is zero. In a similar manner isolation of the weight shows that the force W and the cable force T_{BD} are in equilibrium. These are the two free-body diagrams that would be considered in the solution of the problem.

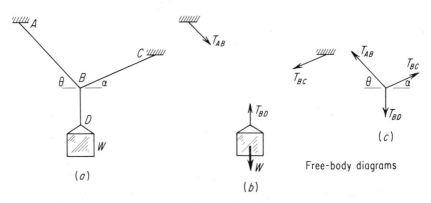

Free-body diagrams

Figure 4-1

A cylinder weighing W lb, shown in Fig. 4-2, is supported by cable AB and a smooth inclined surface C. The free-body diagram shows that the reaction R_C of the surface on the cylinder is normal to both the cylinder and the plane. This is characteristic of contact forces between smooth surfaces.

Still another type of free-body reaction is that found in the *pin-connected support*. This is a mechanical device capable of resisting motion normal to the pin; it cannot, however, resist a moment that acts about the pin axis. To illustrate: consider the ladder in Fig. 4-3 to be pin-connected at B. The top of the ladder rests against a smooth vertical surface and a weight W_C hangs from point C. The weight of the ladder W_L is assumed to act at its *center of gravity*. The ladder isolated as a free-body is shown in Fig. 4-3(b).

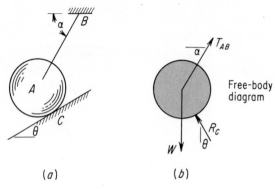

(a)   (b)

Figure 4-2

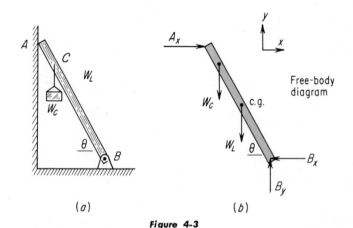

(a)   (b)

Figure 4-3

The weight forces W_C and W_L act downward; A_x is the wall's reaction to the "push" of the ladder; and B_x and B_y are the reactions at the pin.

In some instances, directions of pin reactions—up or down, to the right or to the left—will not be readily apparent. *This does not mean they are to be omitted.* The rule is simply to assume a direction. If the assumption is wrong, the answer for that particular reaction will carry a minus sign, indicating that the reaction should be reversed.

EXAMPLE 1: Draw the free-body diagram of the rod AC, the pulley D, and the weight W shown in Fig. 4-4(a). The rod is pin-connected at A and the pulley pin-connected at D. Assume the surface at C to be perfectly smooth and neglect both the weight of the rod and the weight of the pulley, as they are too small to consider.

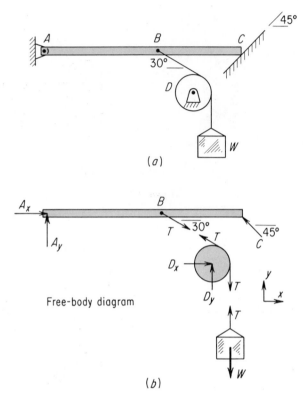

Figure 4-4

Solution:

The weight: A gravity force W and a tensile force T are the two forces that act on the weight.

The pulley: The components of the pin reaction are D_x and D_y. Since the cable is "cut" above and below the pulley, the cable force T appears twice.

The bar: The directions of the pin forces at A are not immediately apparent, so it is merely assumed that they act as shown. The force C, the reaction of the smooth surface on the bar, is normal to the surface.

EXAMPLE 2: Isolate and draw the free-body diagram of the bar AB, the pulley C, and the weight W of the system shown in Fig. 4-5.

Solution:

The weight: A cable force T and a gravity force W act on the weight.

The pulley: The cable tension T acts in both the horizontal and vertical direc-

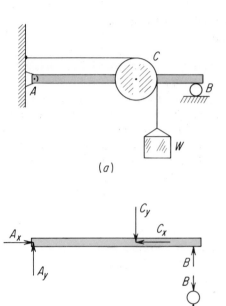

(a)

Free-body
diagram

Figure 4-5

tions as shown, while the pin forces C_x and C_y act at the center of the pulley. It is readily apparent that these pin forces are drawn in the proper direction to maintain equilibrium; C_x opposes the horizontal force T and C_y opposes the vertical force T.

The bar: Since the smooth roll support at B is free to move horizontally, it can exert only a vertical force on the bar. The reaction of the pulley on the bar is opposite to that of the bar on the pulley. In other words, C_x acts to the right on the pulley and to the left on the bar; in a similar manner, C_y acts vertically upward on the pulley and vertically downward on the bar. A_x and A_y, the pin reactions, are the two remaining forces that act on the bar.

4-2 Equilibrium of Two-Dimensional Force Systems

The two dimensional body shown in Fig. 4-6 is acted upon by a group of forces, each of which can be expressed in terms of two similarly directed components. The body and the forces that act upon it are referred to as a *two-dimensional force system*. To maintain equilibrium, *the resultant force must be zero and the resultant moment of the forces about any arbitrary point O must be zero.* Since the resultant is the vector sum of force components, the first necessary condition for equilibrium is mathematically stated as

$$R = \sqrt{(\sum F_x)^2 + (\sum F_y)^2} = 0 \qquad (4\text{-}2)$$

where
$$\sum F_x = 0 \qquad (4\text{-}3)$$

$$\sum F_y = 0 \qquad (4\text{-}4)$$

The second necessary condition for equilibrium, mathematically stated, is

$$\sum M_o = 0 \qquad (4\text{-}5)$$

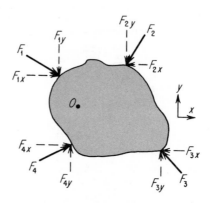

Figure 4-6

4-3 Simplification of the Equations of Equilibrium for Three Special Cases

Case I: Collinear force system. When no more than two forces act upon a body, these forces must: (1) be parallel and be on the same line of action, (2) be oppositely directed, and (3) have equal magnitudes. If the forces are parallel but have different action lines, the condition $\sum M_o = 0$ cannot be satisfied; if the action lines are not parallel, then $\sum F_x = \sum F_y = 0$ cannot be satisfied.

Case II: Concurrent force systems. When no more than three nonparallel forces act on a body (Fig. 4-7), their lines of action must be concurrent—they must pass through a common point. If this were not true, the second condition of equilibrium, that of $\Sigma M_o = 0$, could not be satisfied. Another way of looking at this is to imagine two of the three forces to be added vectorally, thereby reducing the system to one composed of only two forces; as shown in Case I, two forces acting on a body must be collinear.

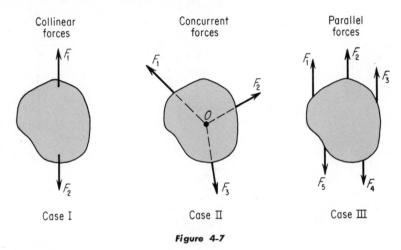

Figure 4-7

Case III: Parallel force systems. This is perhaps the simplest of force systems, since one orthogonal direction, either x or y, is eliminated from the computations. The equations of equilibrium reduce to $\Sigma F = 0$ and $\Sigma M_o = 0$. The examples that follow will illustrate the method of approach and analysis of two-dimensional force systems.

EXAMPLE 3: A 100 lb weight is supported by two cables as shown in Fig. 4-8. Determine the tensile force in each of the cables.

Solution: Cut the cables and draw the free-body diagram of joint B as shown in Fig. 4-8(b). Then write the equations of equilibrium, $\Sigma F_x = 0$ and $\Sigma F_y = 0$, for the three forces.

$$\Sigma F_x = 0$$
$$T_{BC} \cos 45° - T_{AB} \cos 30° = 0$$
$$0.707 T_{BC} = 0.866 T_{AB} \tag{a}$$

and
$$\Sigma F_y = 0$$
$$T_{AB} \sin 30° + T_{BC} \sin 45° - 100 = 0$$
$$0.5 T_{AB} + 0.707 T_{BC} = 100 \tag{b}$$

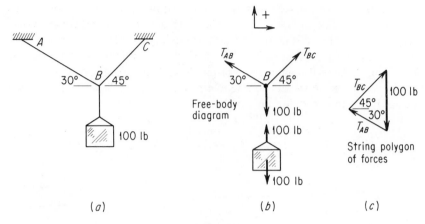

(a) (b) (c)

Figure 4-8

Solving Eqs. (a) and (b) simultaneously gives

$$T_{AB} = \frac{0.707}{0.866} T_{BC} = 0.816 T_{BC}$$

$$[(0.5)0.816 + 0.707]T_{BC} = 100$$

$$1.115 T_{BC} = 100$$

$$T_{BC} = 89.7 \text{ lb}$$

and $$T_{AB} = \frac{0.707}{0.866}(89.7) = 73.2 \text{ lb}$$

Alternate Solution: The string polygon of vector forces must close, since the resultant is zero. First draw the 100 lb force to scale; then draw lines parallel to T_{BC} and T_{AB} to form the closed triangle of forces shown in Fig. 4-8(c). The lengths of the legs of a triangle, when measured to scale, are equal to the unknown forces.

$$T_{AB} = 73 \text{ lb and } T_{BC} = 90 \text{ lb}$$

EXAMPLE 4: Determine the reactions at the carriage wheels A and B of the double trolley crane shown in Fig. 4-9. Assume the weight of the main beam, 1000 lb, to be concentrated at its center of gravity.

Solution: Draw the free-body diagram as shown in Fig. 4-9(b). Since this is a system of parallel forces, two equations of equilibrium, $\sum M_o = 0$ and $\sum F_y = 0$, are all that are required to calculate the desired quantities. As a check, write a third equation in which moments are taken about some arbitrary point other than $O;$ if the solution is correct, this equation will equal zero.

$$\sum F_y = 0$$

$$R_A + R_B - 7000 - 1000 - 3000 = 0$$

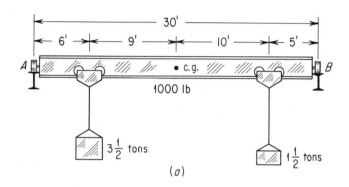

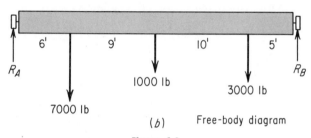

(b)   Free-body diagram

Figure 4-9

$$R_A + R_B = 11,000 \text{ lb} \qquad (a)$$
$$\Sigma M_A = 0$$
$$7000(6) + 1000(15) + 3000(25) - 30R_B = 0$$
$$R_B = \frac{42,000 + 15,000 + 75,000}{30} = \frac{132,000}{30}$$
$$R_B = 4400 \text{ lb}$$

Substitution of R_B into Eq. (a) gives

$$R_A = 11,000 - R_B = 11,000 - 4400$$
$$R_A = 6600 \text{ lb}$$

Check: Moments are taken about point B

$$\Sigma M_B = 0$$
$$R_A 30 - 7000(24) - 1000(15) - 3000(5) = 0$$
$$6600(30) - 7000(24) - 1000(15) - 3000(5) = 0$$
$$198,000 - 168,000 - 15,000 - 15,000 = 0$$

EXAMPLE 5: The portable jib crane shown in Fig. 4-10 weighs 500 lb and is supported on a column by the slotted bracket A and the smooth fulcrum B. The weight of the crane may be assumed to act somewhere on a vertical line passing through point C. Determine the reactions at points A and B required to support the crane.

Solution: The pin A resists both horizontal and vertical downward motion; two force components, A_x and A_y, therefore, are shown in the free-body diagram. The fulcrum B, assumed to be smooth, exerts a single force, B_x, on the crane. Since there are three unknown quantities to be found, three equations of equilibrium are required. These are $\Sigma F_x = 0$, $\Sigma F_y = 0$, and $\Sigma M_o = 0$.

$$\Sigma F_x = 0$$
$$B_x - A_x = 0$$

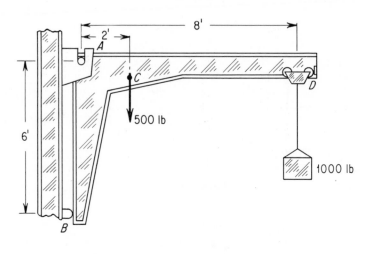

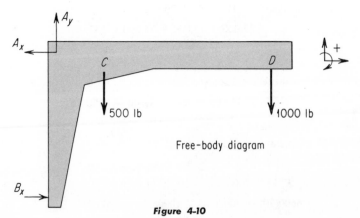

Free-body diagram

Figure 4-10

Therefore $$A_x = B_x \qquad \text{(a)}$$

and $$\Sigma F_y = 0$$

$$A_y - 500 - 1000 = 0$$

$$A_y = 1500 \text{ lb}$$

A moment summation is next taken about point A.

$$\Sigma M_A = 0$$

$$500(2) + 1000(8) - 6B_x = 0$$

$$B_x = \frac{9000}{6} = 1500 \text{ lb} \qquad \text{(b)}$$

From Eq. (a) $$A_x = B_x = 1500$$

The reaction at A is the vector sum of A_x and A_y, where

$$A = \sqrt{(A_x)^2 + (A_y)^2} = \sqrt{(1500)^2 + (1500)^2}$$

$$A = 2121 \text{ lb}$$

4-4 Equilibrium of Forces in Space

The resultant of a group of space forces was shown in Chapter 2 to have, at most, three rectangular components: R_x, R_y, and R_z. It was also shown that the resultant could conceivably have a moment about all three axes: M_x, M_y, and M_z. These six quantities, when set equal to zero, form the basis of three-dimensional equilibrium.

$$R_x = 0, \qquad\qquad M_x = 0$$
$$R_y = 0, \quad \text{and} \quad M_y = 0 \qquad (4\text{-}6)$$
$$R_z = 0, \qquad\qquad M_z = 0$$

One could expect, in the most complicated problem in three-dimensional equilibrium, to compute as many as six unknown quantities. Fortunately, however, in a good many situations these six equations can be reduced to as few as three by inspection alone.

The examples that follow will illustrate the types of problems that are encountered and the approach to their solution.

EXAMPLE 6: A weight of 300 lb is raised by means of a force F applied to the crank as shown in Fig. 4-11. Neglect the weights of all the members and find the reactions at bearings A and B and the force F.

Solution: The free-body diagram, which has been superimposed on an x-, y-, z-coordinate system, indicates the absence of x-components of force. This reduces the six equations of equilibrium to the following five:

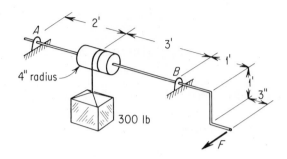

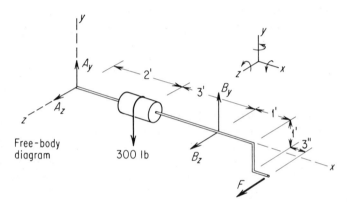

Figure 4-11

$$\Sigma \, F_y = 0, \qquad \Sigma \, M_x = 0$$
$$\Sigma \, F_z = 0, \qquad \Sigma \, M_y = 0, \qquad \Sigma \, M_z = 0$$

Determine the crank force F by equating moments about the x-axis.

$$\Sigma \, M_x = 0$$
$$-F(12) + 300(4) = 0$$
$$F = 100 \, \text{lb}$$

Next, write a moment equation to include the free-body forces that tend to produce a rotation about the z-axis. These include the weight force of 300 lb and the bearing reaction B_y.

$$\Sigma \, M_z = 0$$
$$5B_y - 300(2) = 0$$

Therefore $B_y = 120 \, \text{lb}$

Then write a moment equation for the forces that tend to produce rotation in the system about the y-axis. These forces include B_z and F; the latter, found in the first step, is 100 lb.

$$\Sigma M_y = 0$$

$$F(6.25) + 5B_z = 0$$

where
$$B_z = \frac{-100(6.25)}{5} = -125 \text{ lb}$$

The minus sign indicates that B_z is improperly directed and should be reversed after the problem is completed. Two unknowns, A_y and A_z, remain to be determined, and two of the original five equations have yet to be used — a force summation in the y-direction and a force summation in the z-direction.

$$\Sigma F_y = 0$$

$$A_y + B_y - 300 = 0$$

Substitute the value of B_y from the previous step and compute A_y.

$$A_y + 120 - 300 = 0$$

$$A_y = 180 \text{ lb}$$

Finally, for the z-components of force

$$\Sigma F_z = 0$$

$$A_z + B_z + F = 0$$

Substitution in this equation of the known values of B_z and F gives

$$A_z - 125 + 100 = 0$$

$$A_z = 25 \text{ lb}$$

The tabulated answers are

$$F = 100 \text{ lb}$$

$$A_x = 0, \qquad B_x = 0$$
$$A_y = 180 \text{ lb}, \qquad B_y = 120 \text{ lb}$$
$$A_z = 25 \text{ lb}, \qquad B_z = -125 \text{ lb}$$

Indicate positive and negative directions for the force components on the free-body diagram.

EXAMPLE 7: Determine the tension in the three cables, AD, BD, and CD, that support the 500 lb weight shown in Fig. 4-12.

Solution: Three equations of equilibrium are required: $\Sigma F_x = 0$, $\Sigma F_y = 0$, and $\Sigma F_z = 0$. The moment equations are automatically satisfied since the three forces meet at a common point D.

The method of *direction-cosines* described in Chapter 2 will be used to determine the components of space force T_{BD}.

$$(T_{BD})_x = T_{BD} \cos \theta_x = T_{BD} \frac{-3}{\sqrt{(-3)^2 + (-4)^2 + (12)^2}}$$

$$(T_{BD})_x = -\frac{3}{13} T_{BD}$$

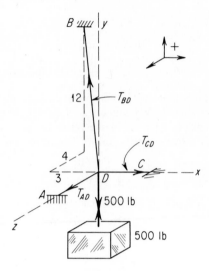

Figure 4-12

In a similar manner $\qquad (T_{BD})_y = T_{BD} \cos \theta_y = \dfrac{12}{13} T_{BD}$

and $\qquad\qquad\quad (T_{BD})_z = T_{BD} \cos \theta_z = -\dfrac{4}{13} T_{BD}$

The force components in each of the rectangular directions are set equal to zero.

$$\Sigma F_x = 0$$

$$-\frac{3}{13} T_{BD} + T_{CD} = 0 \qquad\qquad\qquad (a)$$

$$\Sigma F_y = 0$$

$$\frac{12}{13} T_{BD} - 500 = 0 \qquad\qquad\qquad (b)$$

$$\Sigma F_z = 0$$

$$-\frac{4}{13} T_{BD} + T_{AD} = 0 \qquad\qquad\qquad (c)$$

From Eq. (b)

$$T_{BD} = \frac{500(13)}{12} = 542 \text{ lb}$$

The value T_{BD} when substituted into Eqs. (a) and (c) gives T_{CD} and T_{AD}.
From Eq. (a)

$$T_{CD} = \frac{3}{13} T_{BD} = \frac{3}{13}(542) = 125 \text{ lb}$$

From Eq. (c)

$$T_{AD} = \frac{4}{13} T_{BD} = \frac{4}{13}(542) = 167 \text{ lb}$$

PROBLEMS

Note: In Problems 4-1–4-8 indicate the unknown forces by appropriate symbols; it is not necessary to determine these forces.

4-1. Draw the free-body diagram of the 250 lb cylinder in Fig. P4-1. Assume the contact surfaces to be perfectly smooth.

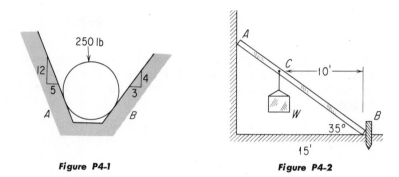

Figure P4-1 **Figure P4-2**

4-2. As shown in Fig. P4-2, a ladder of negligible weight is supported by a smooth vertical wall, a smooth horizontal surface, and a stake driven into the ground at *B*. A 450 lb weight acts at point *C*. Draw the free-body diagram of the ladder.

4-3. As illustrated in Fig. P4-3, a weight of 500 lb is supported by a cable attached to end *B* of the horizontal bar; the bar in turn is supported by a pin at *A* and a smooth roller at *C*. Draw the free-body diagram of the bar *AB*.

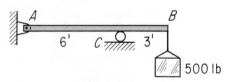

Figure P4-3

4-4. Isolate beams *AB* and *ED* in Fig. P4-4 and draw the free-body diagram of each. Smooth rollers act at points *B* and *C*.

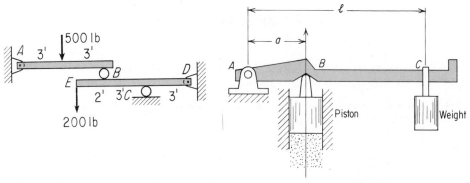

Figure P4-4   **Figure P4-5**

4-5. The lever shown in Fig. P4-5 is pin-supported at one end. The weight can be moved along the axis to balance the pressure force on the piston. Draw the free body diagram of the lever and indicate the forces in terms of the variables.

4-6. Fig. P4-6 indicates the essential features of a drilling machine clamp. The pins at A and B are smooth. Draw the free-body diagrams of the rod and the lever.

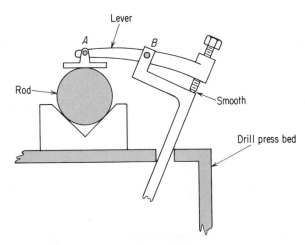

Figure P4-6

4-7. A device used to draw a variable curve is shown in Fig. P4-7. If all hinges are to be pin-connected, draw the free-body diagram of members A, B, and C.

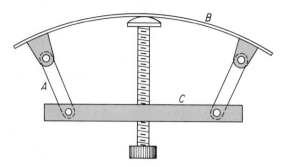

Figure P4-7

4-8. The arrangement of blocks and tackles shown in Fig. P4-8 is called a "bell purchase." Draw a free-body diagram of each pulley and show that the force F is one seventh of the weight W.

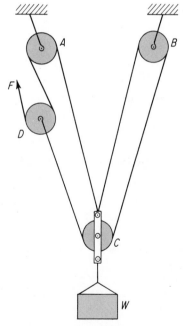

Figure P4-8

4-9. Determine the tensile force in cord AB and in cord BC that support the 100 lb weight in Fig. P4-9. Assume all lines to be vertical.

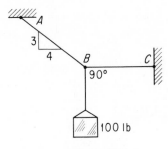

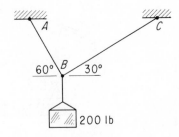

Figure P4-9   **Figure P4-10**

4-10. Determine the tensile force in each of the cords that support the 200 lb weight in Fig. P4-10.

4-11. Find the horizontal force F that must be applied to the 50 lb weight in Fig. P4-11 in order that the cord AB makes a 20 deg angle with the vertical.

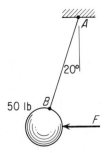

Figure P4-11

4-12. The bolt of the holding jig shown in Fig. P4-12 is tightened to produce a tensile force of 200 lb. Find the forces at A, B, and C that act on the cylinder.

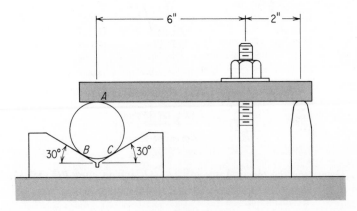

Figure P4-12

4-13. Determine the weight W that a man is capable of supporting if he applies a force $F = 50$ lb directed as shown in Fig. P4-13 on the handles of a truck.

4-14. Find the reaction on the axle A, of the truck shown in Fig. P4-13.

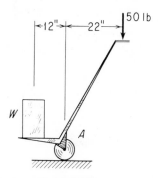

Figure P4-13

4-15. The hairpin conveyor shown in Fig. P4-15 is used to transport tires in an assembly plant. If each tire weighs 30 lb find the bolt reaction at A and at B. Assume that friction between the components is negligible.

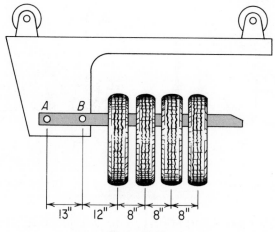

Figure P4-15

4-16. Find the tension in each of the chains of the notched-beam conveyor transport shown in Fig. P4-16.

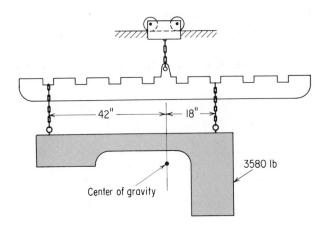

Figure P4-16

4-17. A double lever plug cock is shown in Fig. P4-17. If a steady force of 20 lb is maintained as constant tension and the resisting moment within the cock is 10 lb ft, find the required tension in the cable at *B* to close the cock.

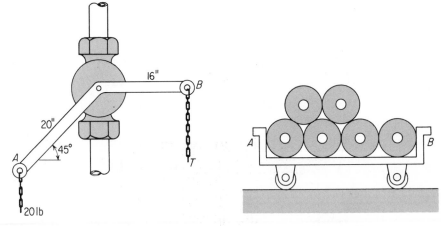

Figure P4-17   **Figure P4-18**

4-18. Six identical 500 lb coils of steel are stacked on a truck as shown in Fig. P4-18. Determine the reactions at *A* and *B* on the truck.

4-19. Determine the weight *W* required to prevent the pulleys in Fig. P4-19 from rotating, and the bearing reactions at *A* and *B*. The pulleys *A* and *B* weigh 60 lb and 30 lb respectively.

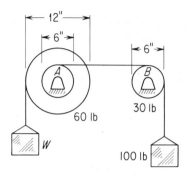

Figure P4-19

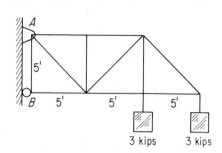

Figure P4-20

4-20. The wall truss shown in Fig. P4-20 is pin-supported at A and roller-supported at B. Determine the reactions at the pin and at the roller if the truss supports two 3 kip loads as shown. Neglect the weight of the truss in the calculations.

4-21. Find the force F required to pull the 1000 lb spool of wire in Fig. P4-21 over the 2 in. obstruction. Assume the weight of the spool to act through its geometric center.

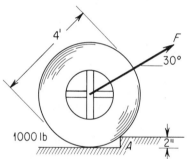

Figure P4-21

4-22. Determine the lifting force at A that can be exerted by the crowbar shown in Fig. P4-22.

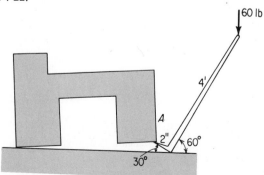

Figure P4-22

4-23. Determine the reactions at pin *A* and at roller *B* for the system shown in Fig. P4-23. The weight of the beam, 500 lb, may be assumed to act at the center of gravity *C*.

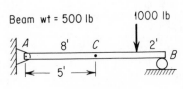

Figure P4-23

4-24. Find the reactions at pin *A* and roller *B* of the system shown in Fig. P4-24. The weight of the beam, 600 lb, acts through point *C*, the center of gravity.

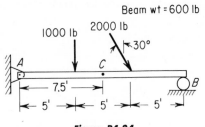

Figure P4-24

4-25. Determine the reactions at *A, B, C,* and *D* in the system shown in Fig. P4-25. The weight of the beams may be neglected in the computations.

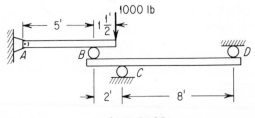

Figure P4-25

4-26. The beam shown in Fig. P4-26 is supported by a pin at *A* and a smooth surface at *B*. If the weight of the beam is negligible, determine the reactions at these two points.

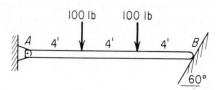

Figure P4-26

4-27. The tractor shown in Fig. P4-27 weighs 10,000 lb. The weight is equally distributed, half on the front wheels and half on the rear wheels. When the tractor is coupled to the trailer, the front wheels scale out to 6000 lb and the rear wheels to 18,000 lb. Determine the distance d that locates the kingpin P.

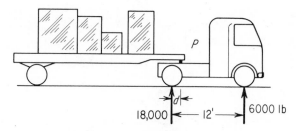

Figure P4-27

4-28. The double-trolley crane in Fig. P4-28 picks up a machine weighing 5 tons. If the weight of the machine is concentrated at point G, determine the tension in cables A and B, and the reactions at the crane wheels C and D.

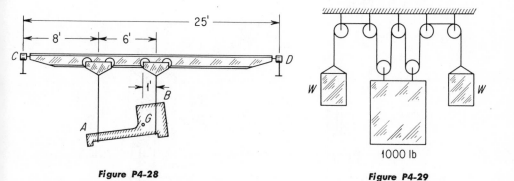

Figure P4-28

Figure P4-29

4-29. Determine the magnitudes of the equal counterweights W that would just balance the 1000 lb elevator shown in Fig. P4-29.

4-30. Each bucket of the elevator shown in Fig. P4-30 weighs 20 lb and when full and rising carries 100 lb of payload. The buckets discharge at the top and then descend empty. Determine the moment required to operate the conveyor at constant speed in the position shown.

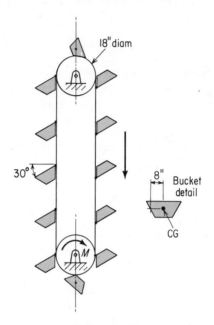

Figure P4-30

4-31. Find the force P required to lift the 300 lb weight in the pulley system shown in Fig. P4-31.

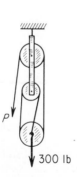

Figure P4-31

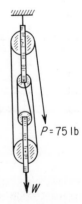

Figure P4-32

4-32. What weight W can be lifted by the 75 lb force with the pulley arrangement shown in Fig. P4-32?

4-33. The double-strut deck truss shown in Fig. P4-33 supports the loads indicated. Determine the pin and roller reactions at A and B.

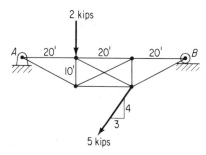

Figure P4-33

4-34. A force of 5000 lb is required at the punch head in the position shown in Fig. P4-34. Assume all joints to be pin-connected and determine for the position shown the necessary driving couple M and the pin reaction at C.

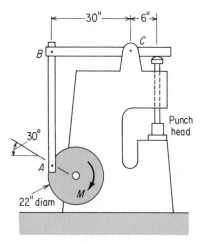

Figure P4-34

4-35. The recorded weights at the axles A, B, and C of the haul-away tractor and trailer in Fig. P4-35 are 6000 lb, 16,000 lb, and 18,000 lb respectively. Determine the magnitude and line of action of the weight of the trailer and its cargo if the uncoupled tractor weighs 10,000 lb, equally distributed over the front and rear wheels.

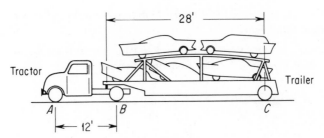

Figure P4-35

4-36. Trucks are often transported in the piggy-back style shown in Fig. P4-36. Determine the reaction at points A, B, and C if each truck weighs 4000 lb at the front axle and 4000 lb at the rear axle when in the horizontal position.

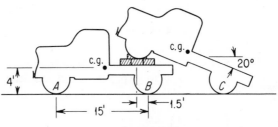

Figure P4-36

4-37. Determine the reactions at A and B on the bracket shown in Fig. P4-37. Consider the weight of the bracket to be negligible.

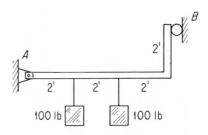

Figure P4-37

4-38. The tensile force exerted by the spring shown in Fig. P4-38 is proportional to the displacement of the end D. The constant of proportionality is called "the spring modulus." If the spring tension is 100 lb for the position shown and the modulus is 200 lb per in., find the spring tension and pin reaction at C for a cam rotation of 180 deg.

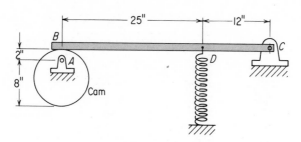

Figure P4-38

4-39. Find the weight W that can be supported by the boom in Fig. P4-39 if the maximum force that the cable AB can exert is 2000 lb. What is the pin reaction at C on the boom when it is supporting the maximum load W?

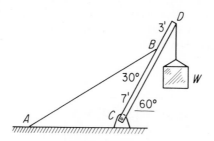

Figure P4-39

4-40. The pulley E and the boom AD are both pin-supported as shown in Fig. P4-40. Determine the tension T in the cable and the pin reaction at A on the boom.

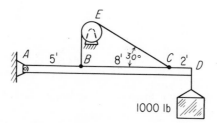

Figure P4-40

4-41. The hydraulic boom and the winch are employed to raise the 5000 lb load as shown in Fig. P4-41. Determine the tension in the cable, the pin reaction on the boom at A, and the force exerted by the hydraulic ram. Neglect the weight of the boom.

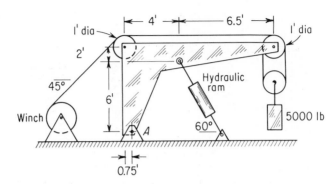

Figure P4-41

4-42. What load W is the portable hoist in Fig. P4-42 capable of lifting if a horizontal force of 30 lb is exerted on the crank at C? What are the reactions on the rollers A and B? Assume that horizontal motion of the hoist is prevented by locked wheels.

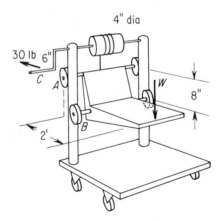

Figure P4-42

4-43. Determine the tension in each of the three cables that support the 100 lb weight in Fig. P4-43.

4-44. Find the tension in each of the three cables that support the 3 kip weight shown in Fig. P4-44.

4-45. The triangular plate in Fig. P4-45 is supported by three cables. Find the tension in each cable if the uniform plate weighs 500 lb.

4-46. Determine the force in each leg of the tripod shown in Fig. P4-46.

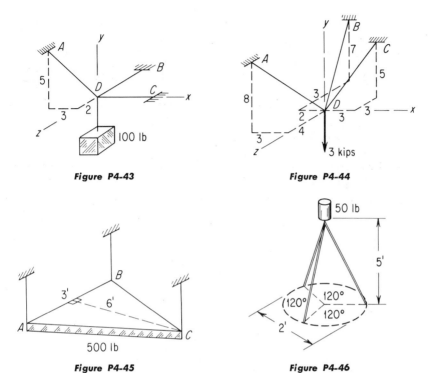

Figure P4-43

Figure P4-44

Figure P4-45

Figure P4-46

4-47. Boom *DC* supports a 500 lb load as shown in Fig. P4-47. Determine the tension in each of the cables and the pin reaction at *D*.

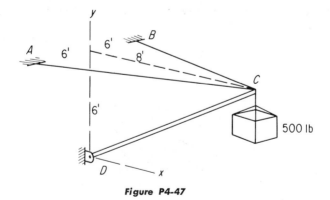

Figure P4-47

4-48. A steel *I* beam weighing 75 lb per ft is supported as shown in Fig. P4-48. Find the force in each of the cables.

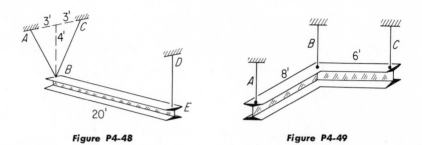

Figure P4-48   Figure P4-49

4-49. Beams weighing 35 lb per ft are welded to form an ell as shown in Fig. P4-49. Determine the force in each of the cables that support this frame.

4-50. Find the bearing reactions at A and D on the shaft shown in Fig. P4-50.

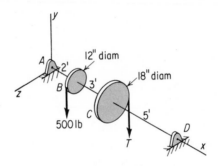

Figure P4-50

4-51. The "jack-shaft" supports three pulleys as shown in Fig. P4-51. Determine the tension T required to maintain equilibrium and the bearing reactions at A and E on the shaft.

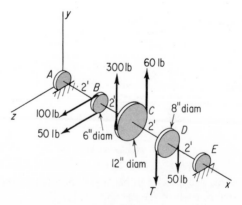

Figure P4-51

4-52. A schematic diagram of a single cylinder air compressor is shown in Fig. P4-52. Determine the belt tension T on the pulley and the bearing reactions at A and B on the crankshaft if the compressed gas in the cylinder exerts a force of $P = 800\,\text{lb}$ on the piston.

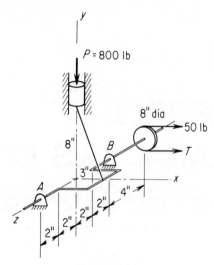

Figure P4-52

Chapter 5

FORCE ANALYSIS OF STRUCTURES

A structure is an assembled group of beams, cables, and columns which is capable of supporting loads while it remains stable in geometric form. The conditions and equations of equilibrium, when they are applied to the structure as a unit, to sections of it, or to the individual members within it, constitute a force analysis.

5-1 Simple Trusses

A *simple truss* is a structure, lying in a single plane, that consists of straight members connected together to form a series of joining triangles. In practice the members are welded, bolted, or riveted together and heavy cover plates, called *gussets*, are used to reinforce each joint.

The first step in the analysis is to make certain simplifying assumptions so that the basic equations of equilibrium can be used to determine the forces that act in the various members.

First, the weights of the individual members are disregarded since they are small compared to the loads they carry. Second, the members are joined: not by riveting, welding, or bolting, but by smooth pins; each joint behaves as a perfect hinge. Third, the loads are applied on the structure only at the pinned joint; thus, each component of the truss is a *two force member*.

5-2 Determination of Tension or Compression

To know whether the members are pulling or pushing is just as important as the force determination. A tension member—one that is pulling on the joint—can be a light bar or cable, while a compression member—one that pushes on the joint—must be heavy and bulky so that it will not buckle under the tremendous loads that it usually carries. The designer must know how the load is applied as well as its magnitude before he can suggest a proper structural member.

Member *AB* of the wall truss shown in Fig. 5-1 is a tension member; isolated as a free-body, it tends to stretch because of the action of the loads that are applied to it. Member *EF* on the truss is a compression member;

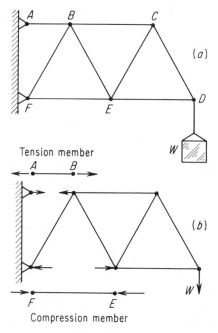

Figure 5-1

it pushes against joints E and F, which in turn push on it and tend to shrink it. A simple test often answers the question of tension or compression: if a flexible cable can support the load, the member is in tension; if it buckles, the member is in compression. A cable would collapse in position EF.

5-3 Analysis by the Method of Joints

The action lines of the forces that act on a simple truss lie on the axes of the individual members; the magnitude and sense of each force are the unknown quantities. One method of determining these forces is to analyze trigonometrically each joint in the truss. Select some initial point—usually either of the ends, where no more than two unknown forces are involved—and proceed from joint to joint, attacking no more than two unknown quantities at a time. The example that follows will illustrate this procedure.

EXAMPLE 1: Determine the force in each member of the truss shown in Fig. 5-2. The structure, supported by a pin at A and a roller at D, is acted upon by a force of 1000 lb at C.

Solution: Isolate the truss from its supports and compute the reactions at A and D.

The reaction A_x is zero, since it is the only x-component of force acting on the free-body:

$$\sum F_x = 0$$
$$A_x = 0$$

A moment summation about pin D gives the reaction A_y,

$$\sum M_D = 0$$
$$20A_y = 5(1000)$$
$$A_y = 250 \, \text{lb}$$

Equilibrium of forces in the y-direction gives the reaction D_y:

$$\sum F_y = 0$$
$$A_y + D_y - 1000 = 0$$
$$D_y = 1000 - 250 = 750 \, \text{lb}$$

Two members are joined at pin A and two at pin D; three members come together at B and C, and four at E. Since a joint with more than two unknown forces cannot be solved, the obvious place to start is either A or D. If joint A is selected, members AB and AE are cut and the free-body diagram is drawn as shown in Fig. 5-2(c). The conditions of equilibrium, $\sum F_x = 0$ and $\sum F_y = 0$, are then applied and the unknown forces are computed. If the sense of a particular force is not obvious,

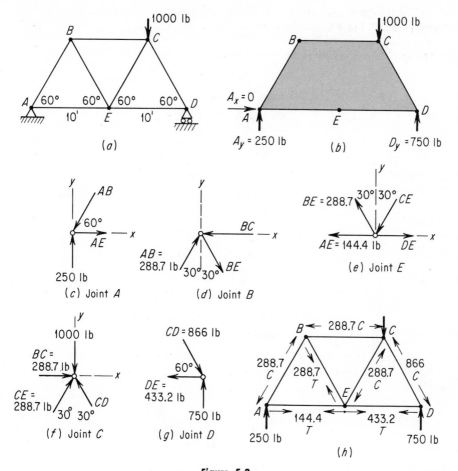

Figure 5-2

it must be assumed. An incorrect guess is indicated by an answer whose magnitude is correct but whose sign is negative.

$$\Sigma F_y = 0$$

$$250 - AB \sin 60° = 0$$

$$AB = \frac{250}{0.866} = 288.7 \text{ lb (compression)}$$

$$\Sigma F_x = 0$$

$$AE - AB \cos 60° = 0$$

$$AE = 288.7(0.5) = 144.4 \text{ lb (tension)}$$

The free-body diagram is next drawn for joint B and the force AB is used to compute BC and BE. BE must pull on the pin to balance the compressive push of AB. BC acts to the left, thereby balancing the horizontal components of force. The equations of equilibrium written for this joint are

$$\Sigma F_y = 0$$
$$288.7 \cos 30° - BE \cos 30° = 0$$
$$BE = 288.7 \text{ lb (tension)}$$

and
$$\Sigma F_x = 0$$
$$288.7 \sin 30° + BE \sin 30° - BC = 0$$
$$BC = 288.7 \text{ lb (compression)}$$

Next, the equations of equilibrium are applied to the free-body diagram of joint E.

$$\Sigma F_y = 0$$
$$288.7 \cos 30° - CE \cos 30° = 0$$
$$CE = 288.7 \text{ lb (compression)}$$

and
$$\Sigma F_x = 0$$
$$DE - 144.4 - 288.7 \cos 60° - CE \cos 60° = 0$$
$$DE = 144.4 + 288.7(0.5) + 288.7(0.5)$$
$$DE = 433.2 \text{ lb (tension)}$$

One unknown force, that in member CD, remains to be determined and joint C will be employed for this computation.

$$\Sigma F_y = 0$$
$$288.7 \cos 30° + CD \cos 30° - 1000 = 0$$
$$CD = \frac{1000 - 288.7(0.886)}{0.866}$$

$$CD = \frac{750}{0.866} = 866 \text{ lb (compression)}$$

Since so many calculations, each dependent upon the one preceding it, are involved, some sort of check should be made. The easiest method is to see if the forces balance at joint D.

$$\Sigma F_x = 0$$
$$433.2 - 866 \cos 60° = 0$$
$$433.2 - 433.2 = 0$$
$$\Sigma F_y = 0$$
$$750 - 866 \sin 60° = 0$$
$$750 - 750 = 0$$

A final sketch showing the magnitudes and directions of the forces within the truss completes the problem. This is shown in Fig. 5-2(h).

5-4 Members That Carry No Load

Often a truss that appears at the outset to be very complicated in reality is quite simple since many of its members are not load supporting. From the practical point of view these members do have a purpose; they are used either to stiffen the truss or to keep certain critical compression members from buckling. As far as the equations of equilibrium are concerned, however, the force within them is zero. To illustrate, consider the truss shown in Fig. 5-3. At first glance it appears that there are 29 members to be determined; this would require the writing of 29 simultaneous equations for a complete analysis. Close inspection, fortunately, shows the entire inner maze to be composed of non-load-carrying members. In the final analysis,

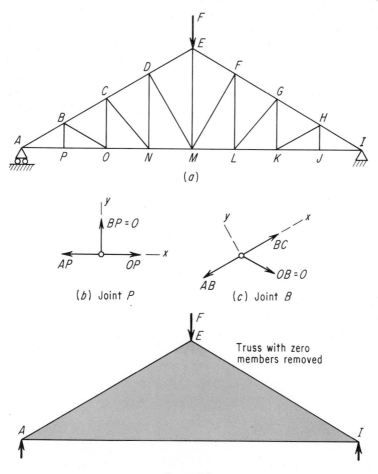

Figure 5-3

only three members, *AE, EI,* and *AI,* actually support loads. The free-body diagram of joint *P* shows *BP* to be the only member that can support a force in the *y*-direction; there is nothing to balance this force, so *BP* must be zero. A similar situation exists at joint *B,* where the component of *OB* along the *y*-axis stands alone: *OB* is zero. If this *analysis by inspection* is continued and the zero members are removed, all that will remain of the truss will be the outer frame *AEI.* Obviously, one of the first steps in the force analysis should be to locate and remove the non-load-carrying members.

5-5 Analysis by The Method of Sections

By isolating as a free-body a section of a truss, it is possible to determine the forces that act in certain members without resorting to the tedious step-by-step method described in the previous sections. Consider again, for example, the truss that was analyzed by the method of joints in Example 1. After the reactions at *A* and *D* have been found, the truss is sectioned along line *a-a* by cutting members *BC, BE,* and *AE* as shown in Fig. 5-4. The left hand portion is isolated as a free-body and the equations of equilibrium are applied to it. The force in member *AE* is found by summing moments about point *B.*

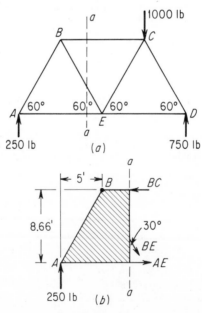

Figure 5-4

$$\Sigma M_B = 0$$

$$8.66AE - 5(250) = 0$$

$$AE = \frac{1250}{8.66} = 144.3 \text{ lb (tension)}$$

BE is the only one of the three members that has a component capable of balancing the 250 lb upward reaction at *A*. Therefore, it is a tension member and the load it carries can be found by a force summation in the *y*-direction.

$$\Sigma F_y = 0$$

$$250 - BE \cos 30° = 0$$

$$BE = \frac{250}{0.866} = 288.7 \text{ lb (tension)}$$

Finally, the components of force in the horizontal direction must balance.

$$\Sigma F_x = 0$$

$$AE + BE \sin 30° - BC = 0$$

$$BC = 144.3 + 288.7(0.5) = 288.7 \text{ lb (compression)}$$

The method of sections is particularly useful when a force analysis of only a few members is required. Occasionally both methods, joints and sections, are used together, since some members are more easily determined by one method than the other. It should be noted, however, that the method of sections does not render a solution when more than three members with unknown loads are cut by the section.

5-6 Analysis of Frames

A *frame*, like a truss, is a structure; they differ only in the way the loads are applied. A frame is capable of supporting loads at points other than the extremities of its members. To illustrate, the frame shown in Fig. 5-5 is composed of three pin-connected members. A force *P* acts on the horizontal member *BD*. The analysis proceeds, in this case, by first determining the reactions at the supports *A* and *E*. Free-body diagrams are then drawn for each member; when necessary, a direction is assumed for the components of force at the various pins. A wrong assumption, just as in truss analysis, will give an answer of correct magnitude, but it will carry a negative sign. The equations of equilibrium are written for each member and the unknown forces are computed.

EXAMPLE 2: Determine the pin reactions at *A*, *B*, and *C* on the members of the frame shown in Fig. 5-6.

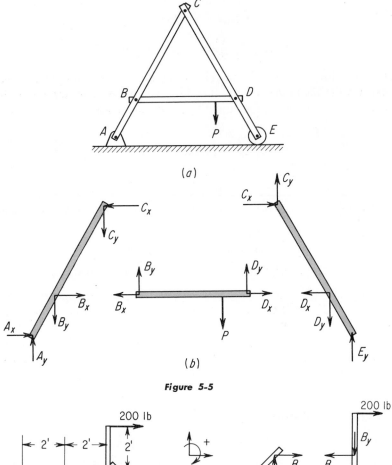

Figure 5-5

Figure 5-6

Solution: Draw a free-body diagram for each member; assume the force directions at the pins. Attempt to find as many of the reactions as possible by single, rather than simultaneous, equations.

C_x can be found by summing moments with respect to point B on the vertical member.

$$\Sigma M_B = 0$$
$$200(2) - 4C_x = 0$$
$$C_x = 100 \text{ lb}$$

A force summation in the x-direction on this same member gives the force B_x.

$$\Sigma F_x = 0$$
$$200 + C_x - B_x = 0$$
$$B_x = 200 + 100 = 300 \text{ lb}$$

A force summation in the y-direction shows B_y and C_y to be equal.

$$\Sigma F_y = 0$$
$$C_y - B_y = 0$$
$$C_y = B_y$$

Now apply the equations of equilibrium to member AB. Moments taken with respect to point A give the force B_y.

$$\Sigma M_A = 0$$
$$4B_x + 2(100) - 4B_y = 0$$
$$B_y = \frac{4(300) + 2(100)}{4} = 350 \text{ lb}$$

Summing forces on member AB in the x- and y-directions completes the analysis.

$$\Sigma F_x = 0$$
$$B_x - A_x = 0$$
$$A_x = B_x = 300 \text{ lb}$$
$$\Sigma F_y = 0$$
$$B_y - A_y - 100 = 0$$
$$A_y = 350 - 100 = 250 \text{ lb}$$

Summarized, the answers are

$$A_x = 300 \text{ lb}, \qquad B_x = 300 \text{ lb}, \qquad C_x = 100 \text{ lb}$$
$$A_y = 250 \text{ lb}, \qquad B_y = 350 \text{ lb}, \qquad C_y = 350 \text{ lb}$$

As a check, both the horizontal forces and the vertical forces must balance on the frame considered a free-body in itself.

Vertical forces:

$$C_y - A_y - 100 = 0$$
$$350 - 250 - 100 = 0$$
$$0 = 0$$

Horizontal forces:

$$200 + C_x - A_x = 0$$
$$200 + 100 - 300 = 0$$
$$0 = 0$$

PROBLEMS

5-1. Determine the force in members AB and BC of the cantilever truss shown in Fig. P5-1. The truss is pin-supported at A and C.

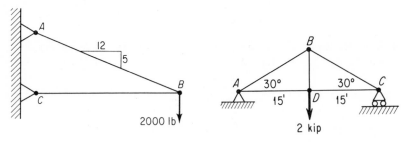

Figure P5-1   **Figure P5-2**

5-2. A simple bridge truss shown in Fig. P5-2 is pin-supported at A and roller-supported at C. Determine the force in each member if a 2 kip load is applied at point D.

5-3. Determine the force in each member of the roof truss shown in Fig. P5-3. The truss is pin-supported at A and roller-supported at F.

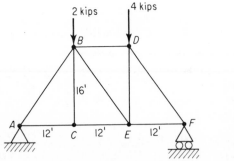

Figure P5-3

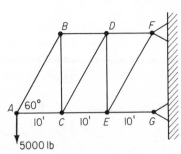

Figure P5-4

5-4. The cantilever truss supports a 5000 lb load directed as shown in Fig. P5-4. Determine the force in each member.

5-5. Determine the force in each member of the truss shown in Fig. P5-5. A vertical load of 2000 lb acts downward as shown.

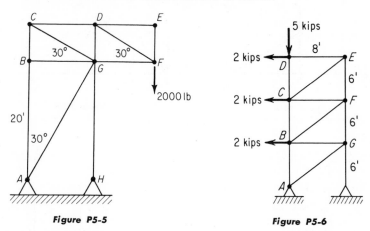

Figure P5-5   **Figure P5-6**

5-6. A section of a vertical tower supports the loads shown in Fig. P5-6. Determine the force in each member of the tower.

5-7. Determine the force in each member of the sign truss in Fig. P5-7.

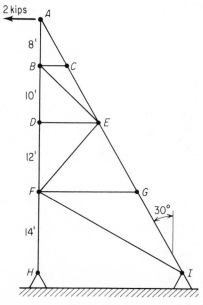

Figure P5-7

5-8–5-13. Locate by inspection the members of the truss that carry no load in Figs. P5-8–P5-13.

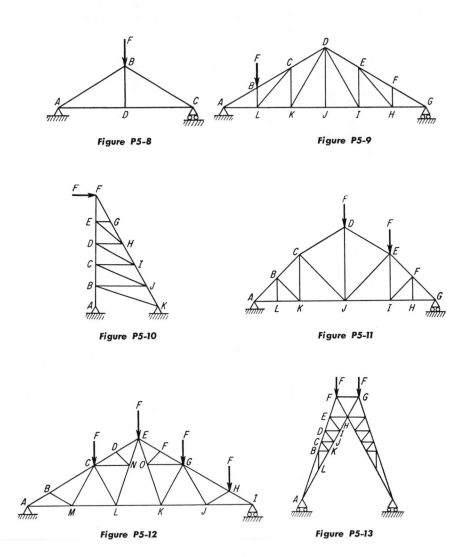

Figure P5-8

Figure P5-9

Figure P5-10

Figure P5-11

Figure P5-12

Figure P5-13

5-14. Use the method of sections to determine the force in members CD, DH, and GH in Fig. P5-14.

5-15. Determine the force in members BC and BF of the cantilever truss in Fig. P5-15. Use the method of sections.

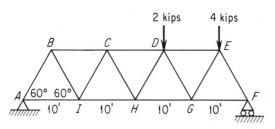

Figure P5-14

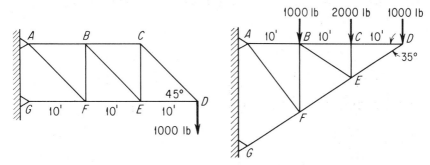

Figure P5-15　　　　　　　**Figure P5-16**

5-16. Use the method of sections to find the force in members *BC*, *BE*, and *EF* in the cantilever truss in Fig. P5-16.

5-17. Use the method of sections to determine the force in members *BC*, *CG*, and *FG* of the overhanging truss in Fig. P5-17.

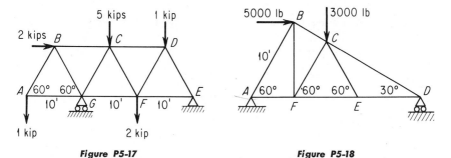

Figure P5-17　　　　　　　**Figure P5-18**

5-18. Determine the force in member *CE* in the triangular truss in Fig. P5-18.

5-19. Determine the force in members *BC* and *BK* in the bridge truss in Fig. P5-19.

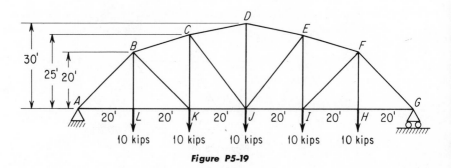

Figure P5-19

5-20. Determine the pin reactions at A, B, and C for the frame loaded as shown in Fig. P5-20.

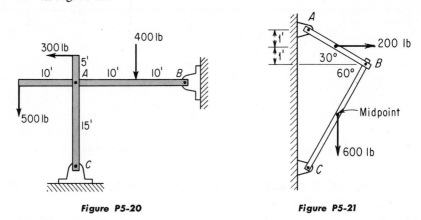

Figure P5-20   **Figure P5-21**

5-21. Determine the pin reactions at A, B, and C that act on the wall bracket in Fig. P5-21.

5-22. Find the pin reactions at A, B, and C that act on the frame in Fig. P5-22.

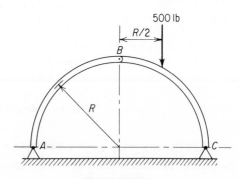

Figure P5-22

5-23. The "A" frame supports a load of 1000 lb as shown in Fig. P5-23. Determine the reactions on the horizontal member at pins B and D. The frame itself is supported by a pin at A and a roller at E.

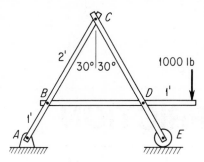

Figure P5-23

5-24. Determine the reactions that act on the double link in Fig. P5-24 at the wall supports A and C.

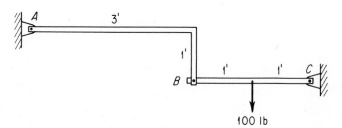

Figure P5-24

Chapter 6

FRICTION

Friction and gravity are the two forces that are most frequently encountered in mechanics, yet they are the least understood. Some 300 years of the combined efforts of scientists and engineers have failed to answer questions concerning their origin and nature.

Friction is both an aid and a hindrance; we are dependent upon it in belt drives, clutches, and brakes, and we seek ways to increase it and thereby increase mechanical efficiency. On the other hand, friction causes bearings, gear teeth, and even space vehicles to wear away; we seek ways to decrease friction to preserve these devices.

6-1 The Laws of Friction

From the practical point of view, three laws describe the retarding force of friction. These laws state that when one solid body slides over another, the frictional force is:

1. *Proportional to the pressure force between the bodies,*
2. *Independent of the area of contact, and*
3. *Independent of the sliding velocity.*

A simple experiment will illustrate these three laws. Body *A* of weight *W* rests on body *B* as shown in Fig. 6-1. A spring scale attached to a rigid support is used to indicate the dragging force of body *B* on body *A*.

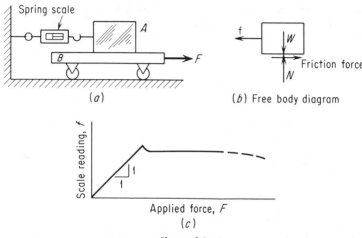

(*a*)

(*b*) Free body diagram

(*c*)

Figure 6-1

The force *F* is applied to body *B* and readings of the scale force *f* are taken. The scale force increases as the applied force increases in a one-to-one ratio until slipping occurs. Once the blocks slide on one another, the scale force drops slightly, and thereafter remains constant and completely independent of the force *F* that acts on body *B*. The relationship between the friction force and the applied force is shown in Fig. 6-1(c). The ratio of the maximum friction force that acts between the surfaces and the normal pressure force *N* is called the *coefficient of static friction* and is symbolized by the Greek letter *mu* with a subscript *s*.

$$\mu_s = \frac{f_{\max}}{N} \qquad (6\text{-}1)$$

The coefficient of kinetic friction, μ_k, is the ratio of the frictional force to the normal force when sliding occurs.

$$\mu_k = \frac{f_{\text{sliding}}}{N} \qquad (6\text{-}2)$$

Two types of problems involving friction are encountered in mechanics. In the first type, the static coefficient of friction is used to determine whether or not a body will move under the action of a given system of forces or to determine the force necessary to just overcome a state of rest. The second type of problem involves bodies that are moving relative to one another; the coefficient of kinetic friction applies to the force analysis. The three examples that follow will illustrate the general class of problems involving static friction.

EXAMPLE 1: A 100 lb block rests on an inclined plane as shown in Fig. 6-2. Determine the maximum inclination angle θ that can exist without allowing the block to move. The coefficient of static friction between the contact surfaces is $\mu_s = 0.65$.

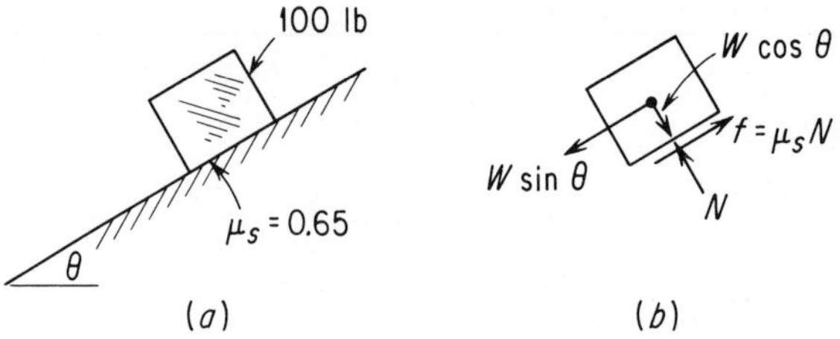

Figure 6-2

Solution: To maintain equilibrium, the component of the weight force must balance the maximum available frictional force

$$W \sin \theta = \mu_s N$$

where N, the normal force, is equal to the component of weight, $W \cos \theta$. Therefore,

$$W \sin \theta = \mu_s W \cos \theta$$

Dividing both sides of this equation by $W \cos \theta$ gives

$$\tan \theta = \mu_s$$

or $\theta = \text{arc tan } 0.65 = 33°$

EXAMPLE 2: Determine the range of values for the force F so that the 100 lb block shown in Fig. 6-3(a) will slide neither up nor down the inclined surface. The coefficient of static friction between the block and the plan is $\mu_s = 0.40$.

Solution: The force of friction always opposes the direction of motion or the direction of *impending* motion. Two free-body diagrams are therefore required:
   1. to describe the force system when impending motion is upward, and
   2. to describe the force system when impending motion is downward.
These two diagrams are shown in Fig. 6-3(b) and in Fig. 6-3(c).
   To start the block upward, the applied force F must overcome the gravity force $W \sin \theta$ and the friction force $f = \mu_s N$.

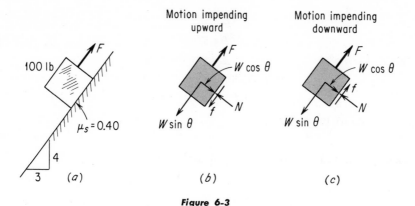

Figure 6-3

$$F = W \sin \theta + \mu_s N = W \sin \theta + \mu_s W \cos \theta$$
$$= 100(\tfrac{4}{5}) + 0.40(100)\tfrac{3}{5} = 104 \text{ lb}$$

For impending downward motion the direction of the friction force reverses; in this case, friction helps support the weight on the plane.

$$F = W \sin \theta - \mu_s W \cos \theta$$
$$= (100)\tfrac{4}{5} - 0.40(100)\tfrac{3}{5} = 56 \text{ lb}$$

The block will not move if F is not less than 56 lb or does not exceed 104 lb.

EXAMPLE 3: The bracket shown in Fig. 6-4(a) is a *self-locking* device; if the weight is far enough outward, the bracket will not slide downward. Determine the minimum distance d at which the weight W can be placed without causing the bracket to slip downward. The coefficient of static friction between the sliding surfaces is $\mu_s = 0.25$.

Solution: The bracket bears on the vertical rod at edges A and B; the reactions at these two points are N_A and N_B. Frictional forces at these two points are upward, since they oppose the impending downward motion. Equilibrium in the x- and y-directions gives

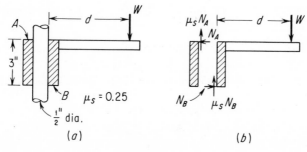

Figure 6-4

$$\Sigma F_x = 0$$

$$N_A = N_B \tag{a}$$

and $$\Sigma F_y = 0$$

$$\mu_s N_A + \mu_s N_B - W = 0$$

$$0.25(N_A + N_B) = W \tag{b}$$

Combining Eqs. (a) and (b) gives

$$N_A = N_B = 2W \tag{c}$$

Taking moments about corner B completes the solution:

$$\Sigma M_B = 0$$

$$Wd + 0.5\mu_s N_A - 3N_A = 0$$

Simplifying gives

$$Wd = [3 - (0.5)(0.25)]N_A = 2.875\ N_A \tag{d}$$

The distance d is computed by combining Eqs. (c) and (d):

$$Wd = 2.88(2)W$$

where $$d = 5.75 \text{ in.}$$

This is the minimum distance to prevent slipping.

6-2 Angle of Friction

In solving many problems involving friction, it is sometimes more convenient to use the resultant of the friction force f and the normal force N rather than the two separately. The angle, shown in Fig. 6-5, between the resultant force R and the normal force N is called the *angle of friction*, and is defined by

$$\tan \alpha = \frac{f}{N} \tag{6-3}$$

The angle of friction has a maximum value when $f = \mu_s N$, thus

$$\tan \alpha_{\max} = \frac{\mu_s N}{N} = \mu_s \tag{6-4}$$

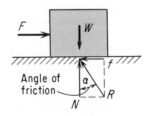

Figure 6-5

Eq. (6-4) states that *the tangent of the angle of friction is equal to the coefficient of friction.*

6-3 Wedges

The angle of friction is most advantageously employed in problems dealing with *wedges*. This is illustrated in the typical wedge problem shown in Fig. 6-6: a force, applied to wedge A, lifts the weight W. The free-body diagram shows A to be acted upon by three forces: the applied force F, the reaction R_1 at the horizontal surface, and the reaction R_2 between wedge A and block B. Both R_1 and R_2 represent the combined effect of the friction force and the normal force between the sliding surfaces. In a similar manner three forces R_2, R_3, and W act on body B.

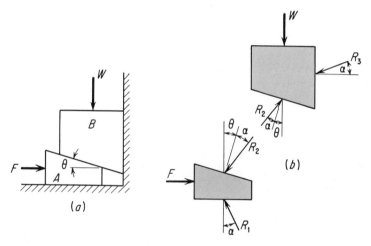

Figure 6-6

EXAMPLE 4: A 5 deg wedge is used to raise a 1000 lb weight as shown in Fig. 6-7(a). Determine the force F required to start the wedge if the coefficient of static friction between all sliding surfaces is $\mu_s = 0.30$.

Solution: The angle of friction is given by Eq. (6-4).

$$\tan \alpha = 0.30$$

$$\alpha = 16.7°$$

The free-body diagram of block A, shown in Fig. 6-7(b), indicates the three forces that are equilibrium: 1000 lb acting downward, the rope tension T to the right, and the resultant R_1 at an angle of $(\alpha + 5°)$ with the vertical.

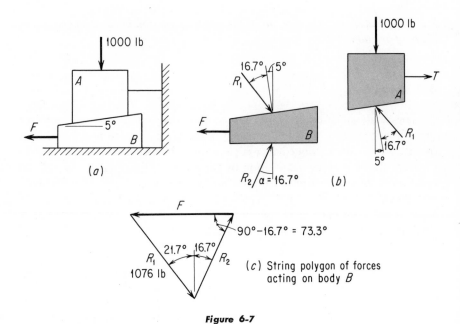

Figure 6-7

A force summation in the y-direction on body A gives

$$\Sigma F_y = 0$$

$$R_1 \cos (5° + \alpha) - 1000 = 0$$

$$R_1 = \frac{1000}{\cos 21.7°} = \frac{1000}{0.9291}$$

$$R_1 = 1076 \text{ lb}$$

The required force F is found by applying the sine law to the string polygon of forces acting on wedge B.

$$\frac{F}{\sin (21.7° + 16.7°)} = \frac{1076}{\sin 73.3°}$$

Solving for F gives

$$F = 1076 \frac{\sin 38.4°}{\sin 73.3°} = 1076 \left(\frac{0.6212}{0.9578}\right)$$

where

$$F = 698 \text{ lb}$$

6-4 Belt Friction

The friction developed between a flat belt or a rope and a cylindrical surface is used to *transmit* power, while band brakes, capstans and similar devices make use of belt friction to *retard* motion. A typical free-body diagram of a rope that has impending motion against a rough cylindrical surface is shown in Fig. 6-8. A force T_L is applied to the rope causing the weight to move upward. The normal reactions of the cylinder on the rope vary from zero to a maximum value and then to zero again. T_L and T_S are the tensions on either side of the rope. The subscripts L and S distinguish the larger tension from the smaller: *the larger tension always tends to cause impending motion.*

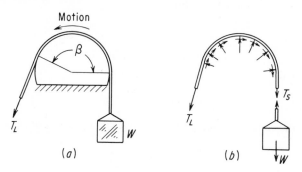

Figure 6-8

The equation that governs the relationship between T_L and T_S states that

$$T_L = T_S e^{\mu\beta} \tag{6-5}$$

where: e = base of the natural logarithm = 2.718
μ = coefficient of friction
β = angle of contact in radians

The term $e^{\mu\beta}$ represents an exponential power of the number 2.718. To determine the magnitude of the exponential term for values of $\mu\beta$ refer to Table II of the Appendix or use a slide rule to determine these values.

EXAMPLE 5: A 100 lb weight is suspended from a rope that passes over a rough cylindrical surface as shown in Fig. 6-9. Determine the force F that must be applied

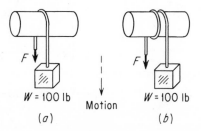

Figure 6-9

to the free end of the rope to just prevent the weight from slipping downward if:
(a) the rope is in contact with one-half of the cylindrical surface; (b) the rope is
wrapped one and one-half times around the cylinder. The coefficient of static
friction between the rope and the cylinder is $\mu_s = 0.40$.

Solution: Since the larger tension always opposes the direction of impending
motion, $T_L = 100$ lb and T_S is the desired force. For a one-half turn, the contact
angle β equals π radians, and for one and one-half turns β equals 3π radians.
The data are substituted into Eq. (6-5):

Part (a):

$$T_L = T_S e^{\mu \beta}$$
$$100 = T_S e^{(0.40)\pi}$$

solving for T_S gives

$$T_S = \frac{100}{e^{1.26}}$$

Table II of the Appendix gives the value of the exponential term as $e^{1.26} = 3.525$;

therefore $$T_S = \frac{100}{3.525} = 28.4 \text{ lb}$$

Part (b): The exponential term assumes a much larger value as β increases

$$e^{\mu \beta} = e^{(0.40)3\pi} = e^{3.77}$$
$$e^{\mu \beta} = 43.31$$

The force required to support the weight in this case is considerably less than that
required in Part (a):

$$T_S = \frac{100}{43.31} = 2.31 \text{ lb}$$

It is interesting to note that the size of the bar has no bearing on the required force.

EXAMPLE 6: The band brake shown in Fig. 6-10(a) is used to arrest the motion
of the flywheel. Determine the tension in either side of the band if a force of
$F = 20$ lb is applied at point D as shown. The coefficient of kinetic friction between
the wheel and the band is $\mu_k = 0.60$.

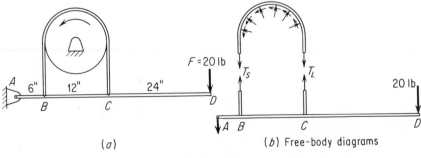

(a)   (b) Free-body diagrams

Figure 6-10

Solution: Two equations are required, since two unknowns, T_L and T_S, are involved in the computation. The belt friction equation governs the ratio of T_L to T_S.

$$\frac{T_L}{T_S} = e^{\mu\beta} = e^{(0.60)\pi}$$

$$T_L = 6.554 \, T_S \tag{a}$$

A moment summation about point A on the lever gives a second equation involving the two unknowns.

$$\Sigma M_A = 0$$

$$6T_S + 18T_L - 42(20) = 0$$

$$T_S + 3T_L = 140 \tag{b}$$

The simultaneous solution of Eqs. (a) and (b) gives the desired answers:

$$T_S + 3(6.554)T_S = 140$$

$$T_S = \frac{140}{20.66} = 6.78 \, \text{lb}$$

$$T_L = 6.554(6.78) = 44.4 \, \text{lb}$$

6-5 Rolling Resistance

Rolling friction, which is usually referred to as *rolling resistance*, results when the surface that supports a rolling load deforms. Figure 6-11 is an exaggerated illustration of this effect. W is the vertical load acting on the wheel and F the force required to pull the wheel out of the depression or rut. Three forces, F, W, and R are in equilibrium. A moment summation about point A gives

$$\Sigma M_A = 0$$

$$W \cdot a - F \cdot d = 0$$

Since the depression is usually very small, the distance d may be replaced by the radius r.

$$F = \frac{Wa}{r} \tag{6-6}$$

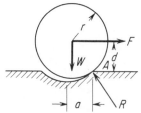

Figure 6-11

The distance *a* is called the *coefficient of rolling resistance;* it may vary from 0.003 in. for steel on steel to 4 in. for steel on soft ground.

EXAMPLE 7: The coefficient of rolling resistance between a 24 in. in diameter steel drum and a level pavement is 0.05 in. Determine the force necessary to overcome rolling resistance if the drum weighs 2000 lb.

Solution: The data are substituted into Eq. (6-6).

$$F = \frac{Wa}{r} = \frac{2000(0.05)}{12}$$

$$F = 8.33 \text{ lb}$$

6-6 Disk Friction

Another type of frictional force which has great importance in the field of machine design is that which occurs between circular areas that are thrust together as shown in Fig. 6-12. Pivots, disk brakes, clutches, and thrust bearings are examples of mechanisms in which this type of friction is developed.

Figure 6-12

Of interest is the magnitude of the moment *M* that is required to cause motion to impend. It is assumed in the analysis that the contact pressure between the mated surfaces is uniformly distributed. Each component of pressure is equivalent to a normal force; frictional forces, then, act over the entire contact area. The products of these friction forces and their respective lever arms, when summed, is equivalent to the external moment *M* necessary to cause motion to impend. The value of this moment is given by

$$M = \tfrac{2}{3}\mu FR \qquad\qquad\qquad (6\text{-}7)$$

where F = thrust force
$\quad R$ = radius of contact area
$\quad \mu$ = coefficient of friction

If the shaft were hollow, the contact area would be a ring rather than a complete circle, and the moment *M* would be given by

$$M = \frac{2}{3}\mu F \frac{(R_o^3 - R_i^3)}{(R_o^2 - R_i^2)} \qquad\qquad (6\text{-}8)$$

R_i and R_o are the inside and outside radii respectively.

EXAMPLE 8: A thrust force of 800 lb acts on the pilot bearing shown in Fig. 6-13. Determine the moment M that must be applied to cause the shaft to rotate. The coefficient of kinetic friction at the contact surface is $\mu_k = 0.10$.

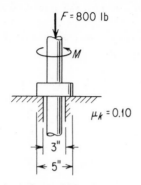

Figure 6-13

Solution: Since a ring of area is involved, Eq. (6-8) is used to find the moment M:

$$M = \frac{2}{3}\mu F \frac{(R_o^3 - R_i^3)}{(R_o^2 - R_i^2)}$$

$$= \frac{2}{3}(0.10)800 \frac{(2.5)^3 - (1.5)^3}{(2.5)^2 - (1.5)^2}$$

$$= 163 \text{ lb in.}$$

PROBLEMS

6-1. The 100 lb body shown in three positions in Fig. P6-1 is at rest; in each case the coefficient of static friction between the surfaces is 0.25. Determine the frictional forces developed between the body and the surface.

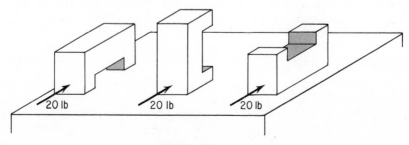

Figure P6-1

6-2. The force F in Prob. 6-1 is increased to 30 lb; find the frictional force developed between each body and the horizontal surface. Are the bodies in equilibrium?

6-3. Plot a curve which will show the magnitude of the frictional force developed between the block and the plane shown in Fig. P6-3 as the angle of elevation is increased from zero to 60 deg. The coefficient of friction is 0.30.

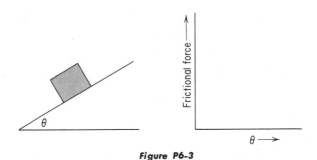

Figure P6-3

6-4. The wooden crate is on the verge of moving downward when the plane is titled 20 deg as shown in Fig. P6-4. Determine the coefficient of static friction between the contacting surfaces.

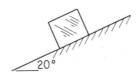

Figure P6-4

6-5. If $\mu_k = 0.9\mu_s$ in Prob. 6-4, by how much can the angle θ be reduced and still have motion downward after the crate overcomes static friction?

6-6. Determine whether the block shown in Fig. P6-6 is moving or is at rest. The coefficients of friction between the contact surfaces are $\mu_s = 0.22$ and $\mu_k = 0.18$.

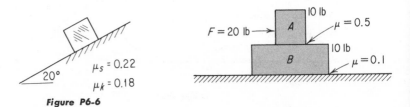

Figure P6-6

6-7. The two blocks shown in Fig. P6-7 are resting upon one another and in turn the two are resting on the rough plane. Will block *A* move relative to *B*? Will block *B* move relative to the plane? Prove your answers by drawing free-body diagrams.

6-8. Find the couple *C* necessary to cause the 200 lb cylinder in Fig. P6-8 to begin rotating clockwise. The coefficient of static friction at both *A* and *B* is $\mu_s = 0.30$.

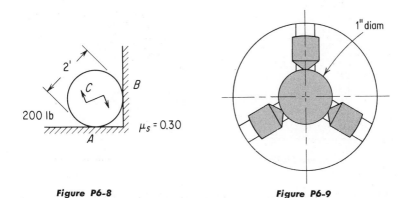

Figure **P6-8**   Figure **P6-9**

6-9. Determine the twisting moment required to cause the 1 in. cylindrical bar to slip in the three-jaw-face chuck shown in Fig. P6-9. Assume a coefficient of static friction of 0.5 and a normal jaw force of 200 lb.

6-10. Solve Prob. 6-9 assuming that the chuck has four equispaced jaws instead of the three as shown.

6-11. In Fig. P6-11, a ladder weighing 25 lb supports a man weighing 180 lb at point *C*. The vertical surface is smooth; the floor is rough. Determine the minimum angle θ at which the ladder will stand without slipping if the coefficient of static friction at *A* is $\mu_s = 0.30$.

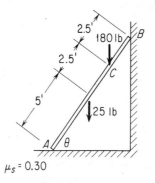

Figure **P6-11**

6-12. Determine the frictional force developed at point *A* in Prob. 6-11 if θ is 75 deg.

6-13. Find the maximum value of the distance *h* in order that the 50 lb block in Fig. P6-13 will slide without tipping. The coefficient of friction between the block and the plane is $\mu = 0.35$.

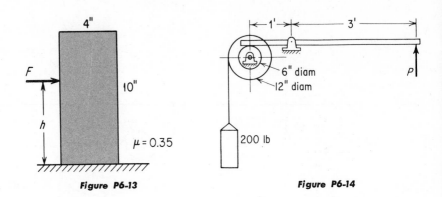

Figure P6-13   Figure P6-14

6-14. Find the force *P* required to prevent rotation of the 100 lb wheel in Fig. P6-14. The coefficient of static friction between the wheel and the brake shoe is $\mu_s = 0.40$.

6-15. A 26 ft ladder of negligible weight rests against a wall as shown in Fig. P6-15. Determine how high a 200 lb man can climb before the ladder slips. The coefficient of static friction at both *A* and *B* is $\mu_s = 0.25$.

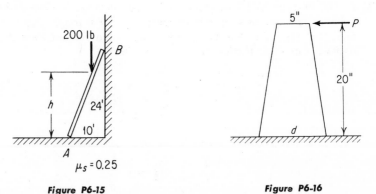

Figure P6-15   Figure P6-16

6-16. Determine the smallest allowable width *d* if the 20 lb block in Fig. P6-16 is to slide rather than tip as *P* is gradually increased. The coefficient of friction between the block and the plane is $\mu_s = 0.20$.

6-17. The 100 lb cylinder is supported by a roller free to turn as shown in Fig. P6-17. Determine the magnitude of the couple required to turn the cylinder if the coefficient of friction between the cylinder and vertical wall is 0.5.

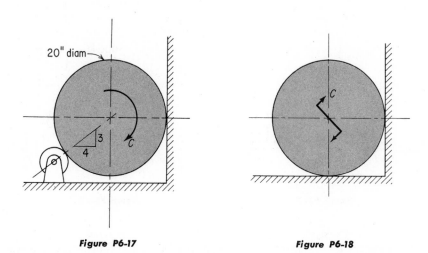

Figure P6-17   **Figure P6-18**

6-18. Determine the torque C required to spin the cylinder of weight W against the wall as shown in Fig. P6-18. The coefficient of friction is μ at both surfaces.

6-19. In Fig. P6-19, the wedge A is used to raise the 2000 lb weight that rests on block B. Determine the force P required to cause motion to impend. The coefficient of static friction between all surfaces is $\mu_s = 0.30$.

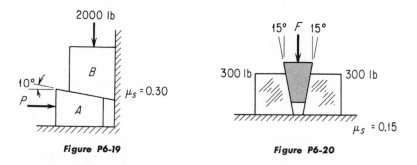

Figure P6-19   **Figure P6-20**

6-20. Determine the force P required to start the wedge in Fig. P6-20 downward. The coefficient of static friction between all contact surfaces is $\mu_s = 0.15$.

6-21. A uniformly distributed load of 100 lb per ft acts on the 12 ft pivoted beam as shown in Fig. P6-21. Determine the force P that must be applied to the 5 deg wedge to cause it just to move. The coefficient of static friction between all surfaces at the wedge is $\mu_s = 0.20$.

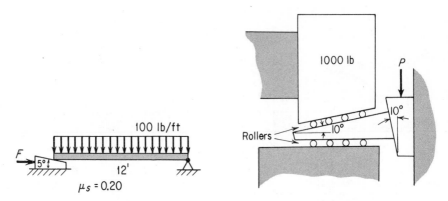

Figure P6-21   Figure P6-22

6-22. A 10 deg wedge is used to raise the 1000 lb weight as shown in Fig. P6-22. Find the force P if the coefficient of friction for all sliding surfaces is 0.2.

6-23. Find the force necessary to just hold the 50 lb weight in Fig. P6-23. The coefficient of kinetic friction between the rope and the cylindrical surface is $\mu_k = 0.20$.

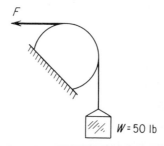

Figure P6-23

6-24. Two turns of rope are wrapped around a horizontal, cylindrical bar. A pull of 20 lb on one end of the rope just prevents a 150 lb weight attached to the other end from slipping downward. Determine the coefficient of friction between the rope and the bar.

6-25. In Fig. P6-25, the coefficient of kinetic friction between the cylindrical surfaces and the rope that supports the 300 lb weight is $\mu_k = 0.25$. Find the force F and the cable tension at A if the weight is on the verge of moving downward.

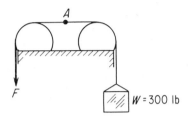

Figure P6-25

6-26. A weight of 500 lb is supported by a force of 50 lb applied to a rope that is passed around a horizontal, cylindrical bar. How many turns are required if the coefficient of friction between the rope and the post is $\mu_s = 1/\pi$?

6-27. In Fig. P6-27, the band brake is used to stop the motion of the flywheel. What force P must be applied to the lever if the flywheel is rotating counterclockwise and the tension in the vertical portion of the belt is 200 lb? The coefficient of kinetic friction between the belt and the wheel is $\mu_k = 0.20$.

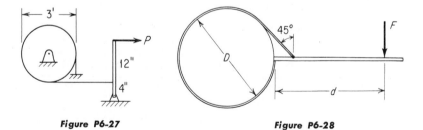

Figure P6-27   **Figure P6-28**

6-28. A strap pipe wrench is shown in Fig. P6-28. Find the least value of d which is necessary so that the wrench will not slip. Assume the coefficient of friction between the belt and pipe is 0.20 and neglect any frictional force between the handle and pipe.

6-29. Determine the horizontal pull required to move a 1500 ton train along a level track. The coefficient of rolling resistance is 0.01 in. and the wheels are 3 ft in diameter.

6-30. Determine the coefficient of rolling resistance if a force of 8 lb is required to move the hand truck in Fig. P6-30 at a constant velocity. The wheels are 12 in. in diameter.

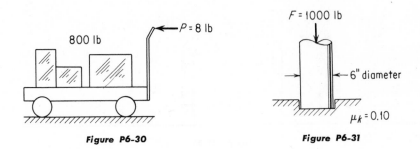

Figure P6-30   Figure P6-31

6-31. A solid circular shaft 6 in. in diameter pivots in a flat socket as shown in Fig. P6-31. Find the frictional moment developed as the shaft rotates. The shaft carries a thrust load of 1000 lb, and the coefficient of kinetic friction μ_k is 0.10.

6-32. If a torque of 35 lb ft is required to move the shaft shown in Prob. 6-31, determine the coefficient of kinetic friction at the contact surfaces.

6-33. Determine the moment required to rotate the pressure plate shown in Fig. P6-33. The coefficient of friction at the contact surface is 0.15.

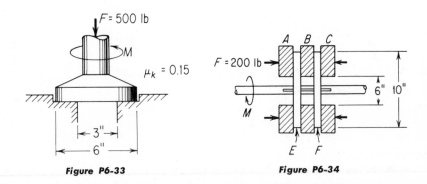

Figure P6-33   Figure P6-34

6-34. A double-disk clutch is shown in Fig. P6-34. Disks A, B, and C can move axially but cannot rotate, while disks E and F are keyed to the shaft and rotate with it. Find the moment M that must be applied to slip the clutch. The coefficient of kinetic friction between all contact surfaces is $\mu_k = 0.15$.

Chapter 7

MOMENT
OF INERTIA

The *moment of inertia*, or *second-moment*, as it is sometimes called, is a particular mathematical expression that appears in mechanics: it is used in the study of the strength of beams, columns, and torsion bars; in the study of fluids; and in the study of angular motion and vibrations. Because this important quantity is frequently encountered, it is essential to know how it is determined.

7-1 Moment of Inertia of an Area
by Approximation

Moment of inertia I is always computed relative to a reference point, line, or plane. In the case of the small element of area ΔA shown in Fig. 7-1, I is equal to the product of the area and the square of its distance from a particular axis. Thus, the moment of inertia with reference to the x-axis is

$$I_x = y^2(\Delta A) \tag{7-1}$$

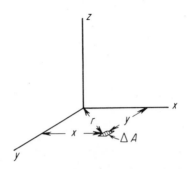

Figure 7-1

With reference to the y-axis the moment of inertia of ΔA is given by

$$I_y = x^2(\Delta A) \tag{7-2}$$

The product of ΔA and the square of its distance from the z-axis, which is perpendicular to the plane of the area, is called the *polar moment of inertia* and is symbolized by the letter J.

$$J = r^2(\Delta A) \tag{7-3}$$

Since r can be expressed in terms of x and y, the polar moment of inertia is related to I_x and I_y; thus

$$J = r^2(\Delta A) = (x^2 + y^2)\Delta A = x^2(\Delta A) + y^2(\Delta A)$$

and

$$J = I_x + I_y \tag{7-4}$$

The moment of inertia of an area with respect to an axis is the sum of the moments of inertia of the elements that comprise the area. This statement provides a means of approximating I_x, I_y, or J when exact formulas are not available:

$$I_x = \Sigma \, y^2(\Delta A)$$
$$I_y = \Sigma \, x^2(\Delta A) \tag{7-5}$$

The smaller the elements selected, the more accurate will be the approximation.

EXAMPLE 1: Determine the approximate value of I_x of the area shown in Fig. 7-2(a).

Solution: The area is divided into 10 strips parallel to the x-axis as shown in Fig. 7-2(a). All elements of area within each strip are assumed to be the same distance from the axis; the error in the computation lies in this assumption.

The area of the first strip, 3 sq. in., is at a mean distance of 7.5 in. from the x-axis. The moment of inertia $(I_x)_1$ is

$$(I_x)_1 = (\text{area}) \times (\text{distance})^2 = 3(1)(7.5)^2 = 168.75 \text{ in.}^4$$

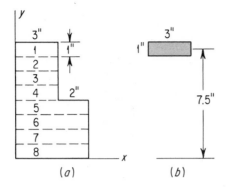

Figure 7-2

The moments of inertia of the remaining strips are computed in a similar manner.

$$(I_x)_2 = 3(1)(6.5)^2 = 126.75 \text{ in.}^4$$
$$(I_x)_3 = 3(1)(5.5)^2 = 90.75 \text{ in.}^4$$
$$(I_x)_4 = 3(1)(4.5)^2 = 60.75 \text{ in.}^4$$
$$(I_x)_5 = 5(1)(3.5)^2 = 61.25 \text{ in.}^4$$
$$(I_x)_6 = 5(1)(2.5)^2 = 31.25 \text{ in.}^4$$
$$(I_x)_7 = 5(1)(1.5)^2 = 11.25 \text{ in.}^4$$
$$(I_x)_8 = 5(1)(0.5)^2 = 1.25 \text{ in.}^4$$

The moment of inertia I_x is the sum of the individual values

$$I_x = \Sigma \, (I_x)_n$$
$$I_x = 168.75 + 126.75 + 90.75 + 60.75 + 61.25 + 31.25 + 11.25 + 1.25$$
$$I_x = 552 \text{ in.}^4$$

An exact answer, obtained by methods that will be described later, gives a value of $I_x = 554.7$ in.^{4} The error in the approximation is less than 0.5 per cent.

The method of finding moments of inertia illustrated in Example 1 has particular value when the area of concern has an irregular shape. Formulas for the more common shapes, such as rectangles, triangles, and circles, are readily available in handbooks that deal with properties of areas.

7-2 Parallel Axis Theorem

The centroidal moment of inertia, that which is computed with reference to an axis through the centroid, can be used to find the value of moments of inertia about other parallel axes. Consider the area shown in Fig. 7-3, where the y-axis is assumed to pass through the centroid O. The moment of

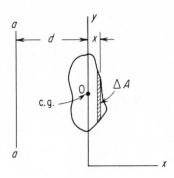

Figure 7-3

inertia of an element of area ΔA about axis a-a parallel to the y-axis is $(x + d)^2 \, \Delta A$, and the moment of inertia of the entire area about axis a-a is

$$I_{a-a} = \Sigma \, (x + d)^2 \Delta A$$

Expanding the bracketed term gives

$$\begin{aligned} I_{a-a} &= \Sigma \, (x^2 + 2xd + d^2)\Delta A \\ &= \Sigma \, x^2(\Delta A) + \Sigma \, 2xd(\Delta A) + \Sigma \, d^2 \, \Delta A \\ &= \bar{I} + 2d\bar{x}A + Ad^2 \end{aligned}$$

The term $\bar{x}$ in the expression is zero, since the y-axis lies on the centroid of the area: the equation reduces to

$$I_{a-a} = \bar{I} + Ad^2 \tag{7-6}$$

where $\bar{I}$ is the moment of inertia with respect to the centroidal axis and Ad^2 is the product of the area and the square of its distance to the parallel axis. This expression is called the *parallel axis theorem*.

EXAMPLE 2: The area of 25 sq in. shown in Fig. 7-4 has a centroidal moment of inertia of $\bar{I}_y = 60$ in.[4] Determine the moment of inertia with respect to line a–a, 10 in. to the left of the y-axis.

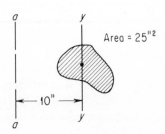

Figure 7-4

Solution: The moment of inertia is given by Eq. (7-6).

$$I_{a-a} = I_y + Ad^2$$
$$= 60 + 25(10)^2 = 2560 \text{ in.}^4$$

7-3 Radius of Gyration

The *radius of gyration* is a number, symbolized by the letter k, which, when squared and multiplied by the area, equals the moment of inertia of that area.

$$I = Ak^2 \qquad (7\text{-}7)$$

As with moment of inertia, it is difficult to attach a physical meaning to the radius of gyration of an area; it is simply a term that is frequently used in mechanics.

EXAMPLE 3: The 12 in. by 5 in. I beam shown in Fig. 7-5 weighs 35 lb per lineal ft. I_x and I_y are 227.0 in.^{4} and 10.0 in.^{4} respectively, and the cross-sectional area of the beam is 10.2 sq in. Determine the radius of gyration with respect to the x-axis and with respect the y-axis.

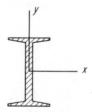

Figure 7-5

Solution: The data are substituted into Eq. (7-7).

$$k = \sqrt{\frac{I}{A}}$$

$$k_x = \sqrt{\frac{227}{10.2}} = 4.72 \text{ in.}$$

$$k_y = \sqrt{\frac{10}{10.2}} = 0.99 \text{ in.}$$

7-4 Composite Areas

Formulas can be derived which give the exact value of the moment of inertia for the various geometric shapes. Several of these are listed in Table 7-1; others, particularly those for structural sections, can be found in handbooks which list the properties of geometric sections.

Table 7-1. Moments of Inertia of Areas

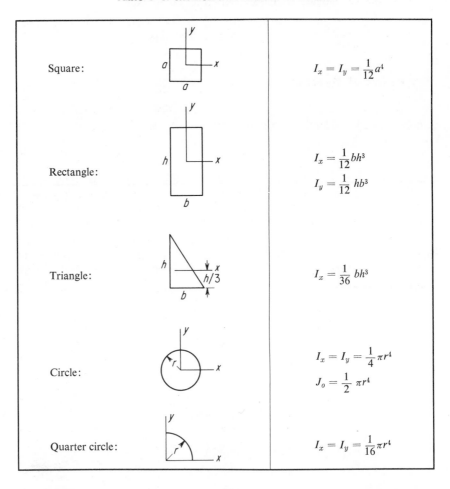

Square:	$I_x = I_y = \dfrac{1}{12}a^4$
Rectangle:	$I_x = \dfrac{1}{12}bh^3$ $I_y = \dfrac{1}{12}hb^3$
Triangle:	$I_x = \dfrac{1}{36}bh^3$
Circle:	$I_x = I_y = \dfrac{1}{4}\pi r^4$ $J_o = \dfrac{1}{2}\pi r^4$
Quarter circle:	$I_x = I_y = \dfrac{1}{16}\pi r^4$

When an area is composed of two or more simple areas, its moment of inertia is the sum of the individual values all with respect to a common reference line. The parallel axis theorem is employed in this type of problem to transfer the individual inertias to a common reference line.

The examples that follow illustrate both the use of the table and the method of determining the moment of inertia of composite areas.

EXAMPLE 4: Determine the values of the centroidal moments of inertia $\bar{I}_x$ and $\bar{I}_y$ for the area shown in Fig. 7-6.

Solution: The moment of inertia of the composite area is the sum of the moments of inertia of its parts, each found with reference to the centroidal axis

Structural Shapes

		Size (in.)	Weight per ft (lb)	Area (in.²)	w (in.)	d (in.)	$\bar{x}$ (in.)	I_x (in.⁴)	I_y (in.⁴)
Wide flange beam:		12 × 12	120	35.31	12.32	13.12	0	1072	345
		10 × 10	100	29.43	10.35	11.12	0	625	207
Channel:		12 × 3	30	8.79	3.17	12.00	0.68	161.2	5.2
		6 × 2	13	3.81	2.16	6.00	0.52	17.3	1.1
Equal leg angle:		$6 \times 6 \times \frac{1}{2}$	19.6	5.75	6	6	1.68	19.9	19.9
		$3 \times 3 \times \frac{3}{8}$	7.2	2.11	3	3	0.89	1.8	1.8

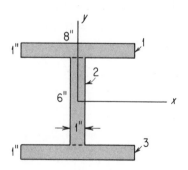

Figure 7-6

of the composite area before addition. In this example, the centroid is found simply by inspection.

The y-axis passes through the centroid of each of the three rectangles. The formulas from Table 7-1 can be used directly to find $\bar{I}_y$.

$$\bar{I}_y = (\bar{I}_y)_1 + (\bar{I}_y)_2 + (\bar{I}_y)_3$$

Hence

$$I_y = \tfrac{1}{12}(1)(8)^3 + \tfrac{1}{12}(6)(1)^3 + \tfrac{1}{12}(1)8^3$$
$$= 42.67 + 0.5 + 42.67$$
$$= 85.84 \text{ in.}^4$$

To find I_x, the parallel axis theorem must be employed to transfer the inertias of areas A_1 and A_3 to the centroidal x-axis.

$$(I_x)_1 = \bar{I}_1 + Ad^2$$
$$= \tfrac{1}{12}(8)(1)^3 + 8(1)(3.5)^2$$
$$= 0.67 + 98.00$$
$$= 98.67 \text{ in.}^4$$

$(I_x)_1$ and $(I_x)_3$ are numerically equal to one another, since the areas A_1 and A_3 are the same distance from the centroidal x-axis.

$(I_x)_2$ can be found directly by formula

where
$$(I_x)_2 = \tfrac{1}{12}bh^3 = \tfrac{1}{12}(1)(6)^3$$
$$(I_x)_2 = 18.00 \text{ in.}^4$$

The moment of inertia of the composite area about the centroidal x-axis is, then, the sum of the three component inertias.

$$(\bar{I}_x) = (I_x)_1 + (I_x)_2 + (I_x)_3$$
$$= 98.67 + 18.00 + 98.67$$
$$= 215.34 \text{ in.}^4$$

EXAMPLE 5: A rectangular plate 8 in. high by 6 in. wide has a hole 4 in. in diameter drilled through as shown in Fig. 7-7. Determine the moment of inertia of the plate with reference to axis a–a.

Solution: The missing area is assumed to contribute a negative moment of inertia to the section.

The moment of inertia of the rectangle, transferred to axis a–a, is

$$(I_{a-a})_1 = \tfrac{1}{12}bh^3 + Ad^2$$
$$= \tfrac{1}{12}(6)(8)^3 + 6(8)(4)^2$$
$$= 256 + 768 = 1024 \text{ in.}^4$$

The moment of inertia of the circle, also transferred to axis a–a, is

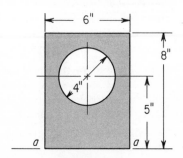

Figure 7-7

$$(I_{a-a})_2 = \frac{\pi r^4}{4} + Ad^2$$

$$= \frac{\pi(2)^4}{4} + \pi(2)^2(5)^2$$

$$= 12.56 + 314.00$$

$$= 326.56 \text{ in.}^4$$

The moment of inertia of the composite section is

$$I_{a-a} = (I_{a-a})_1 - (I_{a-a})_2$$

$$= 1024 - 326.56$$

$$= 697.44 \text{ in.}^4$$

7-5 Moment of Inertia of Bodies

The mathematical expression $\sum (\Delta W/g)r^2$ is frequently encountered in problems concerned with rotation of solid bodies. The term [weight]/[gravity] is called the *mass* of the body and for this reason the mathematical expression is referred to as the *mass moment of inertia*. The equation indicates a process of summation of the products of the individual elements of mass and the square of their distance from the particular reference axis.

The term W/g is called a *slug* and has the dimensions

$$\frac{W}{g} = \frac{\text{lb}}{\text{ft/sec}^2}$$

Mass moment of inertia has the dimensions, therefore, of slug ft² or ft lb sec²

$$I = \frac{W}{g}r^2 = \frac{\text{lb}}{\text{ft/sec}^2} \times \text{ft}^2 = \text{ft lb sec}^2$$

7-6 Radius of Gyration of Bodies

The *radius of gyration* with reference to an inertia axis is a number k, which, when squared and multiplied by the mass of a solid body, is equal to the moment of inertia of the body with reference to the same inertia axis.

$$I = mk^2 = \frac{W}{g}k^2 \qquad (7\text{-}8)$$

A physical meaning can be attached to mass radius of gyration; it is the radius of a ring of concentrated mass which has the same moment of inertia as the body in question.

EXAMPLE 6: A solid body weighing 64.4 lb has a mass moment of inertia about a particular axis of 10 slug ft². Determine the radius of gyration of the body about the same inertia axis.

Solution: The mass, based upon the accepted value of gravity, 32.2 ft per sec², is

$$m = \frac{W}{g} = \frac{64.4}{32.2} = 2 \text{ slugs}$$

Substitution of the data into Eq. (7-8) gives the value of the radius of gyration:

$$k = \sqrt{\frac{I}{m}} = \sqrt{\frac{10 \text{ slug ft}^2}{2 \text{ slug}}} = 2.24 \text{ ft}$$

7-7 Transfer of Inertia Axis

Just as with areas, the mass moments of inertia can be transferred from a centroidal axis to some prescribed axis by the parallel axis theorem. In this instance, mass replaces area in the formula.

$$I = \bar{I} + md^2 \tag{7-9}$$

This equation, together with the values of centroidal moments of inertia of solid bodies given in Table 7-2, permits finding the moment of inertia of a body about a variety of axes. The example that follows illustrates the method.

EXAMPLE 7: Determine the mass moment of inertia of a solid right circular cylinder of radius r about an axis parallel to the longitudinal axis and at a distance r from it.

Solution: Table 7-2 gives the value of the centroidal moment of inertia as

$$\bar{I} = \tfrac{1}{2} mr^2$$

By the parallel axis theorem, the desired value of I is

$$I = \bar{I} + md^2$$
$$= \tfrac{1}{2} mr^2 + mr^2 = \tfrac{3}{2} mr^2$$

7-8 Moment of Inertia of Composite Bodies

The mass moments of inertia of several geometric bodies are given in Table 7-2. These, together with the parallel axis theorem, are used to compute the mass moments of inertia of composite bodies in a manner similar to that employed for composite areas. Moments of inertia of the components are computed with reference to a common axis and then added; the absence of a portion of the body merely indicates a negative contribution to the moment of inertia of the system.

EXAMPLE 8: Determine the moment of inertia of the brass collar shown in Fig. 7-8 about the geometric axis *o–o*. Brass has a specific weight of 0.31 lb per cu in.

Table 7-2. Moments of Inertia of Uniform Masses

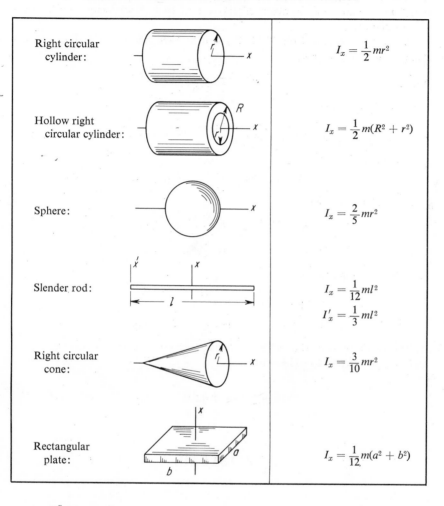

Right circular cylinder:		$I_x = \dfrac{1}{2}mr^2$
Hollow right circular cylinder:		$I_x = \dfrac{1}{2}m(R^2 + r^2)$
Sphere:		$I_x = \dfrac{2}{5}mr^2$
Slender rod:		$I_x = \dfrac{1}{12}ml^2$ $I'_x = \dfrac{1}{3}ml^2$
Right circular cone:		$I_x = \dfrac{3}{10}mr^2$
Rectangular plate:		$I_x = \dfrac{1}{12}m(a^2 + b^2)$

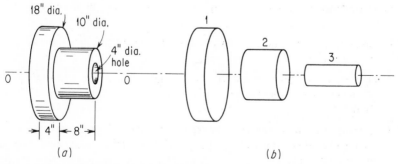

Figure 7-8

Solution: Three cylindrical elements, each with a different mass, make up the collar: the section 18 in. in diameter, the section 10 in. in diameter, and the hole 4 in. in diameter.

Before the formulas from Table 7-2 can be used, the mass in slugs of each element must be computed.

Where: $$m = \frac{W}{g} = \frac{[\text{volume}] \times [\text{specific weight}]}{\text{gravity}}$$

a. The 18 in. cylinder:

$$m_1 = \frac{[\pi(9)^2 4] \text{ in.}^3 [0.31] \text{ lb/in.}^3}{32.2 \text{ ft/sec}^2} = 9.79 \text{ slugs}$$

from Table 7-2 $$I = \tfrac{1}{2} mr^2$$

$$I_1 = \tfrac{1}{2}(9.79)(\tfrac{9}{12})^2 = 2.75 \text{ slug ft}^2$$

b. The 10 in. cylinder:

$$m_2 = \frac{[\pi(5)^2 8] \times [0.31]}{32.2} = 6.05 \text{ slugs}$$

$$I_2 = \tfrac{1}{2} mr^2 = \tfrac{1}{2}(6.05)(\tfrac{5}{12})^2 = 0.53 \text{ slug ft}^2$$

c. The 4 in. diameter hole:

$$m_3 = \frac{[\pi(2)^2 12] \times [0.31]}{32.2} = 1.45 \text{ slugs}$$

$$I_3 = \tfrac{1}{2} mr^2 = \tfrac{1}{2}(1.45)(\tfrac{2}{12})^2 = 0.02 \text{ slug ft}^2$$

The moment of inertia of the composite section is equal to the sum of the moments of inertia of its elements:

$$I = I_1 + I_2 - I_3$$
$$= 2.75 + 0.53 - 0.02 = 3.26 \text{ slug ft}^2$$

PROBLEMS

7-1. Determine I_x, I_y, and J of 1 sq. in. of area located in the *x-y* plane at $x = 5$ in., $y = 10$ in.

7-2. Determine I_x, I_y, and J of an element of area of 2 sq. in. located in the *x-y* plane at 6, −3.

7-3. One sq. in. of area in the *x-y* plane has a polar moment of inertia of 169 in.[4] and a moment of inertia with respect to the *x*-axis of 25 in.[4] Find I_y.

7-4. Determine by approximation the second moment I_x about the base of the rectangular area shown in Fig. P7-4. Divide the area into 6 equal strips for the computation.

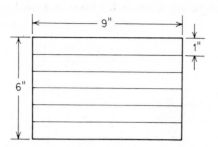

Figure P7-4

7-5. The exact answer for I_x in Prob. 7-4 is 648 in.[4] What is the per cent error in the approximation?

7-6–7-8. Determine by approximation the value of I_x about the horizontal base line of the area shown in Figs. P7-6–7-8. Use 1 in. high horizontal strips of area.

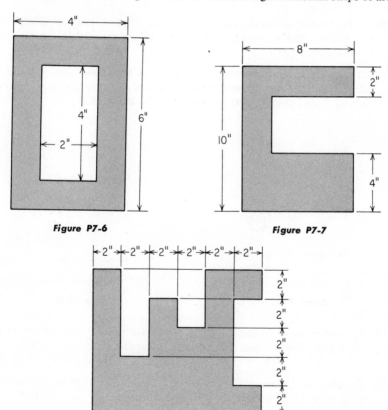

Figure P7-6   **Figure P7-7**

Figure P7-8

7-9. Use 1 in. strips to approximate the value of I_x and I_y of the area shown in Fig. P7-9.

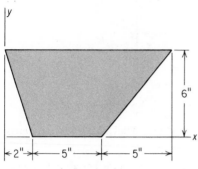

Figure P7-9

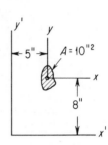

Figure P7-10

7-10. If the centroidal moments of inertia of the 10 sq in. area in Fig. P7-10 are $\bar{I}_x = 25$ in.^{4} and $\bar{I}_y = 40$ in.^{4}, determine the moments of inertia about the x'-axis and y'-axis.

7-11. In Fig. P7-11, the moments of inertia of the area about axes a–a and b–b are 250 in.^{4} and 450 in.^{4} respectively. Determine the centroidal moment of inertia $\bar{I}_y$ and the quantity of area A in the element.

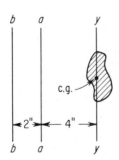

Figure P7-11

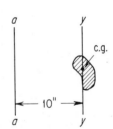

Figure P7-12

7-12. The centroidal moment of inertia of the element of area shown in Fig. P7-12 is $\bar{I}_y = 50$ in.^{4} and the moment of inertia about a parallel axis a–a is $I_{a-a} = 400$ in.^{4} Determine the amount of area in the element.

7-13. The centroidal moment of inertia of the 10 sq in. area shown in Fig. P7-13 is $\bar{I}_x = 40$ in.^{4} Determine the distance d for which $I_{a-a} = 120$ in.^{4}

7-14. Determine the second moment of an area of 40 sq in. if the radius of gyration of the area is $k = 8$ in.

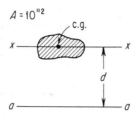

Figure P7-13

7-15. Find the centroidal radius of gyration of an area $A = 15$ in.^{2} with respect to the x-axis if the area has a moment of inertia of $\bar{I}_x = 60$ in.^{4}

7-16. Find the polar radius of gyration of the area described in Prob. 7-2.

7-17. Determine the radius of gyration with reference to the x-axis of the area described in Prob. 7-1.

7-18. As shown in Fig. P7-18, the radius of gyration of the 10 sq in. area about axis a–a is $k = 11$ in. Determine the centroidal moment of inertia I_y.

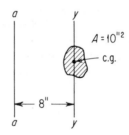

Figure P7-18

Note: Refer to Tables 7-1 and 7-2 for exact values of moments of inertia where required in the problems that follow.

7-19. A rectangle is 4 in. wide by 12 in. high. Find its moment of inertia with respect to a line drawn along the short side.

7-20. Determine the centroidal polar moment of inertia of a rectangle 5 in. wide by 7 in. high.

7-21. Find the polar moment of inertia of a 10 in. by 12 in. rectangle with respect to a line perpendicular to the plane of the rectangle and passing through a corner.

7-22. The rectangular plate section in Fig. P7-22 has a square hole cut from it. Determine the moment of inertia of the plate with respect to the centroidal x-axis and with respect to axis a–a.

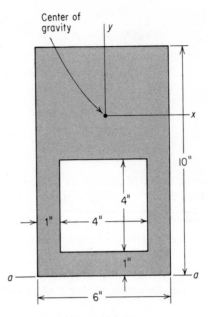

Figure P7-22

7-23. Find the radius of gyration of the plate described in Prob. 7-22 about an axis perpendicular to the plate at the center of gravity.

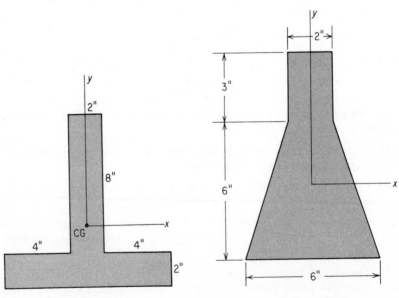

Figure P7-24   **Figure P7-25**

7-24. Locate the centroid of the area shown in Fig. P7-24 and find the moment of inertia with respect to the $\bar{x}$-axis.

7-25. Locate the centroid of the area shown in Fig. P7-25 and find the moment of inertia with respect to the $\bar{x}$-axis.

7-26. Determine the polar moment of inertia of the area shown in Fig. P7-26 with respect to its centroidal axis.

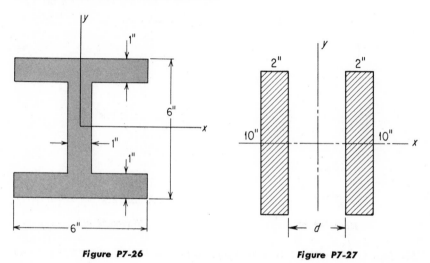

Figure P7-26   **Figure P7-27**

7-27. Find the distance d between the two rectangular areas in Fig. P7-27 in order that $I_x = I_y$.

7-28. Three 2 in. by 10 in. timbers are nailed together to form a tee-beam as shown in Fig. P7-28. Locate the center of gravity of the cross-section and determine I_x and I_y.

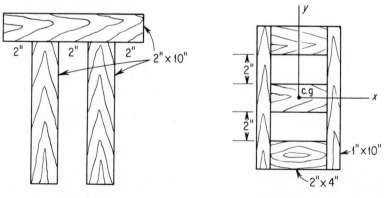

Figure P7-28   **Figure P7-29**

7-29. A box-beam is fabricated from two 1 in. by 10 in. and three 2 in. by 4 in. planks. Determine the centroidal moments of inertia I_x and I_y of the cross-section shown in Fig. P7-29.

7-30. Find the moment of inertia I_y of the hexagonal area shown in Fig. P7-30.

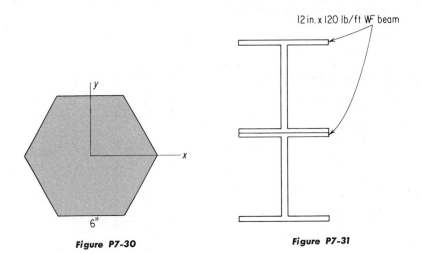

Figure P7-30   **Figure P7-31**

7-31. Two 12 in. by 120 lb/ft wide flange beams are welded to form the section shown in Fig. P7-31. Determine the centroidal moments of inertia and the centroidal radius of gyration.

7-32. An *I* beam is fabricated by welding 4 angles to a plate as shown in the section in Fig. P7-32. Determine the centroidal moments of inertia of the section.

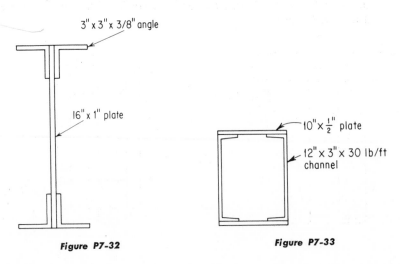

Figure P7-32   **Figure P7-33**

7-33. A box-beam is made by welding a 10 in. by $\frac{1}{2}$ in. cover plate to two 12 in. by 3 in. channels as shown in Fig. P7-33. Find I_x, I_y, and J of their combined area.

7-34. Find the spacing d between the two 12 in. by 3 in. channels in Fig. P7-34 in order that $I_x = I_y$.

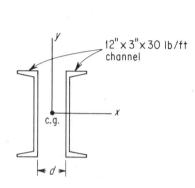

Figure P7-34

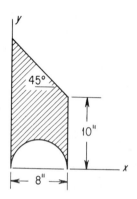

Figure P7-35

7-35. Determine the moments of inertia of the area shown in Fig. P7-35 with respect to the x- and y-axis.

7-36. Find the radius of gyration of a 4 slug mass that has a moment of inertia of 16 slug ft².

7-37. Determine the mass moment of inertia of a 64.4 lb right circular cylinder about axis a–a. The cylinder, shown in Fig. P7-37, has a diameter of 1 ft.

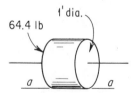

Figure P7-37

7-38. Find the mass moment of inertia about a diametral axis of an aluminum sphere with a diameter of 12 in. The specific weight of aluminum is 160 lb per cu ft³.

7-39. A pendulum consisting of two aluminum spheres welded to a 20 lb uniform slender rod is shown in Fig. P7-39. Determine the mass moment of inertia of the pendulum about axis O–O. The specific weight of aluminum is 160 lb per cu ft.

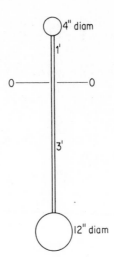

Figure P7-39

7-40. A 10 in. by 8 in. by 1 in. plate weighs 0.30 lb per cu in. Find the mass moment of inertia of the plate about an axis perpendicular to the face of the plate through one corner.

7-41. Determine the moment of inertia of a 128.8 lb right circular disk about an axis perpendicular to the centroidal longitudinal axis. The disk has a diameter of 18 in. Its thickness may be considered negligible.

7-42. A slender rod is 4 ft long and weighs 32.2 lb. Compute the value of the mass moment of inertia of the rod about an axis on the rod that is perpendicular to it and 1 ft from its centroid.

7-43. Find the centroidal radius of gyration of the hollow steel cylinder shown in Fig. P7-43. The specific weight of steel is 0.28 lb per cu in.

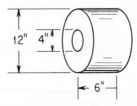

Figure P7-43

7-44. A 6 in. square bar weighing 0.30 lb per cu in. has two 3 in. diameter holes drilled through as shown in Fig. P7-44. Determine the mass moment of inertia about a longitudinal centroidal axis *x–x*.

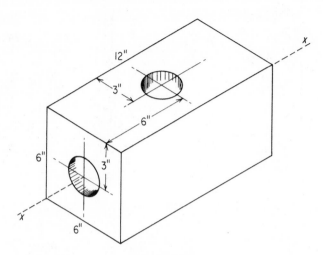

Figure P7-44

7-45. The rectangular plate, made of a material weighing 0.25 lb per cu in., has four holes drilled through as shown in Fig. P7-45. Find the mass moment of inertia of the plate about a centroidal axis normal to the plate.

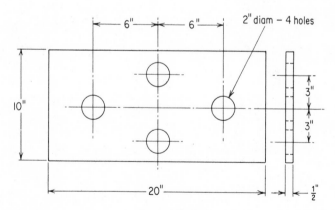

Figure P7-45

7-46. A pulley, made of material weighing 0.30 lb per cu in., has the cross section shown in Fig. P7-46. Assume the rim, hub, and web to be hollow cylinders and compute the mass moment of inertia of the pulley about its polar axis.

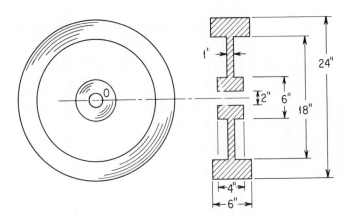

Figure P7-46

Chapter 8

APPLICATIONS
OF STATICS

The science of statics is used extensively in many branches of engineering. Its role in two of these branches, the study of beams and the study of fluids, will be introduced in this chapter.

PART A: BEAMS

8-1 Classification of Beams

Structural members that are capable of sustaining loads normal to their axes are called *beams*. Some of the ways that these members can be supported are shown in Fig. 8-1. A beam that rests on two supports, one a hinge and the other a smooth roller, is called a *simple beam;* a *cantilever beam* is one that is supported only at the end. As the name implies, an *overhanging beam* is a beam that extends beyond its supports at either one end or both ends. If

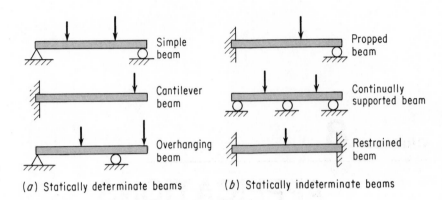

(a) Statically determinate beams   *(b)* Statically indeterminate beams

Figure 8-1

the reaction forces which support the beam can be found by the equations of statics alone, the beam is *statically determinate*, while beams that have more supports than are necessary to maintain equilibrium are *statically indeterminate*. Beams that are *propped*, *continually supported*, or *built-in* are examples of this latter class. Since theory beyond the scope of this book is required for the analysis of indeterminate beams, only those that are statically determinate will be considered.

8-2 Types of Loads

There are four types of loads which can act on a beam; these are illustrated in Fig. 8-2. The *concentrated load*, the simplest, acts at a single point on the beam. *Distributed load*, as the name implies, is one that acts over a given length of the beam; the latter may be either *uniform* or *non-uniform*, as illustrated. A fourth type of loading occurs when the beam is subjected to a pure *moment* in the form of a couple. Fig. 8-3(a) shows how all four of these basic loads might act in combination.

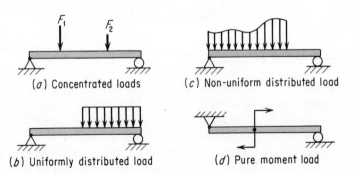

(a) Concentrated loads   *(c)* Non-uniform distributed load

(b) Uniformly distributed load   *(d)* Pure moment load

Figure 8-2

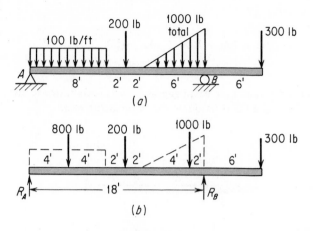

Figure 8-3

The equations of equilibrium, $\Sigma F_x = 0$, $\Sigma F_y = 0$, and $\Sigma M = 0$, are employed to find the reactions which support the beam. Since there are usually two unknown parallel forces to be computed, two equations are all that need be written. Answers obtained by these two equations should always be checked by writing the third equation of equilibrium.

EXAMPLE 1: Determine the reactions at the supports A and B that act on the beam shown in Fig. 8-3. The beam supports a uniformly distributed load of 100 lb per ft over a portion of its span, a triangular load of 1000 lb over another portion, and two concentrated loads of 200 lb and 300 lb each.

Solution: The free-body diagram is drawn as shown in Fig. 8-3(b). The uniformly distributed load of 100 lb per ft is represented by a net load of 800 lb acting at the center of gravity. In a similar manner, the 1000 lb triangular load is represented by a single force 2 ft to the left of support B.

The reaction R_B is found by taking moments about support A.

$$\Sigma M_A = 0$$

$$18R_B - 800(4) - 200(10) - 1000(16) - 300(24) = 0$$

$$R_B = \frac{3200 + 2000 + 16,000 + 7200}{18}$$

$$= 1578 \text{ lb}$$

The reaction R_A is computed in a similar manner by taking moments about point B.

$$\Sigma M_B = 0$$

$$18R_A - 1000(2) - 200(8) - 800(14) + 300(6) = 0$$

$$R_A = \frac{2000 + 1600 + 11,200 - 1800}{18}$$

$$= 722 \text{ lb}$$

A force summation in the y-direction serves as a check.

$$\Sigma F_y = 0$$
$$800 + 200 + 1000 + 300 - 1578 - 722 = 0$$
$$0 = 0$$

EXAMPLE 2: A cantilever beam supports two concentrated loads as shown in Fig. 8-4(a). Determine the reaction on the beam at the wall.

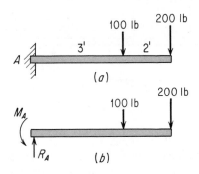

Figure 8-4

Solution: The wall reacts to the beam in two ways: first, it prevents vertical movement, and second, it restrains rotation. The two reactions R_A and M_A are found by evaluating the equations of equilibrium; thus

$$\Sigma F_y = 0$$
$$R_A - 100 - 200 = 0$$

where
$$R_A = 300 \text{ lb}$$

and
$$\Sigma M_A = 0$$
$$M_A - 100(3) - 200(5) = 0$$

where
$$M_A = 1300 \text{ lb ft}$$

8-3 Shear and Moment Diagrams

Beams with concentrated loads. The reactions of the supports A and B on the beam shown in Fig. 8-5(a) are Pb/l and Pa/l respectively. The free-body diagram of this beam shows it to be in complete equilibrium with its surroundings, where

$$\Sigma F_x = 0, \qquad \Sigma F_y = 0, \qquad \Sigma M = 0$$

If the beam is cut at a distance x from the left end, a force V and a moment M are required to keep the severed sections in equilibrium. These

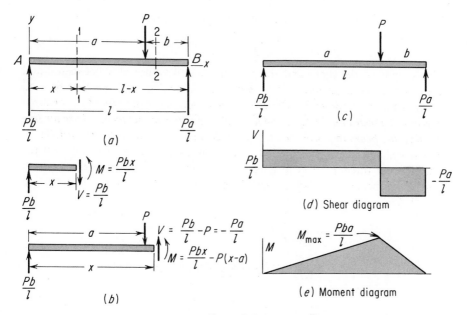

Figure 8-5

two internal reactions in the beam are called the *shear* and the *moment* at x. A force summation $\sum F_y = 0$ and a moment summation $\sum M = 0$ on the left hand portion will show V and M to be

$$V = \frac{Pb}{l}$$

and

$$M = \frac{Pb}{l}x$$

The shear remains constant between the limits of $x = 0$ and $x = a$, while the moment between these same limits increases as x increases. At $x = a$ the moment is

$$M = \frac{Pab}{l}$$

If a second free-body is drawn, this time to the right of load P, the shear and moment are

$$V = \frac{Pb}{l} - P = \frac{P(b-l)}{l} = -\frac{Pa}{l}$$

and

$$M = \frac{Pb}{l}x - P(x-a)$$

A study of the moment equation indicates that as x increases, M decreases, and that at $x = l$ the moment is zero.

$$M = \frac{Pbl}{l} - P(l - a)$$

$$= Pb - Pb = 0$$

The graphs of the shear and the moment for all values of x between 0 and l are called the *shear* and *moment diagrams*. A sign convention must be used in plotting these diagrams: **Positive shear results when the sum of the external forces act upward on the left hand free-body; positive moments are those tending to bend the beam in a way to cause its radius of curvature to be upward.** Thus, positive shear means that the left hand segment would rise if it were not for the internal force V to keep it in equilibrium; a positive moment tends to cause the beam to bend upward. This sign convention is illustrated in Fig. 8-6.

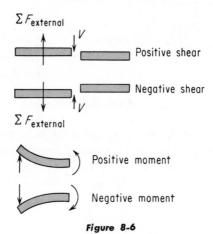

Figure 8-6

EXAMPLE 3: Draw the shear and the moment diagram for the simply supported beam shown in Fig. 8-7. Determine the maximum value of V and of M.

Solution: The reactions at A and D are first computed:

$$\sum M_A = 0$$
$$12R_D - 6(200) - 10(300) = 0$$
$$R_D = 350 \text{ lb}$$

and

$$\sum M_D = 0$$
$$12R_A - 2(300) - 6(200) = 0$$
$$R_A = 150 \text{ lb}$$

Check:

$$\sum F_y = 0$$
$$200 + 300 - 350 - 150 = 0$$
$$0 = 0$$

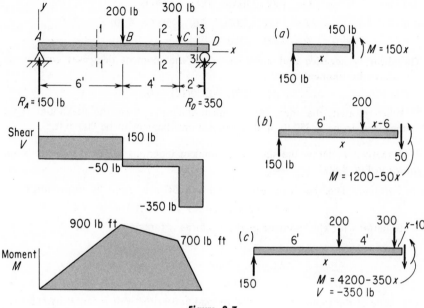

Figure 8-7

To plot the shear and moment diagrams, free-body diagrams of three sections of the beam are required. These three free-bodies are illustrated in Fig. 8-7(a), (b), and (c).

The first free-body results when a cut is made at section 1–1 a distance x to the right of end A. The shear in this section is constant and equal to

$$V = +150 \text{ lb}$$

while the moment increases uniformly as x increases.

$$M = +150x \text{ lb ft}$$

At $x = 6$ ft, the moment in the beam is 900 lb ft.

The second free-body diagram results when a cut is made at section 2–2, again at a distance x from end A. The shear in this section of the beam is now

$$V = 150 - 200 = -50 \text{ lb}$$

and the moment is

$$M = 150x - 200(x - 6)$$

or

$$= 1200 - 50x$$

In the portion of the beam between $x = 6$ ft and $x = 10$ ft, the moment decreases uniformly with x; at $x = 10$ ft, M is 700 lb ft, thus

$$M = 1200 - 50(10) = 700 \text{ lb ft}$$

The third and final free-body diagram, that of a section to the left of cut 3–3, shows the shear and moment to be

$$V = 150 - 200 - 300 = -350 \text{ lb}$$

and
$$M = 150x - 200(x - 6) - 300(x - 10)$$
$$= 4200 - 350x$$

The shear is negative and constant, while the moment decreases with x; at $x = 12$ ft, the moment is zero.

$$M = 4200 - 350(12) = 0$$

When plotted, the shear and moment diagrams show the maximum value of the shear to be -350 lb, and the maximum moment to be 900 lb ft.

EXAMPLE 4: Draw the shear and moment diagrams for the cantilever beam shown in Fig. 8-8(a).

Solution: The shears in sections AB and BC are found by inspection to be
$$V_{AB} = -200 \text{ lb} \quad \text{and} \quad V_{BC} = -700 \text{ lb}.$$

Equations for the moment in the beam as a function of x are

$$M_{AB} = -200x$$

and
$$M_{BC} = -200x - 500(x - 4)$$
$$= 2000 - 700x$$

The value of the moment at the 500 lb load and at the wall is found by substitution; thus

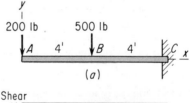

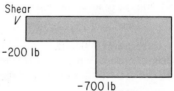

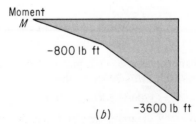

Figure 8-8

at $x = 4$ ft,

$$M = -200(4) = -800 \text{ lb ft}$$

and

at $x = 8$ ft,

$$M = 2000 - 700(8) = -3600 \text{ lb ft}$$

The shear and moment diagrams appear as shown in Fig. 8-8(b).

Beams with distributed loads. The general procedure for drawing shear and moment diagrams, outlined in the previous paragraphs, applies to any loading arrangement; it follows, however, that these diagrams become more complex as the loading becomes more involved. An example follows that will illustrate the drawing of a shear and a moment diagram for a beam that supports a distributed load.

EXAMPLE 5: Draw the shear and moment diagrams for the beam shown in Fig. 8-9.

Solution: The reactions are found by moment summations about A and C:

$$\Sigma M_A = 0$$

$$10R_C - 6(100)3 = 0$$

$$R_C = 180 \text{ lb}$$

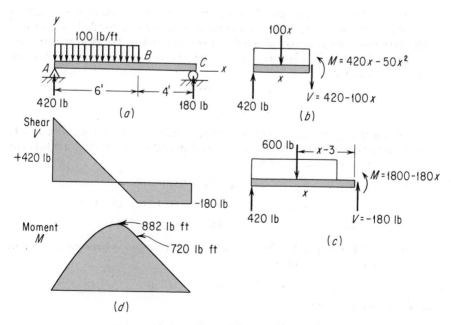

Figure 8-9

and
$$\Sigma M_C = 0$$
$$10R_A - 6(100)7 = 0$$
$$R_A = 420 \text{ lb}$$

Check:
$$\Sigma F_y = 0$$
$$6(100) - 420 - 180 = 0$$
$$0 = 0$$

A free-body diagram is next drawn, as shown in Fig. 8-9(b), for a portion of the beam x ft in length; x is any value greater than zero but less than 6 ft. The forces that act in this free-body are the upward reaction of 420 lb at A and a downward force of $100x$ lb. The vertical shear at the cut is computed by evaluating $\Sigma F_y = 0$, thus

$$V = 420 - 100x$$

By this equation, the curve of the shear as a function of x is shown to be a straight line sloping downward to the right. At a value of $x = 0$, the shear is $+420$ lb and at a value of $x = 6$ ft, the shear is -180 lb.

The same two external forces that produced the vertical shear also tend to bend the beam. The sum of the moments of these two forces is equal to the internal moment at the cut:

$$M = 420x - 100x\left(\frac{x}{2}\right) = 420x - 50x^2$$

Since the value of the moment depends both on x and x^2, the moment diagram has the shape of a *parabola*. The careful plotting of this parabola shows that *the maximum moment occurs at a point in the beam where the shear is zero.* This statement, which is true for any type of loading, places the maximum moment at $x = 4.2$ ft, thus

$$V = 420 - 100x = 0$$
$$x = 4.2 \text{ ft}$$

The moment magnitudes evaluated at three points: $x = 0$, $x = 4.2$ and $x = 6$, are all that need be computed to sketch adequately the moment diagram between the limits of $x = 0$ and $x = 6$ ft.

at $x = 0$: $M = 420(0) - 50(0)^2 = 0$

at $x = 4.2$: $M = 420(4.2) - 50(4.2)^2 = 882 \text{ lb ft}$

at $x = 6$: $M = 420(6) - 50(6)^2 = 720 \text{ lb ft}$

A free-body diagram drawn for a portion of the beam lying between $x = 6$ and $x = 10$ shows the shear to be

$$V = 420 - 600 = -180 \text{ lb}$$

and the moment to be

$$M = 420x - 600(x - 3) = 1800 - 180x$$

Thus, the shear in the portion of the beam between $x = 6$ ft and $x = 10$ ft is constant and negative, while the moment decreases uniformly to zero from its initial value of $+ 720$ lb ft.

PART B: FLUID STATICS

8-4 Solids, Liquids, and Gases

Matter can exist in nature as a solid, a liquid, or a gas. As a *solid*, it has shape and form which it is capable of retaining even if acted upon by forces.

Matter in the form of a liquid or a gas is called a *fluid;* in this state it offers no resistance to shearing forces. A given amount of liquid occupies a definite volume; it always has a horizontal free surface when at rest and when not completely confined. Gas, like a liquid, offers no resistance to shearing forces; its volume, unlike that of a liquid, however, equals the volume of the container to which it is confined.

8-5 Liquid Pressure

The term, pressure, is a measure of the *force per unit area* that a liquid exerts against a surface that it contacts. Pressure, as illustrated in Fig. 8-10, is dependent upon depth. The tank shown contains a liquid having a specific weight, weight per unit volume, of w. An isolated cylinder of liquid within the tank would weigh

$$W = whA$$

where h = height

and A = cross-sectional area.

The force necessary to support this cylinder of liquid must equal W.

$$F = whA$$

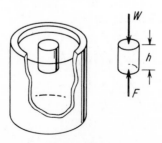

Figure 8-10

Dividing both elements of this equation by A gives F/A, the pressure in terms of specific weight and depth.

$$P = \frac{F}{A} = wd \tag{8-1}$$

The pressure P given in Eq. (8-1) is called the *gage pressure;* the total pressure known as the *absolute pressure*, also incorporates the force of the surrounding atmosphere. The absolute pressure, therefore, is the sum of the gage pressure and the atmospheric pressure. Under normal conditions, the atmospheric pressure is 14.7 lb per in.²

EXAMPLE 6: Determine the gage and absolute pressures in a lake at a depth of 20 ft. Water weighs approximately 62.4 lb per ft.³

Solution: The pressure-depth relationship is given by Eq. (8-1).

$$P = wh = \frac{62.4 \text{ lb}}{\text{ft}^3} \times 20 \text{ ft} \times \frac{\text{ft}^2}{144 \text{ in.}^2}$$

$$= 8.67 \text{ lb per in.}^2$$

The absolute pressure is the gage pressure plus 14.7 lb per in.²

$$P_{ab} = P + 14.7 = 8.67 + 14.7$$

$$= 23.37 \text{ lb per in.}^2$$

8-6 Force on Submerged Surfaces

The force that a liquid exerts on a surface it contacts is always normal to that surface. This is illustrated in Fig. 8-11, where the submerged surface, the wall, retains a quantity of liquid of width d and height h. The line AB, called the *pressure gradient line*, represents the magnitude of the pressure

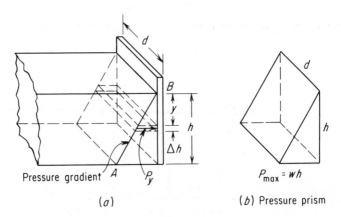

(a)   (b) Pressure prism

Figure 8-11

as a function of depth; the pressure is zero at the free surface and a maximum, wh, at the deepest point. The product of the pressure at some arbitrary depth y and the small increment of area on which it acts is equal to the force ΔF.

$$\Delta F = P_y(\Delta h)d$$

The total force on the wall is the sum of these incremental values of force

$$F = \Sigma \ \Delta F = \Sigma \ P_y(\Delta h)d$$

If P_y is the average pressure acting on the wall, the equation can be rewritten as

$$F = \frac{wh}{2} \Sigma \ (\Delta h)d$$

Where $\Sigma \ (\Delta h)d$ is the wetted area of the wall hd:

$$F = \frac{wh}{2}(hd) = \frac{wh^2 d}{2}$$

This force is exactly equal to the volume of the triangular prism defined by the pressure gradient line, the wall, and the floor.

$$F = \text{volume} = \tfrac{1}{2}[\text{base}] \times [\text{height}] \times [\text{width}]$$

$$F = \tfrac{1}{2}wh^2d \tag{8-2}$$

The line of action of the force is located at the centroid of the prism, in this case at a distance 2/3 down from the top.

When the submerged surface is inclined, the pressure prism is drawn as illustrated in Fig. 8-12; as for the vertical wall, the pressure is zero at the free surface and wh at the deepest point.

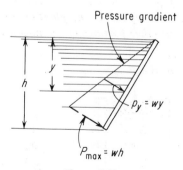

Pressure gradient

$$p_y = wy$$

$$P_{max} = wh$$

Figure 8-12

EXAMPLE 7: A retaining wall, 5 ft wide, is hinged at C. It supports a body of water as shown in Fig. 8-13. Determine the force in the strut AB that supports the wall.

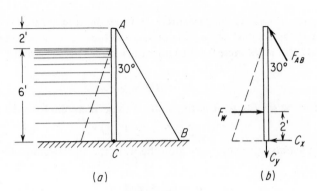

Figure 8-13

Solution: The force of the water against the wall is equal to the volume of the pressure prism.

$$F = \tfrac{1}{2} wh^2 d = (\tfrac{1}{2})62.4(6)^2(5) = 5615 \text{ lb}$$

The line of action of the force is at the centroid of the prism, or 2 ft above the hinge pin C. The force in the strut F_{AB} is computed by summing moments about C.

$$\Sigma M_C = 0$$

$$2F_W - 8F_{AB} \sin 30° = 0$$

$$F_{AB} = \frac{2(5615)}{8(0.5)} = 2808 \text{ lb}$$

8-7 Transmission of Fluid Pressure: Pascal's Law

An important principle in the study of fluid statics, known as Pascal's law, states that *a pressure applied at any point on a confined liquid is immediately transmitted to all other portions of the liquid.* It has been shown that

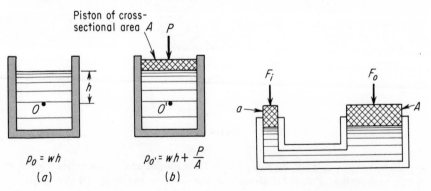

Figure 8-14   **Figure 8-15**

the pressure at a point below a free surface of a liquid is wh. If additional force P is applied by a piston having a cross-sectional area A as shown in Fig. 8-14, the pressure at point O will be immediately increased by an amount P/A.

This principle forms the basis for the design of hydraulic machinery: brakes, presses, jacks, and hoists. The force F, for example, which acts on the small piston of cross-sectional area a of the hydraulic cylinder shown in Fig. 8-15, exerts a pressure F_i/a which is transmitted to the surface of the large piston. The force F_o needed to maintain equilibrium is equal to the product of the pressure and the area.

$$F_o = F_i\left(\frac{A}{a}\right) \qquad (8\text{-}3)$$

The input force F_i is, therefore, magnified by a factor of A/a.

EXAMPLE 8: A force of 20 lb is applied to the handle of the hydraulic jack shown in Fig. 8-16. If the small actuating piston has an area $a = 0.5$ in.^{2} and the output piston has an area of $A = 12$ in.^{2}, find the lifting force P that can be exerted.

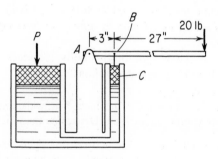

Figure 8-16

Solution: The force exerted by the lever on the small piston is found by taking moments about pin A.

$$\Sigma M_A = 0$$
$$3F - 20(30) = 0$$
$$F = 200 \text{ lb}$$

The force transmitted to the output piston is given by Eq. (8-3).

$$P = F\left(\frac{A}{a}\right) = 200\left(\frac{12}{0.5}\right) = 4800 \text{ lb}$$

The original force of 20 lb is increased to 4800 lb by the lever and by the transmission of fluid pressure. The ratio of the output force to the input force, 240 in this case, is called *mechanical advantage*.

8-8 Buoyancy: Archimedes' Principle

Equilibrium exists throughout the body of a static liquid. As illustrated in Fig. 8-17 an isolated portion of liquid of weight W is balanced by the pressure forces of the surrounding liquid, which must equal W. The sum of

Figure 8-17

these pressure forces is called the buoyant force. If the space occupied by the isolated portion of liquid is filled with some other material, the substance will be buoyed up by forces equal to the weight of the displaced liquid. Archimedes' principle may be stated as follows: *A body totally or partially immersed in a fluid will be acted upon by a buoyant force equal to the weight of the displaced fluid.*

It follows that if the weight of the body is greater than the buoyant force, the body will sink; if less, it will float.

EXAMPLE 9: A plank of wood 4 in. thick, 8 in. wide, and 10 ft long floats on water with half of its volume submerged. Determine the weight of the plank.

Solution: Static equilibrium exists between the plank and the buoyant force. The weight of the plank, therefore, is equal to the buoyant force, which in turn is equal to the weight of the displaced water.

$$W = [\text{volume}] \times [\text{specific weight}]$$

$$\left(\frac{1}{2}\right)\left[\left(\frac{4}{12}\right)\left(\frac{8}{12}\right)(10)\right] 62.4 = 69.4 \text{ lb}$$

EXAMPLE 10. Find the volume of an object that weighs 35 lb in air and 20 lb when suspended in water.

Solution: The buoyant force B, the difference between the weight of the object in air and in water, is equal to the weight of the displaced liquid.

$$B = [\text{volume}] \times [\text{specific weight}] = 15$$

thus
$$62.4 \, V = 15$$

$$V = 0.24 \text{ cu ft}$$

PROBLEMS

8-1–8-9. Find the reactions at the supports *A* and *B* for the beam acted upon by the loads shown in the following figures.

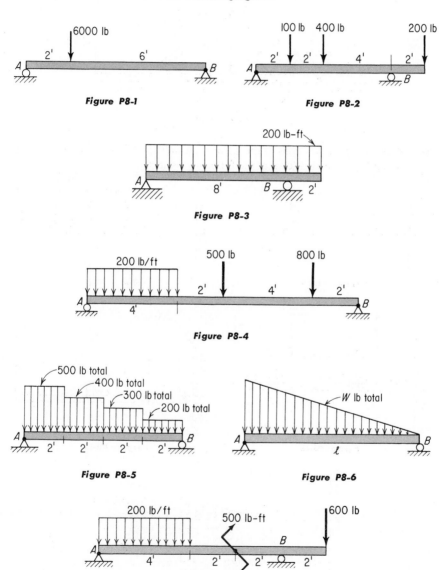

Figure P8-1

Figure P8-2

Figure P8-3

Figure P8-4

Figure P8-5

Figure P8-6

Figure P8-7

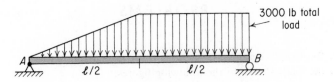

Figure P8-8

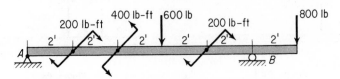

Figure P8-9

8-10–8-18. Find the reactions at the supporting wall for the cantilever beam acted upon by the loads shown in the following figures.

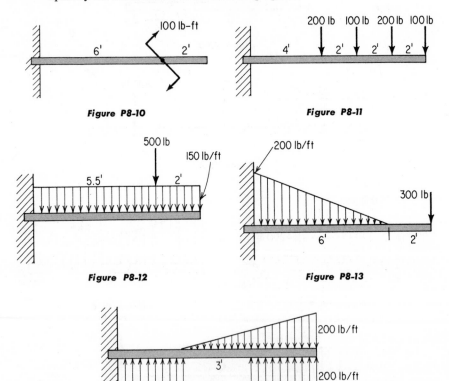

Figure P8-10

Figure P8-11

Figure P8-12

Figure P8-13

Figure P8-14

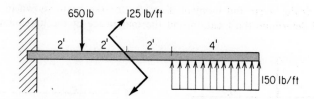

Figure P8-15

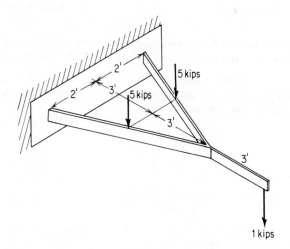

Figure P8-16

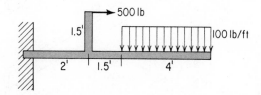

Figure P8-17

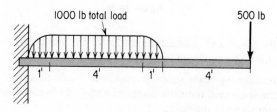

Figure P8-18

8-19. Draw the shear and moment diagrams for the beam shown in Fig. P8-19 and determine the location and the magnitude of the maximum moment.

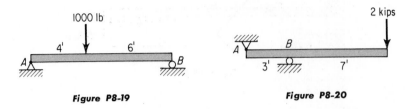

Figure P8-19   Figure P8-20

8-20. Draw the shear and moment diagrams for the beam shown in Fig. P8-20 and determine the location and magnitude of the maximum moment.

8-21. The beams support a load as shown in Fig. P8-21. Draw the shear and moment diagrams and determine the location and magnitude of the maximum moment in each beam.

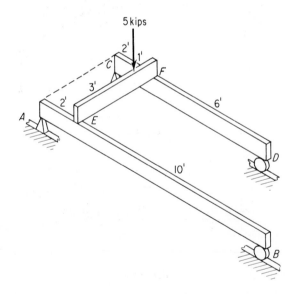

Figure P8-21

8-22. Draw the shear and moment diagrams for the vertical beam shown in Fig. P8-22. Find the maximum moment in the beam.

8-23. The overhanging beam supports the three loads as shown in Fig. P8-23. Draw the shear and moment diagrams and find the maximum moment and maximum shear in the beam.

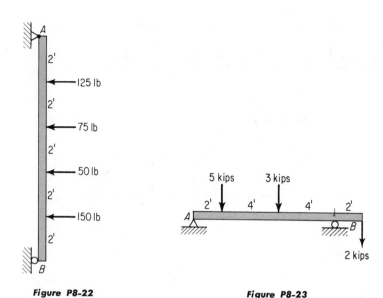

Figure P8-22

Figure P8-23

8-24. The chain hung beam supports symmetrical loads as shown in Fig. P8-24. Draw the shear and moment diagrams and determine the maximum moment in the beam.

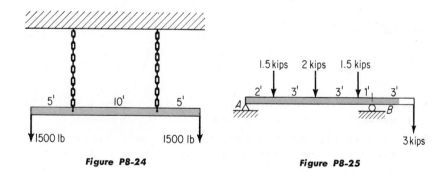

Figure P8-24

Figure P8-25

8-25. Draw the shear and moment diagrams of the beam that is acted upon by the loads as shown in Fig. P8-25. Find the maximum values of the shear and the moment.

8-26–8-28. The cantilever beam supports the concentrated loads shown in Figs. P8-26, P8-27, and P8-28. Draw the shear and moment diagrams and find the value of the maximum moment.

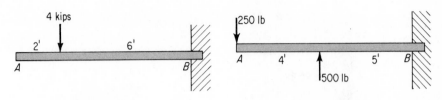

Figure P8-26   Figure P8-27

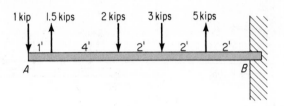

Figure P8-28

8-29. The beam shown in Fig. P8-29 carries a uniformly distributed load over its entire span. Draw the shear and moment diagrams and determine the magnitude and location of the maximum moment.

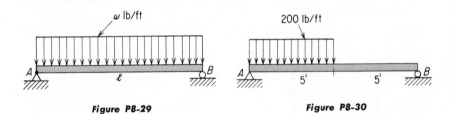

Figure P8-29   Figure P8-30

8-30. Draw the shear and moment diagrams for the beam shown in Fig. P8-30, and determine the location and magnitude of the maximum moment.

8-31. Draw the shear and moment diagrams for the beam shown in Fig. P8-31 and determine the location and magnitude of the maximum moment.

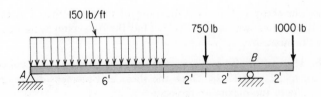

Figure P8-31

8-32. The beam in Fig. P8-32 supports two uniformly distributed loads and a concentrated load. Draw the shear and moment diagrams and determine the magnitude and location of the maximum moment acting in the beam.

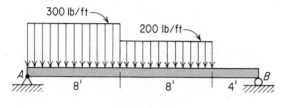

Figure P8-32

8-33. The overhanging beam in Fig. P8-33 carries a uniformly distributed load over its entire span. Draw the shear and moment diagrams and find the magnitude and location of the maximum moment in the beam.

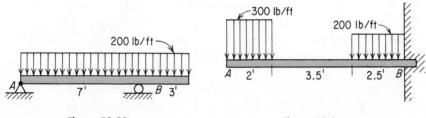

Figure P8-33   *Figure P8-34*

8-34. Draw the shear and moment diagrams for the cantilever beam shown in Fig. P8-34 and determine the moment at the support.

8-35. Draw the shear and moment diagrams for the two beams shown in Fig. P8-35.

8.36. Find the gage and absolute pressures at a depth of 500 ft in fresh water.

8-37. A vertical glass tube 4 ft long is filled with mercury. Determine the gage pressure at the bottom of the tube if mercury is 13.6 times heavier than water.

8-38. A square box 3 ft on edge has an attached 0.15 in. diameter tube that extends 5 ft upward from the top of the box. Find the force exerted on the top of the box when it and the tube are filled with water.

8-39. Man has explored the sea to depths exceeding 2 miles. Determine the water pressure at this depth if sea water has a specific weight of $w = 64$ lb per cu ft.

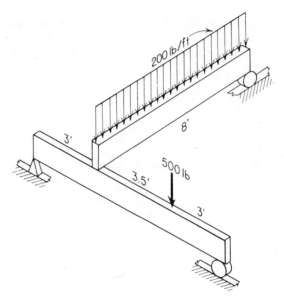

Figure P8-35

8-40. A rectangular trough 3 ft deep, 4 ft wide, and 10 ft long is filled with water. Find the forces which act on the bottom, on the sides, and on the ends of the trough.

8-41. The dam, which is 5 ft wide, is held in position by member *BC* as shown in Fig. P8-41. Assume pinned joints throughout and find the force in this member.

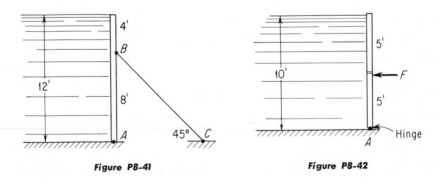

Figure P8-41   **Figure P8-42**

8-42. Find the force *F* required to maintain the hinged gate in the position shown in Fig. P8-42. The dam is 6 ft wide and is used to retain water to a maximum depth of 10 ft.

8-43. Water acts on both sides of a vertical wall 5 ft wide. The depth of the water on one side of the wall is 19 ft; on the other side, the depth is 6 ft. Determine the magnitude and location of the resultant force that acts on the wall.

8-44. The plunger of a hydraulic press is 0.25 in. in diameter and the piston it actuates is 6 in. in diameter. If a force of 100 lb is applied to the plunger, what force must be exerted on the large piston to maintain equilibrium?

8-45. Find the mechanical advantage of the plunger-piston combination described in Prob. 8-44.

8-46. Determine the output force on the large piston if $F = 20$ lb is applied to the foot-operated linkage shown in Fig. P8-46.

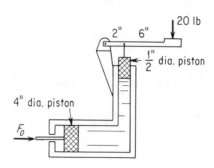

Figure P8-46

8-47. What is the mechanical advantage of the system described in Prob. 8-46?

8-48. Find the volume of a submarine which displaces 1800 tons of sea water weighing 64 lb per ft³.

8-49. A steel drum has a volume of 18 cu ft and weighs 500 lb. How many pounds of lead, weighing 700 lb per ft³, must be fastened to the outside bottom of the drum to make it float half submerged in water?

8-50. How many pounds of lead would be necessary in Prob. 8-49 if the lead is placed inside the drum?

8-51. A rock weighs 50 lb in air and 30 lb in water. Find its volume and specific weight.

8-52. A hollow steel casting weighs 100 lb in air and 40 lb in water. What is the volume of the cavity? Steel weighs 490 lb per ft³.

Chapter 9

KINEMATICS OF PARTICLES: THE GEOMETRY OF MOTION

An object is said to have motion when its position in space varies with time. Some motion is relatively simple and some so complicated that banks of electronic computers are required for its analysis. The same basic definitions apply to the motion of a simple link in a machine and to the trajectory of an intercontinental ballistic missile.

9-1 Types of Motion

A particle has *rectilinear* or *translational* motion when its path is a straight line; when the path is curved, the motion is *curvilinear*. The combination of rectilinear motion and curvilinear motion in a two dimensional plane is called *plane motion*.

Figure 9-1 shows a portion of a machine composed of a piston *A*, a connecting rod *AB*, and a crankshaft *BC*. The axis of the crankshaft is at *C*.

Figure 9-1

The piston is confined by the cylinder walls so that it can move only up and down. The paths of all the particles on the cross-section of the piston are parallel and in a single plane: the piston has *rectilinear plane motion*.

Since the crankshaft is revolving about C, all particles of BC are moving in concentric circles with centers at C. Thus, all points on BC have *curvilinear* or *rotational plane motion*.

The motion of the connecting-rod is somewhat more complicated; end A is translating with the piston, while end B is revolving with the crankshaft. No two particles of AB have the same path; the motion of any particle is partially rotational and partially translational. The connecting rod is moving with *generalized plane motion*.

9-2 Distance and Displacement

The odometer of an automobile records accumulated mileage and does not indicate relative position. It measures the *total distance* traveled—a *scalar* quantity. *Displacement*, on the other hand, is defined as a change in position without reference to time and is, therefore, a vector, since it possesses both magnitude and direction.

EXAMPLE 1: The position of a tool bit T in a lathe can be changed by the independent motions of the carriage A, the crossfeed B, and the compound rest C, as shown in Fig. 9-2. The carriage moves along the axis of the lathe bed, and the crossfeed moves in a direction perpendicular to the carriage. The motion of the compound rest is controlled through the adjustable angle θ. Determine the displacement R of the tool bit if the carriage moves 6 in. to the left, the crossfeed 4 in. toward the lathe center, and the compound rest 3 in. as shown for an angle $\theta = 60$ deg. What is the total distance D, traveled by the tool bit?

Solution: The vector displacements are added, as shown in Fig. 9-2(b), by the string polygon method of Chapter 2. R_x and R_y are the components of the displacement of the tool bit.

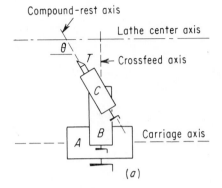

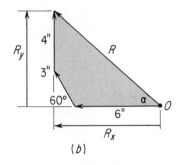

(b)

Figure 9-2

$$R_x = 6 + 3 \cos 60° = 7.5 \text{ in.}$$

$$R_y = 3 \sin 60° + 4 = 6.6 \text{ in.}$$

$$R = \sqrt{R_x^2 + R_y^2} = \sqrt{(7.5)^2 + (6.6)^2} = 10 \text{ in.}$$

$$\tan \alpha = \frac{R_y}{R_x} = \frac{6.6}{7.5} = 0.88$$

$$\alpha = 41.4°$$

$$D = 6 + 3 + 4 = 13 \text{ in.}$$

9-3 Speed and Velocity

Speed is defined as the rate of change of distance. It may be noted that the speedometer of an automobile is correctly named, since it measures the *time rate* in which a unit distance is covered, i.e., miles per hour (mph). Velocity is a vector quantity in that it implies the *speed* and *direction* or *bearing*. It is correct to say that the tip speed of an airplane propeller is constant; it is, however, incorrect to say that the tip velocity is constant, since the direction of the velocity vector is continually changing.

Figure 9-3

Absolute velocity is measured with respect to stationary surroundings; *relative velocity* is measured with respect to moving surroundings. As an example, assume the man in Fig. 9-3 to be running with a velocity of $v_M = 10$ fps up a stationary escalator. If the escalator is set in motion with a velocity of $v_E = 5$ fps, the man's absolute velocity has increased to 15 fps, while his velocity with respect to the escalator is still 10 fps. Thus

$$v_M = v_{M/E} + v_E = 10 + 5 = 15 \text{ fps up and to the right} \qquad (9\text{-}1)$$

v_M and v_E represent absolute velocities, and $v_{M/E}$ represents the velocity of the man relative to the escalator. Note that if the escalator were to move down at the same rate at which the man walks up, his absolute velocity would be zero.

EXAMPLE 2: Two jet planes are flying at a constant speed and a fixed altitude, as shown in Fig. 9-4. They leave formation at O and fly in the directions indicated. The velocities of planes A and B are 500 mph and 700 mph respectively. Determine the velocity of plane A relative to plane B.

Solution: The velocity relationship between planes A and B is given by the vector Eq. (9-1); only the subscripts need be changed.

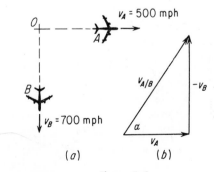

Figure 9-4

$$v_A = v_{A/B} + v_B$$

Solving for the desired quantity $v_{A/B}$

$$v_{A/B} = v_A - v_B$$

To subtract vectors v_B from v_A, reverse v_B and add it to v_A by the string polygon method. This addition is shown in Fig. 9-4(b).

$$v_{A/B} = \sqrt{(v_A)^2 + (-v_B)^2}$$
$$= \sqrt{(500)^2 + (700)^2}$$
$$= 860 \text{ mph}$$

$$\alpha = \arctan \tfrac{7}{5} = 54.5° \measuredangle$$

9-4 Velocity Analysis

Motion involving constant speed in a straight line is called *uniform motion*. If s_o and s_f represent displacements at times t_o and t_f, the velocity is

$$v = \frac{s_f - s_o}{t_f - t_o} = \frac{\Delta s}{\Delta t} \tag{9-2}$$

The expression $\Delta s/\Delta t$ is graphically interpreted as the slope of the displacement-time graph. This is illustrated in Fig. 9-5.

When the speed in a straight line changes, the motion is *non-uniform* and the velocity in Eq. (9-2) is the *average* value over the time interval Δt.

$$v_{\text{avg}} = \frac{\Delta s}{\Delta t} \tag{9-3}$$

The rearrangement of the terms in Eqs. (9-2) and (9-3) gives

$$\Delta s = v(\Delta t)$$

and $$\Delta s = v_{\text{avg}}(\Delta t) \tag{9-4}$$

In either case, the equations state that a change in displacement Δs is equal to the area under the velocity-time diagram.

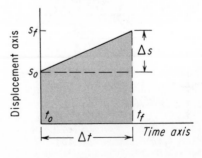

Figure 9-5

EXAMPLE 3: Two automobiles A and B are traveling on the same road. Car A is one mile ahead of car B and is traveling at a speed of 30 mph. At what uniform speed must car B travel in order to pass car A in two minutes?

Solution: The displacement of cars A and B must be the same at the end of 2 minutes.

$$2 \text{ min} \times \frac{1 \text{ hr}}{60 \text{ min}} = \frac{1}{30} \text{ hr}$$

$$s_A = s_B$$

$$1 + 30\frac{1}{30} = v_B\frac{1}{30}$$

$$v_B = 60 \text{ mph}$$

EXAMPLE 4: A velocity-time curve of a moving particle is shown in Fig. 9-6. During the first 10 sec, the velocity increases from zero to 20 fps. It remains constant for the next 20 sec and then decreases to zero in 5 more sec. The total elapsed time is 35 sec. Determine the displacement and average velocity of the particle.

Solution: During the first 10 sec of motion, the average velocity is

$$v_{\text{avg}} = \frac{0 + 20}{2} = 10 \text{ fps}$$

This represents a displacement, in 10 sec, of

$$\Delta s_1 = v_{\text{avg}}(\Delta t) = 10(10) = 100 \text{ ft}$$

During the next 20 sec of motion the velocity is constant, therefore

$$\Delta s_2 = v(\Delta t) = 20(20) = 400 \text{ ft}$$

and finally, during the last 5 sec, an average velocity is again used:

$$v_{\text{avg}} = \frac{20 + 0}{2} = 10 \text{ fps}$$

and $$\Delta s_3 = v_{\text{avg}}(\Delta t) = 10(5) = 50 \text{ ft}$$

The total displacement ΔS is the sum of three individual displacements:

$$\Delta S = \Delta s_1 + \Delta s_2 + \Delta s_3 = 100 + 400 + 50 = 550 \text{ ft}$$

The average velocity over the entire 35 sec of motion is

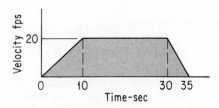

Figure 9-6

$$v_{avg} = \frac{\Delta S}{\Delta t} = \frac{550}{35} = 15.7 \text{ fps}$$

An alternate method of solution would be to determine the area under the velocity-time diagram by direct computation. In this case, the area consists of two triangles and one rectangle.

$$\Delta S = \tfrac{1}{2}(20)10 + 20(20) + \tfrac{1}{2}(20)5 = 550 \text{ ft}$$

9-5 Acceleration

Accelerated motion occurs whenever the velocity changes in either direction or magnitude or both. When the velocity of a point moving in a straight line changes by equal amounts in equal increments of time, acceleration is said to be *uniform*. If Δv represents a change in velocity from v_o to v_f in an increment of time t_o to t_f then

$$a = \frac{v_f - v_o}{t_f - t_o} = \frac{\Delta v}{\Delta t} \qquad (9\text{-}5)$$

and if $t_o = 0$

$$v_f - v_o = at \qquad (9\text{-}6)$$

Eq. (9-5) defines the *average acceleration* over any time interval when the ratio $\Delta v/\Delta t$ is not constant. Acceleration has the dimensions of [velocity]/[time] and it is usually expressed in the units of feet per second per second (fps²).

EXAMPLE 5: A boat moves north at 5 mph; 10 sec later, it moves south at the rate of 15 mph. What is the average acceleration over the 10 sec interval?

Solution: Assume north to be the positive direction and south the negative direction for the velocity vectors.

$$a_{avg} = \frac{\Delta v}{\Delta t} = \frac{5 \text{ mph} - (-15 \text{ mph})}{10 \text{ sec}} = 2 \frac{\text{mi}}{\text{hr sec}}$$

The units of miles per hour per second are converted to fps²:

$$2 \frac{\text{mi}}{\text{hr sec}} \times \frac{5280 \text{ ft}}{\text{mi}} \times \frac{1 \text{ hr}}{3600 \text{ sec}} = 2.93 \text{ fps}^2$$

9-6 Uniformly Acclerated Motion

Many problems—for example, those involving a gravitational free fall—are concerned with a constant acceleration. Consequently, it is convenient to develop mathematical relationships for such motion between the variables: displacement, velocity, acceleration, and time.

A study of Fig. 9-7, a plot of velocity against time, indicates that two

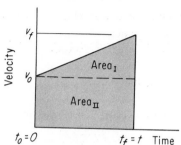

$$\text{Area}_I = \left(\frac{v_f - v_o}{2}\right)t$$

$$\text{Area}_{II} = v_o t$$

Figure 9-7

distinct areas are involved: a triangle and a rectangle. The displacement s is equivalent to the total area enclosed by this curve:

$$s = \text{area}_I + \text{area}_{II}$$

$$= \frac{v_f - v_o}{2}t + v_o t \qquad (a)$$

By definition

$$v_f - v_o = at \qquad (9\text{-}6)$$

Substituting Eq. (9-6) into Eq. (a) gives an equation in which displacement is related to the initial velocity, the acceleration, and time.

$$s = v_o t + \frac{at^2}{2} \qquad (9\text{-}7)$$

Another important relationship is obtained by solving Eq. (9-6) for time t, squaring, and substituting the values of t and t^2 into Eq. (9-7). This results in a formula that relates displacement to the initial velocity, the final velocity, and acceleration.

$$t = \frac{v_f - v_o}{a}$$

squared, gives

$$t^2 = \frac{v_f^2 - 2v_f v_o + v_o^2}{a^2}$$

$$s = v_o t + \frac{at^2}{2}$$

$$= v_o \left(\frac{v_f - v_o}{a}\right) + \frac{a}{2}\left(\frac{v_f^2 - 2v_f v_o + v_o^2}{a^2}\right)$$

$$= \frac{v_f^2 - v_o^2}{2a} \qquad (9\text{-}8)$$

EXAMPLE 6: A car traveling at 15 mph increases its speed uniformly to 45 mph in 11 sec. Determine (a) the acceleration; (b) the distance traveled; (c) the distance traveled in the eighth second; (d) the speed after traveling 100 ft.

Solution: The initial velocity and final velocity are converted to the units of fps.

$$15 \frac{mi}{hr} \times \frac{5280 \text{ ft}}{mi} \times \frac{1 \text{ hr}}{3600 \text{ sec}} = 22 \text{ fps}$$

Therefore

$$45 \frac{mi}{hr} = 3(22) = 66 \text{ fps}$$

Eq. (9-6) is used to calculate the acceleration of the car.

$$a = \frac{v_f - v_0}{t} = \frac{66 - 22}{11} = 4 \text{ fps}^2$$

The distance traveled is determined by substitution of data into Eq. (9-7):

$$s = v_0 t + \frac{at^2}{2} = 22(11) + \frac{4(11)^2}{2} = 484 \text{ ft}$$

The distance traveled in the eighth second is the distance evaluated for a total of 8 seconds less that for a total of 7 seconds.

$$s_{8-7} = s_8 - s_7 = \left[22(8) + \frac{4(8)^2}{2} \right] - \left[22(7) + \frac{4(7)^2}{2} \right] = 52 \text{ ft}$$

Finally, Eq. (9-8) is used to evaluate the speed after traveling a distance of 100 ft.

$$v_f^2 - v_0^2 = 2as$$

Solving for the final velocity v_f gives

$$v_f = \sqrt{2as + v_0^2} = \sqrt{2(4)100 + (22)^2} = 35.8 \text{ fps}$$

EXAMPLE 7: A stone is projected upward with a velocity of 20 fps from a point on a cliff 40 ft above the ground. How high above the cliff will the stone rise, and what total time will elapse before the stone hits the ground? Assume a value of 32.2 fps² for the acceleration of gravity.

Solution: Assume all motion (displacement, velocity and acceleration) in the upward direction to be positive; the gravitational acceleration and the net displacement are both negative.

At the highest point of the motion, the instantaneous velocity is zero. From Eq. (9-8)

$$s = \frac{v_f^2 - v_0^2}{2a} = \frac{0^2 - (20)^2}{2(-32.2)} = \frac{400}{64.4} = 6.21 \text{ ft above cliff}$$

The time of flight is found by substituting the net displacement of the stone, $s = 40$ ft, into Eq. (9-7).

$$s = v_0 t + \frac{at^2}{2}$$

$$-40 = 20t + \frac{(-32.2)t^2}{2}$$

Rearranging terms in the order of descending powers of t gives

$$16.1t^2 - 20t - 40 = 0$$

The time t is then determined by the quadratic equation:

$$t = \frac{-b \pm \sqrt{b^2 - 4ac}}{2a} = \frac{20 \pm \sqrt{(20)^2 + 4(16.1)40}}{2(16.1)} = 0.62 \pm 1.69$$

$$t = +2.31 \text{ sec}$$

Note: Only the positive root is significant; the negative value of time given in the solution has no meaning and is, therefore, discarded.

9-7 The Motion of Projectiles

Two simultaneous, but distinctly different, types of motion are involved in analysis of the flight of a projectile. Disregarding any effects of air resistance, the horizontal component of velocity is constant, while the vertical component is dependent upon a downward gravitational acceleration. The movement resulting from the *superposition* of the two velocities is called *projectile motion.* The path from the origin of the motion to the first point of impact is called the *trajectory.*

The dotted line in Fig. 9-8 represents a trajectory of a projectile having an initial velocity of v_o and a firing angle of θ with the horizontal. An x-y system of coordinates is drawn to coincide with the origin of the motion O and the horizontal and vertical directions. Vectors pointing upward and vectors pointing to the right are therefore positive. Point A in Fig. 9-8 is an arbitrary point on the trajectory having displacement components of x and y.

The initial velocity components are $v_x = v_o \cos \theta$ and $v_y = v_o \sin \theta$. Since v_x has a constant value, the x-component of displacement is given by

$$x = v_x t$$

$$x = (v_o \cos \theta)t$$

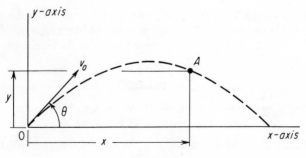

Figure 9-8

The y-component of displacement, which is affected by a constant acceleration, is given by Eq. (9-7):

$$s = v_0 t + \frac{at^2}{2}$$

$$y = (v_0 \sin \theta)t - \frac{gt^2}{2}$$

where g is the downward (negative) acceleration of gravity. The actual
velocity on the trajectory at point A is the vector sum of v_x and v_y:

$$v_A = \sqrt{v_x^2 + v_y^2}$$

where v_x is constant and v_y is given by Eq. (9-5):

$$v_x = v_0 \cos \theta$$

$$v_y = v_0 \sin \theta - gt$$

EXAMPLE 8: A projectile is fired from a cliff 2000 ft above sea level as shown
in Fig. 9-9. The muzzle velocity is 1500 fps and the firing angle is $\theta = 30$ deg.
Determine: (a) the range; (b) the time of flight; (c) the velocity just prior to
hitting the sea; (d) the maximum height reached by the projectile.

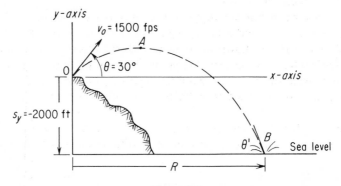

Figure 9-9

Solution: A sketch is drawn using a system of x- and y-coordinates with the
origin O at the firing position. The highest point on the trajectory is at A and
the point of impact is at B. The velocity components at the origin are

$$v_x = 1500 \cos 30° \tag{a}$$

$$v_y = 1500 \sin 30° \tag{b}$$

The equation for the range R is written in terms of v_x and t:

$$R = v_x t = (1500 \cos 30°)t = 1299t \text{ ft} \tag{c}$$

The time of flight is found by substituting the vertical displacement s_y into Eq.
(9-7):

$$S = v_o t + \frac{at^2}{2}$$

$$-2000 = (1500 \sin 30°)t + \frac{(-32.2)t^2}{2}$$

This equation is rewritten in quadratic form and the time t calculated:

$$16.1t^2 - 750t - 2000 = 0$$

$$t = \frac{750 \pm \sqrt{(750)^2 + 4(16.1)2000}}{2(16.1)} = \frac{750 \pm 831}{32.2} = -2.53, +49.1$$

The negative root is discarded; the time of flight is

$$t = 49.1 \text{ sec}$$

The range is then computed by substituting $t = 49.1$ sec into Eq. (c).

$$R = 1299(49.1) = 63,800 \text{ ft}$$

To determine the velocity at point B, v_y is needed; this can be found from Eq. (9-6).

$$v_f - v_o = at$$

$$v_y = 1500 \sin 30° - 32.2(49.1)$$

$$= 750 - 1581 = -831 \text{ fps}$$

where v_B is the vector sum of v_x and v_y; thus

$$v_B = \sqrt{(v_x)^2 + (v_y)^2} = \sqrt{(1299)^2 + (-831)^2} = 1542 \text{ fps}$$

$$\theta' = \text{arc tan } \frac{v_y}{v_x} = \text{arc tan } \frac{831}{1299} = 32.6° \searrow$$

At the maximum height in the trajectory the y-component of velocity is zero. Eq. (9-8) is used to find this height.

$$v_f^2 - v_o^2 = 2as$$

$$s_{\max} = \frac{0^2 - (1500 \sin 30°)^2}{2(-32.2)} = \frac{(750)^2}{64.4} = 8730 \text{ ft}$$

9-8 Normal Acceleration

Fig. 9-10 shows a particle moving with a constant speed on a circular path with radius r. The continual change in direction of the velocity vector is a change in velocity itself; this change, therefore, constitutes an acceleration. This acceleration is defined in the usual manner as

$$a = \frac{v_f - v_o}{t_f - t_o} = \frac{\Delta v}{\Delta t}$$

To find the change in velocity, Δv, the vectors v_f and v_o are subtracted by the string polygon method as shown in Fig. 9-10(b). Since the magnitudes of v_o and v_f are the same, the change in velocity Δv is

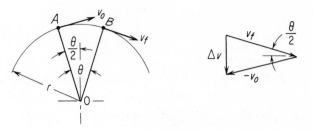

Figure 9-10

$$\Delta v = 2v \sin \frac{\theta}{2} \qquad\qquad (a)$$

where for small angles

$$\sin \frac{\theta}{2} = \frac{\theta}{2}$$

and Eq. (a) becomes

$$\Delta v = v\theta$$

For small central angles the cord length AB is approximately equal to the arc length $r\theta$. This length, in terms of velocity and time, is

$$\overline{AB} = v(\Delta t) = r\theta$$

and

$$\Delta t = \frac{r\theta}{v}$$

where

$$a_n = \frac{\Delta v}{\Delta t} = \frac{v\theta}{r\theta/v} = \frac{v^2}{r} \qquad\qquad (9\text{-}9)$$

a_n is called the *normal acceleration* and is directed toward the center of curvature of the path.

PROBLEMS

9-1. The tool bit shown in Fig. 9-2 is to have a displacement of 5 in. directed toward right center at an angle of 30 deg with the carriage axis. Show how this may be accomplished using: (a) the carriage and crossfeed; (b) the carriage and compound rest; (c) the crossfeed and compound rest; (d) all three elements. Assume the angle θ to be 60 deg.

9-2. Make a half-scale layout of the cam and follower assembly shown in Fig. P9-2 and plot the path of points A, B, and C for one full revolution of the cam. Use 20 deg increments of cam rotation.

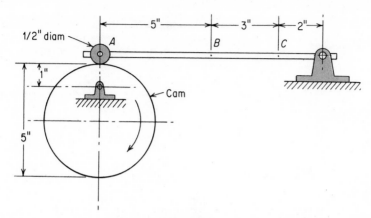

Figure P9-2

9-3. Two ships, A and B, sail away from a marker buoy. Ship A sails 5 mi north and ship B sails 8 mi east. Find the displacement of ship A relative to ship B and the compass bearing of this displacement.

9-4. A 13 ft rod AB is placed in a corner as shown in Fig. P9-4, with end A 5 ft from O. If end A is displaced 7 ft to the right, find (a) the displacement of the mid-point m of the rod; (b) the displacement of end B.

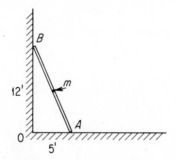

Figure P9-4

9-5. Solve part (a) of Prob. 9-4 if end A of rod AB is moved from the position shown to point O.

9-6. A plane is sighted from two points both at zero ground elevation as shown in Fig. P9-6. Determine the elevation of the plane if the points are 1000 yards apart.

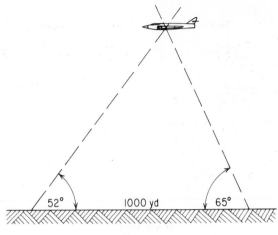

Figure P9-6

9-7. A missile that has been vertically launched is being tracked by a sighting device as shown in Fig. P9-7. If two sightings are made 2.0 sec apart find the average speed in ft per sec during the rise from *A* to *B*.

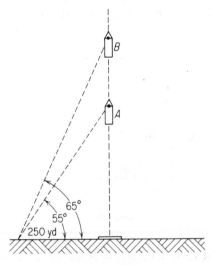

Figure P9-7

9-8. Resolve the 10 ft displacement in each case shown in Fig. P9-8 into components lying along lines *a–a* and *b–b*.

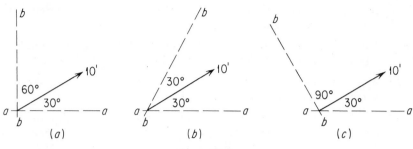

Figure P9-8

9-9. A jet plane is flying at a speed of "Mach 1.2" (1.2 times the speed of sound or 1.2 × 1100 fps) in a direction of 30 deg west of north. Determine the north and west components of its velocity in miles per hour.

9-10. Determine the "Mach" number equivalent to (a) 90 mph; (b) 750 mph; (c) 500 yd per sec. Refer to Prob. 9-9.

9-11. One nautical mile (6076 ft) per hour is called a "knot". Express 10 knots in units of: (a) miles per hour; (b) feet per second; (c) feet per minute.

9-12. Express 30 mph in (a) feet per second; (b) knots; (c) yards per minute.

9-13. A car, Fig. P9-13, travels 500 yards in 30 seconds. Find the speed in miles per hour and the x and y component of velocity in feet per second.

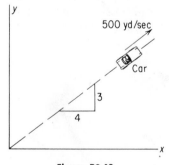

Figure P9-13

9-14. An automobile travels on a straight road at a speed of 40 mph for 15 min. and then at 60 mph for 30 min. Determine: (a) the average speed; (b) the average velocity.

9-15. An automobile leaves a town and travels at a speed of 20 mph for one hour. It then turns around and returns at a speed of 40 mph. Find: (a) the average speed; (b) the average velocity.

9-16. Draw the velocity-time curve for the motion of Prob. 9-15 and justify the answers graphically.

9-17. Light travels at a speed of 186,000 miles per second. How long does it take to reach the earth from the sun, a distance of 92,000,000 miles?

9-18. A star in a far-off constellation is 2 million light-years away. Express this in miles using exponential powers of ten.

9-19. Depth charges exploded in the sea off Australia have been heard 12,000 miles away at Bermuda. The sound waves made the trip in 2 hours and 24 minutes. Determine the average velocity of the sound in the water in units of feet per second. If the sound traveled the same distance in air, how long would it take to make the trip? The velocity of sound in air is 1100 fps.

9-20. A train 500 ft long is traveling at a speed of 120 mph. How long will it take to pass a given point?

9-21. Find the resultant velocity of a missile having velocity components of $V_x = 2000$ ft per sec, $V_y = 500$ ft per sec and $V_z = 5000$ ft per sec.

9-22. Two automobiles, one mile apart, are moving toward one another. One car has a speed of 30 mph and the other a speed of 45 mph. How long will it take them to meet?

9-23. A bullet is fired with a velocity of 1800 fps at an object 50 yards due south. The object is moving 60 mph due east. In what direction should the gun be aimed? Does the direction depend upon the range?

9-24. The current of a river has a velocity of 4 mph north. A boat can travel at a rate of 20 mph relative to the water. Find the velocity of the boat when heading (a) with the current;(b) against the current; (c) due east; (d) southwest.

9-25. Two planes are approaching one another as shown in an elevation view in Fig. P9-25. What is the velocity of plane A relative to plane B? Of plane B relative to plane A?

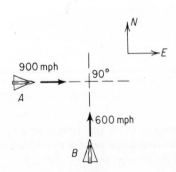

Figure P9-25

9-26. An air ship departs from a mooring and sails due west with a uniform velocity of 10 knots. Simultaneously, a north wind is blowing with a velocity of 20 knots. Find the absolute velocity of the ship and its displacement from the mooring 3 hr after departure.

9-27. A car A traveling with a velocity of 60 mph passes another car B traveling 40 mph in the same direction. Determine (a) the velocity of car A relative to car B; (b) the velocity of car B relative to car A; (c) the distance between them 4 min after passing.

9-28. A man rows a boat 3 mi upstream and 3 mi back in 2 hr. If he can row a boat 7 mph in still water, how fast is the stream flowing?

Note: When the acceleration of gravity is required in the following problems, use a value of 32.2 fps².

9.29. Convert an acceleration of 0.01 mi per min per sec to units of: (a) ft per min per min; (b) ft per min per sec; (c) fps².

9-30. An automobile acquires a speed of 60 mph in 15 sec. What is the average acceleration of the car?

9-31. The velocity-time diagram for the rectilinear motion of a point is shown in Fig. P9-31. Determine: (a) the acceleration for the first 5 sec; (b) the acceleration between the fifth and fifteenth seconds; (c) the acceleration between the fifteenth and thirtieth seconds; (d) the average velocity; (e) the total displacement.

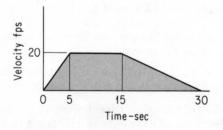

Figure P9-31

9-32. An automobile, traveling at a speed of 60 mph, approaches an intersection. If the brakes can retard the motion at a rate of 5 fps for each second of travel, find: (a) how far ahead of the intersection the brakes should be applied; (b) the time required to stop.

9-33. Starting from rest, an airplane acquires a take-off velocity of 150 mph on a two-mile runway. The acceleration is assumed to be uniform. Calculate the time required to reach take-off speed.

9-34. The brakes are applied on a train moving with a velocity of 120 mph. Determine the deceleration of the train if the speed is reduced by a factor of one-half in 2000 ft. How long will it take to come to rest after applying the brakes?

9-35. A weight is dropped from a helicopter that is rising vertically with a velocity of 20 fps. If the weight reaches the ground in 15 sec, how high above the ground was the helicopter when the weight was dropped and with what velocity does the weight strike the ground?

9-36. What is the uniform acceleration of an elevator if it acquires a speed, from rest, of 600 fpm in a distance of 20 ft?

9-37. Water drips from a faucet at the rate of 4 drops per second. Determine the distance between two successive drops one second after the first one has fallen.

9-38. An object falls freely from rest. Determine the velocity at the end of 3 sec and the distance it has fallen at the end of 5 sec.

9-39. A stone is thrown upward from the edge of a cliff with a velocity of 40 fps. Determine: (a) the maximum height reached; (b) the time to reach the maximum height; (c) the height of the cliff if the stone hits the ground 10 sec after being thrown.

9-40. A gun fires a shell on level terrain at an angle $\theta = 30$ deg with the horizontal. The muzzle velocity is 1800 fps. Determine: (a) the maximum height reached by the shell; (b) the range; (c) the time of flight.

9-41. Determine the muzzle velocity of a projectile if the firing angle is $\theta = 30$ deg and the time of flight is $t = 60$ sec. What is the range of the projectile?

9-42. A projectile is fired from the edge of a cliff 500 ft above level ground. If the firing angle is $\theta = 20$ deg and the muzzle velocity is 1500 fps, determine: (a) the maximum height reached; (b) the horizontal range; (c) its velocity just prior to striking the ground.

9-43. The range of a target on level ground is 50,000 ft. Determine the firing angle θ if a shell is fired with a muzzle velocity of 1800 fps.

9-44. An airplane flies horizontally 10,000 feet above the ground at a speed of 600 mph. How many seconds prior to reaching a target must the plane's bombs be released? With what velocity do the bombs strike the target?

9-45. The range of a projectile is 10,000 yd when fired at an angle of 30 deg with the horizontal. Determine the muzzle velocity of the projectile.

9-46. A stone is dropped into a well and 10 seconds later the sound is heard. If the velocity of sound is 1100 fps, how deep is the well?

9-47. Determine the normal acceleration of an automobile that is traveling at a speed of 60 mph while rounding a curve with a radius of 400 ft.

9-48. A particle moves on a circular path with a radius of 10 ft. Determine the particle's speed if it has a normal acceleration of 4 fps².

9-49. Astronauts are whirled in horizontal apparatus to simulate the great acceleration they are to experience in rocket flight. The apparatus consists of a 50 ft arm pivoted at one end with the would-be space traveler at the other. What speed must he have if he experiences an acceleration of 8 g's (eight times the acceleration of gravity)?

Chapter 10

KINEMATICS
OF RIGID
BODIES

The laws of geometry govern the motion of bodies just as they govern the motion of particles. In this chapter, particular reference will be made to problems involving the translation, rotation, and plane motion of rigid bodies.

10-1 Particles, Bodies, and Machines

When is an object considered a particle and when is it considered a body? The answer to this question depends upon the comparative size of the body to its path. For example, the earth can be considered to be a particle when its motion about the sun is studied—the size of the earth is small compared to the size of its path. At the other extreme, the dimensions of even the smallest gear in a watch are important to the movement of the minute hand and the hour hand. The gear must be treated as a body.

The motion-path comparison can be extended to cover the internal movement of the particles of matter that make up the body. If the internal contractions or expansions are small compared to the overall motion, the object can be assumed to be a *rigid body*. Some care must be used when applying this concept. A spring, for example, cannot be correctly assumed to be rigid since the force it exerts depends upon the amount that it is stretched or compressed.

In the study of mechanics, a *mechanism* is a group of bodies assembled so that their motions are related; a pair of mated gears is an example of a mechanism. A *machine* is simply a mechanism that is capable of performing a useful function.

10-2 Translation of a Rigid Body

When every particle in a body has identical motion the body is said to *translate:* it always moves parallel to itself. *Rectilinear translation* occurs when the particles which make up the body move in straight lines; *curvilinear translation* occurs when the particles that comprise the body have curved paths. In either case, a line AB scribed on the body always remains parallel to itself during translatory motion, as shown in Fig. 10-1.

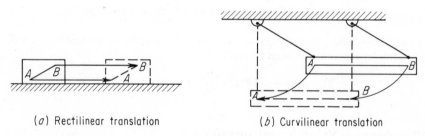

(*a*) Rectilinear translation   (*b*) Curvilinear translation

Figure 10-1

10-3 Pure Rotation

The flywheel shown in Fig. 10-2 moves with pure rotation. The *axis of rotation*, in this case the shaft AB, is always perpendicular to the plane of rotation and all particles in the body move in concentric circles with this axis as their center. The curved arrow ↻ indicates the direction of rotation, clockwise or counterclockwise, as the case may be.

Angular quantities are measured in terms of revolutions, degrees, or radians. Frequently, all three units of measure may be involved in a single problem. The conversion of units is readily accomplished by noting that

$$\text{one revolution} = 360 \text{ degrees} = 2\pi \text{ radians}$$

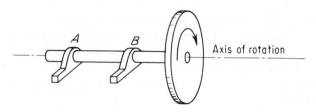

Figure 10-2

Angular motion is analogous to linear motion in that displacement, velocity, and acceleration are defined for both systems in a similar manner. The Greek letter θ (theta) is used to symbolize an *angular displacement*. This quantity, expressed in radians, is a measure of change in angular position. *Angular distance*, on the other hand, is analogous to linear distance; it is a measure of the *total angle* turned by a rotating body.

EXAMPLE 1: A flywheel, similar to that shown in Fig. 10-2, rotates 20 revolutions clockwise and then 10.5 revolutions counterclockwise. Determine the angular distance and the angular displacement of the flywheel.

Solution: Angular distance is the total angle turned without regard to direction, thus

$$\theta_D = |20| + |10.5| = 30.5 \; \text{rev}\left(\frac{2\pi \; \text{rad}}{\text{rev}}\right) = 192 \; \text{rad}$$

A sign convention is necessary to compute the angular displacement; in this problem, let clockwise rotation be positive.

$$\theta = 20 - 10.5 = 9.5 \; \text{rev}\left(\frac{2\pi \; \text{rad}}{\text{rev}}\right) = 59.7 \; \text{rad clockwise}$$

10-4 Angular Velocity and Angular Acceleration

The Greek letter ω (omega) is the symbol used to designate angular velocity—the rate of change of angular displacement. The appropriate units of ω are either radians per second [rad per sec] or revolutions per minute [rpm]. *Average angular velocity*, like average linear velocity, is defined as the time rate of change of displacement.

$$\omega_{\text{ave}} = \frac{\Delta\theta}{\Delta t} \tag{10-1}$$

where $\Delta\theta$ represents a *change* in angular displacement, and Δt represents an increment of elapsed time. *Uniform angular velocity* means simply that the rate of change of displacement is constant.

The average angular acceleration, α (alpha), is defined as the time rate of change of angular velocity. The appropriate units of α are rad per sec^2.

$$\alpha_{\text{ave}} = \frac{\Delta\omega}{\Delta t} \tag{10-2}$$

Employing the methods of Chap. 9, a set of three equations can be written for uniformly accelerated motion:

$$\theta = \omega_0 t + \frac{\alpha t^2}{2} \tag{10-3}$$

$$\alpha = \frac{\omega_f - \omega_0}{t} \tag{10-4}$$

$$2\alpha\theta = \omega_f^2 - \omega_0^2 \tag{10-5}$$

It is important that appropriate signs, plus and minus, be used to indicate a direction of rotation that is consistent for all the terms in the equation.

EXAMPLE 2: A flywheel similar to that shown in Fig. 10-2 is acted upon by a brake which brings it uniformly to rest in 15 sec from an initial clockwise speed of 1800 rpm. Determine the angular acceleration acting on the wheel and the angular displacement of the wheel during the 15 sec period.

Solution: The units of the initial velocity are first converted to radians per second and Eq. (10-4) is then used to calculate the angular acceleration. A clockwise direction is assumed to be positive.

$$1800\frac{\text{rev}}{\text{min}} \times \frac{2\pi \text{ rad}}{\text{rev}} \times \frac{\text{min}}{60 \text{ sec}} = 60\pi \text{ rad per sec}$$

$$\alpha = \frac{\omega_f - \omega_0}{t} = \frac{0 - 60\pi}{15}$$

$$= -12.56 \text{ rad per sec}^2$$

The minus sign indicates that the flywheel is decelerating.

Eq. (10-3) is next used to find the angular displacement of the flywheel during the 15 sec period.

$$\theta = \omega_0 t + \frac{\alpha t^2}{2} = 60\pi(15) - \frac{4\pi(15)^2}{2}$$

$$\theta = 1410 \text{ rad}$$

EXAMPLE 3: A ship's propeller accelerates uniformly from 300 rpm to 500 rpm while turning through 100 revolutions. Find the angular acceleration and the time required to change the speed.

Solution: The variables, displacement and velocity, are converted into units of radians and radians per second. Eqs. (10-5) and (10-4) are then used to compute the angular acceleration and the time respectively.

$$\omega_o = 300\left(\frac{2\pi}{60}\right) = 31.4 \text{ rad per sec}$$

$$\omega_f = 500\left(\frac{2\pi}{60}\right) = 52.3 \text{ rad per sec}$$

$$\theta = 100(2\pi) = 628 \text{ rad}$$

$$\alpha = \frac{\omega_f^2 - \omega_o^2}{2\theta} = \frac{(52.3)^2 - (31.4)^2}{2(628)}$$

$$\alpha = 1.39 \text{ rad per sec}^2$$

$$t = \frac{\omega_f - \omega_o}{\alpha} = \frac{52.3 - 31.4}{1.39}$$

$$t = 15.0 \text{ sec}$$

10-5 Relationship Between Linear and Angular Motion

Figure 10-3 shows weight fastened to a cord which is wrapped around a pulley of radius r. As the pulley rotates clockwise through an angle θ, a length of cord s unwinds and the weight moves downward. In one revolution the weight descends a distance equal to the circumference of the pulley.

$$s = 2\pi r$$

and for any portion of a revolution the distance s equals the product of the radius of the pulley and its angular displacement expressed in radians, thus

$$s = r\theta \tag{10-6}$$

By the substitution of an incremental value $\Delta\theta$ for the angular displacement, the linear displacement given by Eq. (10-6) becomes

$$\Delta s = r(\Delta\theta)$$

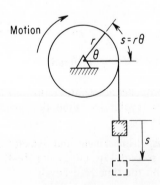

Figure 10-3

Dividing both sides of this equation by Δt gives the linear velocity in v terms of angular velocity ω.

$$\frac{\Delta s}{\Delta t} = r\frac{\Delta \theta}{\Delta t}$$

$$v = r\omega \tag{10-7}$$

Again substituting incremental values in Eq. (10-7), the relationship between linear acceleration and angular acceleration is obtained:

$$\frac{\Delta v}{\Delta t} = r\frac{\Delta \omega}{\Delta t}$$

$$a = r\alpha \tag{10-8}$$

EXAMPLE 4: Two weights, A and B, are attached to cords wrapped around the double pulley as shown in Fig. 10-4. While moving downward, weight A increases its velocity uniformly from 30 fps to 50 fps in 2 sec. Determine the acceleration and displacement of weights A and B, and the angular displacement of the pulley.

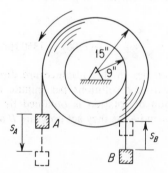

Figure 10-4

Solution: The kinematic equations for linear motion are used to determine a_A and s_A.

$$a_A = \frac{v_f - v_o}{t} = \frac{50 - 30}{2} = 10 \text{ fps}^2 \downarrow$$

and
$$s_A = \frac{v_f^2 - v_o^2}{2a} = \frac{(50)^2 - (30)^2}{2(10)} = 80 \text{ ft} \downarrow$$

The angular displacement and angular acceleration are next calculated, using Eqs. (10-6) and (10-8).

$$\theta = \frac{s}{r} = \frac{80}{\frac{15}{12}} = 64 \text{ rad } \circlearrowright$$

$$\alpha = \frac{a}{r} = \frac{10}{\frac{15}{12}} = 8 \text{ rad per sec}^2 \circlearrowright$$

Eqs. (10-6) and (10-8) are again employed, in this instance, to find the displacement and acceleration of body B.

$$s_B = r\theta = \frac{9}{12}(64) = 48 \text{ ft} \uparrow$$

$$a_B = r\alpha = \frac{9}{12}(8) = 6 \text{ fps}^2 \uparrow$$

EXAMPLE 5: Gear A, the driver of the three-gear transmission shown in Fig. 10-5, is rotating counterclockwise with an angular velocity of 1800 rpm. Find the angular velocities of gears B and C.

Solution: Since the rim velocities of gears A and B are equal at point P, their angular velocities are related.

$$v_P = r_A\omega_A = r_B\omega_B$$

where

$$\omega_B = \frac{r_A}{r_B}\omega_A = \frac{4.5}{3}(1800) = 2700 \text{ rpm} \,\circlearrowright$$

In a similar manner, the rim velocities of gears B and C are equal at point Q.

$$v_Q = r_B\omega_B = r_C\omega_C$$

where $$\omega_C = \frac{r_B}{r_C}\omega_B = \frac{3}{6}(2700) = 1350 \text{ rpm} \,\circlearrowleft$$

Because the angular velocities in this instance are direct ratios of each other, the conversion of units from revolutions per minute to radians per second is unnecessary. The direction of rotation is obtained by observing the directions of the velocity vectors v_P and v_Q as they act on gears B and C.

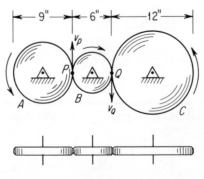

Figure 10-5

10-6 Normal and Tangential Components of Acceleration

It was shown in Chapter 9 that a directional change in velocity is always accompanied by a component of acceleration a_n normal to the path and directed towards the center of curvature. If the velocity v along the path is expressed in terms of the angular velocity ω, the normal component of acceleration becomes

$$a_n = \frac{v^2}{r} = \frac{(r\omega)^2}{r} = r\omega^2 \tag{10-9}$$

Point P on the rotating body shown in Fig. 10-6 has two orthogonal components of acceleration. These two components, one normal and the other tangent to the path of P, exist because both the magnitude and the direction of the velocity at the point are changing. The total acceleration a_P is the vector sum of these two components.

$$a = \sqrt{a_n^2 + a_t^2} = \sqrt{(r\omega^2)^2 + (r\alpha)^2} \tag{10-10}$$

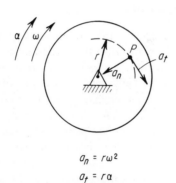

$$a_n = r\omega^2$$
$$a_t = r\alpha$$

Figure 10-6

EXAMPLE 6: A point P is located on the rim of a flywheel as shown in Fig. 10-7(a). Determine the total acceleration of point P if the flywheel has a clockwise angular velocity of 5 rad per sec and a counterclockwise angular acceleration of 20 rad per sec^2.

Solution: The total acceleration, using Eq. (10-10), is the vector sum of a_n and a_t, where

$$a_n = r\omega^2 = 1.5(5)^2 = 37.5 \text{ fps}^2$$

and

$$a_t = r\alpha = 1.5(20) = 30 \text{ fps}^2$$

thus

$$a = \sqrt{a_n^2 + a_t^2} = \sqrt{(37.5)^2 + (30)^2} = 48 \text{ fps}^2$$

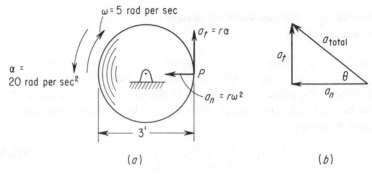

Figure 10-7

The vector representing the total acceleration is directed at an angle θ as shown in Fig. 10-7(b), where

$$\theta = \text{arc tan} \left(\frac{30}{37.5} \right) = 38.7 \text{ deg}$$

10-7 The Coriolis Acceleration

Few people realize, while they travel 60 miles per hour on a north-south road, that there is a tendency to drift off the road at the rate of some 15 feet per mile. Friction between the tires and the road prevents this, of course, but the tendency still exists. This drift, caused in part by the rotation of the earth, was discovered by a French engineer G. G. Coriolis in 1835 and is called the *Coriolis drift*, or the *Coriolis acceleration*; it affects the motion of projectiles, satellites, aircraft, ocean currents, and even the weather. In mechanisms, the Coriolis acceleration occurs whenever a body is subjected to a combination of rotation and relative translation. This is the case illustrated in Fig. 10-8; the slider moves outward along the rod with a constant relative velocity v_r, while the rod rotates about O.

The rather complicated path of the slider is greatly simplified when viewed in terms of its components. The slider can be imagined to move from B to E in three basic steps: first, along arc BC, next, along line CD, and finally, along arc DE. The first two motions occur with constant velocity; during the third motion, along arc DE, the slider must accelerate to keep up with the rod.

$$\text{arc } BC = r_1\theta \tag{a}$$

$$\text{arc } FE = r_2\theta \tag{b}$$

$$\text{distance } DC = v_r t \tag{c}$$

$$\text{velocity along rod} = v_r = \frac{(r_2 - r_1)}{t} \tag{d}$$

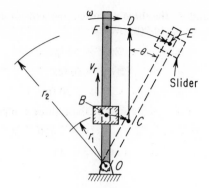

Figure 10-8

$$\text{angular velocity of the rod} = \omega = \frac{\theta}{t} \tag{e}$$

The acceleration along arc DE can be found by the kinematic equation $S = at^2/2$:

$$\text{arc } DE = (r_2 - r_1)\theta = \frac{at^2}{2} \tag{f}$$

The Coriolis acceleration is obtained by combining Eqs. (d), (e), and (f):

$$\frac{at^2}{2} = (v_r t)(\omega t)$$

$$a_c = 2v_r\omega \tag{10-11}$$

A simple rule exists for establishing the direction of a_c—rotate the vector representing the radial velocity 90 deg in the direction of ω; it will point in the direction of the Coriolis acceleration.

EXAMPLE 7: The rod shown in Fig. 10-9(a) has an angular velocity of 5 rad per sec and an angular acceleration of 10 rad per sec², both directed counterclockwise. The slider is 2 ft from O and is moving outward along the rod at the rate of $v_r = 3$ fps. Determine the normal, tangential, and Coriolis components of acceleration of the slider.

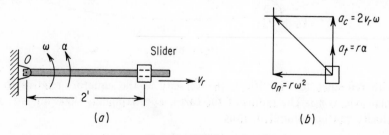

Figure 10-9

Solution: a_n, a_t, and a_c, the three vector components of acceleration acting on the slider, are shown in Fig. 10-9(b), where

$$a_n = r\omega^2 = 2(5)^2 = 50 \text{ fps}^2 \leftarrow$$
$$a_t = r\alpha = 2(10) = 20 \text{ fps}^2 \uparrow$$
$$a_c = 2v_r\omega = 2(3)5 = 30 \text{ fps}^2 \uparrow$$

The total acceleration is the vector sum of these three components.

$$a_{\text{total}} = \sqrt{(a_n)^2 + (a_t + a_c)^2} = \sqrt{(50)^2 + (20 + 30)^2} = 70.7 \text{ fps}^2$$
$$\theta = \text{arc tan } \tfrac{50}{50} = 45°$$

10-8 The Earth as a Rotating Body

In the ordinary problem in mechanics, the effect of the earth's rotation can be safely ignored, just as it is still safe, in general, to assume that what goes up comes down. In many instances, however, the earth's motion is a prime factor; it must be considered, for example, in the launching and guidance of missiles, satellites, rockets, and high-speed aircraft.

While the overall motion of the earth is rather complex, its two primary rotations can be considered here. These are, first, a rotation about the polar axis at the rate of one revolution per day, and second, a rotation of the polar axis about the sun at the rate of one revolution every 365 days. The path about the sun, or *orbit* as it is called, as seen in Fig. 10-10, is very nearly circular. The rate of rotation about the polar axis, called the *spin velocity*, can be readily calculated; it is found to be

$$\omega = \frac{2\pi}{24(3600)} = 7.27 \times 10^{-5} \text{ rad per sec}$$

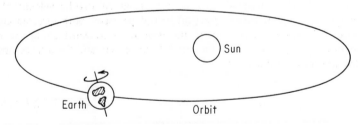

Sun

Earth   Orbit

Figure 10-10

With reference to Fig. 10-11, the velocity at the equator, relative to the polar axis, is $r\omega$. The radius of the earth, approximately 4000 mi, is r. This velocity can be computed, thus

$$v_E = r\omega = 4000 \text{ mi (5280 ft/mi)} 7.27 \times 10^{-5} \text{ rad per sec}$$
$$= 1540 \text{ fps or 1050 mph}$$

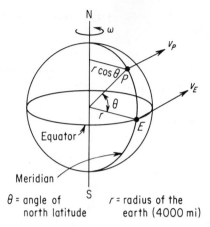

Figure 10-11

θ = angle of r = radius of the
north latitude   earth (4000 mi)

At any other point P on the surface of the earth, the effective radius is $r \cos \theta$, where θ is the angle of north or south latitude. The velocity in this instance would be given by

$$v_P = (r \cos \theta)\omega$$

If a satellite were launched due east from Cape Kennedy, Florida (latitude 28°28′N), the earth's rotation would impart an initial velocity relative to the polar axis of

.87990

$$V = (r \cos \theta)\omega = [4000(5280) \cos 28°28′]7.27 \times 10^{-5}$$

$$V = 1350 \text{ fps}$$

(In all probability, the satellite would be aimed slightly south of east or north of east, so that its path as it orbits the earth would cross the equator.)

A particle moving with uniform velocity over the surface of a rotating sphere, the earth, for example, experiences the three independent components of acceleration shown in Fig. 10-12. The first component, a_{n1}, a normal

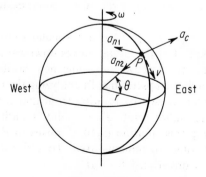

Figure 10-12

acceleration directed towards the polar axis, is caused by the particle's rotation with the earth.

$$a_{n1} = (r \cos \theta)\omega^2$$

The second component, a_{n2}, also a normal acceleration, is directed towards the center of the earth and is caused by a directional change in the particle's velocity.

$$a_{n2} = \frac{v^2}{r}$$

The Coriolis component a_c, the third component of acceleration, results when the particle moves outward from the polar axis as it rotates with the earth.

$$a_c = 2(v \sin \theta)\omega$$

EXAMPLE 8: A sphere, 4 ft in diameter, similar to the one shown in Fig. 10-12, is rotating with an angular velocity of 20 rad per sec. A particle P is moving along a meridian (north-south) line with a velocity of 10 fps. Find the components of acceleration due to the combined motion if at the instant shown $\theta = 60$ deg.

Solution: The components of acceleration are a_{n1} directed towards the polar axis, a_{n2} directed towards the center of the sphere, and a_c directed eastward as shown on the figure.

$$a_{n1} = (r \cos \theta)\omega^2 = 2(\cos 60°)(20)^2 = 400 \text{ fps}^2$$

$$a_{n2} = \frac{v^2}{r} = \frac{(10)^2}{2} = 50 \text{ fps}^2$$

$$a_c = 2v(\sin \theta)\omega = 2(10)(\sin 60°)20 = 346 \text{ fps}^2$$

10-9 Plane Motion

The introductory discussion of Chap. 9 defined plane motion as motion, partially rotational and partially translational, that is confined to a single plane. The rolling wheel of an automobile and the oscillating connecting rod of a stationary gasoline engine are two familiar examples of objects that have plane motion.

The ladder shown in Fig. 10-13 is a particular example of a body that has plane motion. End A of the ladder moves downward while end B moves outward; the dotted figure represents some new position that the ladder occupies after a period of elapsed time. In analyzing the motion, it is possible to separate the portion caused by rotation from that caused by translation. For instance, let the ladder rotate about point A until it is parallel to its final position. During this rotation point B moves to B' while A, imagined to be the center of rotation, remains fixed. To arrive at the final position, the ladder translates downward to $A'B''$.

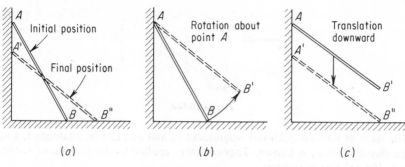

Figure 10-13

During the rotational phase of the motion, the velocity of point B is equal to the product of the length of the ladder and the angular velocity ω. This velocity is called *the velocity of B relative to A*, and is symbolized as $v_{B/A}$. Since the entire ladder next moves as point A moves, the *absolute* velocity of end B is the vector sum of $v_{B/A}$ and v_A.

$$v_B = v_{B/A} + v_A \tag{10-12}$$

In this problem the directions of the three velocities are known: v_B is horizontal, $v_{B/A}$ is perpendicular to the ladder, and v_A is vertical.

EXAMPLE 9: A 10 ft ladder is placed against a wall as shown in Fig. 10-14(a). If, at this instant, the velocity of end A is 10 fps downward, find the absolute velocity of end B and the angular velocity of the ladder.

Solution: Data concerning the magnitude and directions of the velocities are substituted into Eq. (10-12), and the string polygon of vectors is constructed as shown in Fig. 10-14(c), where

$$v_B = v_{B/A} + v_A$$

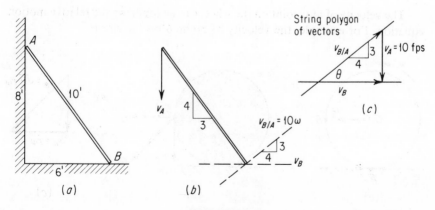

Figure 10-14

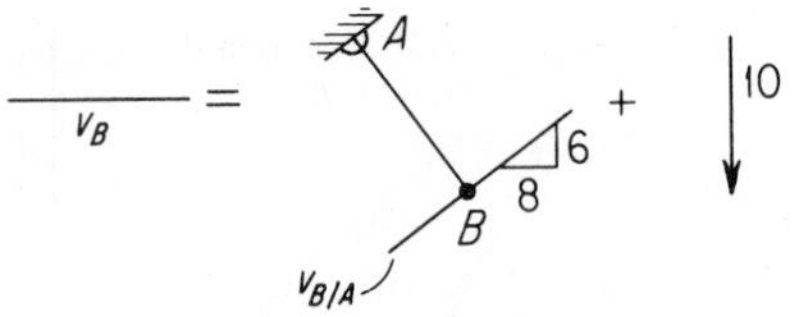

$$\frac{\qquad\qquad}{v_B} \; =$$

Figure 10-14A

The sense of the two unknown magnitudes v_B and $v_{B/A}$ can be established, since the direction of v_A is known. Trigonometry, applied to the triangle of vectors, gives the polygon of vectors:

$$v_B = v_{B/A} \cos \theta = (10\omega)\tfrac{4}{5} = 8\omega \qquad\qquad (a)$$

and $$v_{B/A} \sin \theta = 10 \qquad\qquad (b)$$

$$(10\omega)\tfrac{3}{5} = 10$$

$$\omega = \tfrac{5}{3} = 1.67 \text{ rad per sec}$$

Therefore $$v_B = 8(1.67) = 13.3 \text{ fps}$$

10-10 The Rolling Wheel

A rolling wheel, like that shown in Fig. 10-15(a), is an interesting example of an object having plane motion. An untrained observer will insist that the wheel rotates about geometric center O; this is only true, of course, if the wheel spins without moving forward. Since the axis of rotation is actually the point of contact between the wheel and the road, the angular velocity is simply

$$\omega = \frac{v_o}{r}$$

The velocity of any point on the wheel can be found by the relative motion equation. For example, the velocity of point B on the rim is

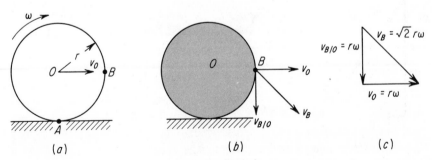

Figure 10-15

$$v_B = v_{B/O} + v_O$$

The relative component $v_{B/O}$ is directed downward and is equal to $r\omega$, while v_O, also equal to $r\omega$, is directed to the right. The absolute velocity of point B is the vector sum of the two components.

$$v_B = \sqrt{(r\omega)^2 + (r\omega)^2} = r\omega\sqrt{2}$$

EXAMPLE 10: The wheel of Fig. 10-16, which has a diameter of 4 ft, is rolling to the right with a center velocity $v_O = 30$ fps. Find the angular velocity of the wheel and the velocities of points B and C.

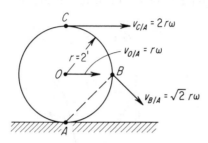

Figure 10-16

Solution: One approach to this problem is to relate the unknown velocities, one by one, to point A. This appears to be a particularly good reference point, because it has a velocity equal to zero. The angular velocity is first found by writing Eq. (10-12) in terms of points O and A.

$$v_O = v_{O/A} + v_A$$
$$30 = 2\omega + 0$$

therefore

$$\omega = 15 \text{ rad per sec}$$

$$v_B = v_{B/A} + v_A = (r\sqrt{2})\omega + 0$$
$$= (2\sqrt{2})15 = 42.4 \text{ fps}$$

Once again Eq. (10-12) is employed, this time in terms of points C and A:

$$v_C = v_{C/A} + v_A = 2r\omega + 0$$
$$= 2(2)15 = 60 \text{ fps}$$

10-11 Instantaneous Center of Rotation

On every object which has plane motion there is one point, the *instantaneous center of rotation*, that has zero linear velocity. On gears, flywheels, and pulleys that have fixed axes, the instantaneous center is the axis itself. On bodies which have plane motion, the position of the instantaneous center changes with the position of the body. Whether it be fixed or moving, the instantaneous center is that point about which rotation occurs. The linear velocity of any particle on the body is always perpendicular to a radial line drawn from the instantaneous center to the particle. The converse of this statement provides a method of finding the instantaneous center—*perpendiculars drawn from velocity vectors on the body must intersect at a common point—the instantaneous center.* As an example, consider the ladder shown in Fig. 10-17, which has been placed in a corner and released. The velocity of point A on the ladder is vertical, while the velocity of point B is horizontal. The instantaneous center O_{ic} is the point of intersection of lines drawn perpendicular to the velocities at points A and B. If the velocity at either point is known, the angular velocity ω can be calculated:

$$\omega = \frac{v_A}{OA} \quad \text{or} \quad \omega = \frac{v_B}{OB}$$

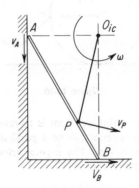

Figure 10-17

The velocity of point P on the ladder is perpendicular to a line drawn from O_{ic} to P, and is equal to

$$v_P = (\overline{O_{ic}P})\omega$$

EXAMPLE 11: A piston, connecting rod, crankshaft mechanism is shown in Fig. 10-18. The crankshaft is rotating with a clockwise angular velocity of 30 rad per sec and at the instant shown is 30 deg from "top dead center" (the position of the crank when the piston is at the extreme left). Find the velocity of the piston P.

Solution: The velocity of point A is common to both the connecting rod and the crankshaft, and its direction and magnitude are known. A second point on the connecting rod, where it joins the piston P, has a velocity directed along the axis of the piston. Perpendiculars drawn to these two points will intersect at the instantaneous center of the connecting rod. Trigonometry is employed to find the necessary distances to the instantaneous center, although a graphical solution would be just as correct.

The sine law is used to find the angle θ between the connecting rod and a horizontal reference line:

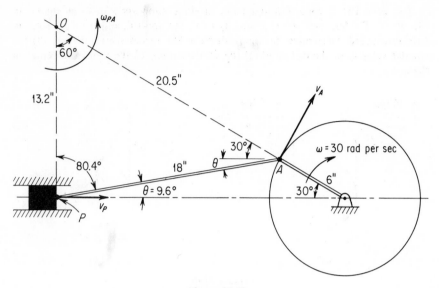

Figure 10-18

$$\frac{\sin \theta}{6} = \frac{\sin 30°}{18}$$

$$\theta = \text{arc sin } (0.167) = 9.6°$$

The angle PAO is then

$$\angle PAO = 30° + 9.6° = 39.6°$$

By inspection, angle POA is found to be 60°; therefore, angle OPA is

$$\angle OPA = 180° - 60° - 39.6° = 80.4°$$

Next, the sine law is used to find the distances $\overline{OP}$ and $\overline{OA}$, where

$$\overline{OP} = 18\frac{\sin 39.6°}{\sin 60°} = 13.2 \text{ in.}$$

and

$$\overline{OA} = 18\frac{\sin 80.4°}{\sin 60°} = 20.5 \text{ in.}$$

The velocity of point A can now be calculated, since the angular velocity of the crankshaft is given:

$$v_A = r\omega = 6(30) = 180 \text{ in. per sec}$$

The angular velocity of the connecting rod is then

$$\omega_{PA} = \frac{v_A}{\overline{OA}} = \frac{180}{20.5} = 8.78 \text{ rad per sec } \circlearrowleft$$

The velocity of the piston is finally calculated

$$v_P = \overline{OP}\,\omega = 13.2(8.78) = 116 \text{ in. per sec} \rightarrow$$

Example 12: A rope, fashioned into a sling, supports a disk, as shown in Fig. 10-19. The left rope A has a velocity of 15 fps upward, and the right rope B, 5 fps downward. Determine: (a) the position of the instantaneous center, (b) the angular velocity of the disk, and (c) the velocity point C, the geometric center of the disk.

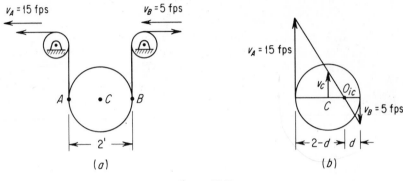

Figure 10-19

Solution: The instantaneous center of the disk lies somewhere on AB, a line perpendicular to both v_A and v_B. Imagine this to be point O, a distance d from the right rope and $(2 - d)$ from the left rope. By the ratio of corresponding sides of similar triangles

$$\frac{2 - d}{15} = \frac{d}{5}$$

$$2 - d = 3d$$

$$d = 0.5 \text{ ft to the left of } B$$

The angular velocity of the disk in terms of v_B and d is

$$\omega = \frac{v_B}{d} = \frac{5}{0.5} = 10 \text{ rad per sec } \circlearrowright$$

The velocity of the center of the pulley is, therefore

$$v_C = \overline{OC}\,\omega = (0.5)10 = 5 \text{ fps upward}$$

PROBLEMS

10-1. Determine the angular displacement of a flywheel that rotates for 30 sec with a clockwise angular acceleration of 4 rad per sec^2 if it (a) starts from rest; (b) has an initial clockwise angular velocity of 10 rad per sec; (c) has an initial counterclockwise angular velocity of 10 rad per sec.

10-2. Find the average angular velocity in rad per sec of an outboard motor propeller that rotates through 1000 revolutions in 20 min.

10-3. Express an acceleration of 100 rev per min per sec in units of (a) rev per sec^2; (b) rad per sec^2; (c) rad per min^2.

10-4. A flywheel increases its speed uniformly from 60 rpm to 120 rpm while turning through 20 revolutions. Determine the angular acceleration of the wheel and the time required for the speed to change.

10-5. Find the angular acceleration and angular displacement of a flywheel if it completely reverses its speed from 1800 rpm counterclockwise to 1800 rpm clockwise in 45 sec.

10-6. The speed of a flywheel decreases from 1800 rpm to 600 rpm in 20 sec; determine the average angular deceleration.

10-7. What angular velocity will a propeller acquire in 120 revolutions if it has an average angular acceleration of 10 rad per sec^2 clockwise and it (a) starts from rest; (b) has an initial clockwise angular velocity of 600 rpm; (c) has an initial counterclockwise angular velocity of 1200 rpm?

10-8. An acceleration-time curve for a rotating mechanism is shown in Fig. P10-8. If the mechanism starts from rest, determine its angular displacement and angular velocity (a) after 10 sec; (b) after 15 sec.

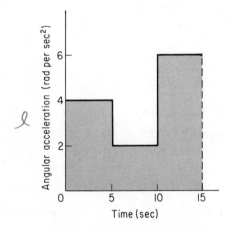

Figure P10-8

10-9. A velocity-time curve for a rotating gear is shown in Fig. P10-9. Find the (a) acceleration during the first 10 sec; (b) acceleration between 10 and 15 sec; (c) acceleration between 15 and 30 sec; (d) angular displacement for the entire 30 sec period.

10-10. A "day" on the planet Venus is approximately 30 hours long. Find its

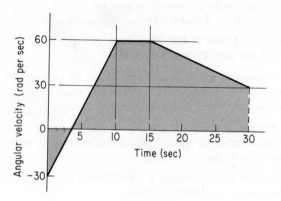

Figure P10-9

angular velocity and equatorial rim speed if the planet has a diameter of 7700 mi.

10-11. Jupiter, the largest planet in the solar system, has a diameter of 85,700 mi, and it turns one revolution about its axis every 9.9 hr. Determine the linear velocity of a point on the equator.

10-12. The stepped-bar shown in Fig. P10-12 is being turned at 600 rpm in a lathe. Determine the velocity in ft per min of a point located on the (a) 3 in. diameter section; (b) 2 in. diameter section; (c) 1.5 in. diameter section.

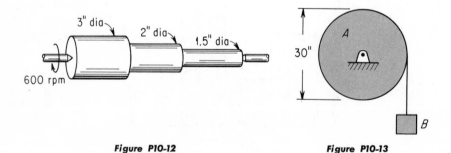

Figure P10-12   *Figure P10-13*

10-13. Determine the angular displacement and angular acceleration of the pulley A shown in Fig. P10-13, if the weight B acquires a speed from rest of 30 fps in 2 sec.

10-14. Weight B in Fig. P10-14 accelerates uniformly from a velocity of 10 fps to a velocity of 30 fps while descending 10 ft. Determine the acceleration of weight A during this period.

10-15. A pair of parallel axes internal contact spur gears are shown in Fig. P10-15.

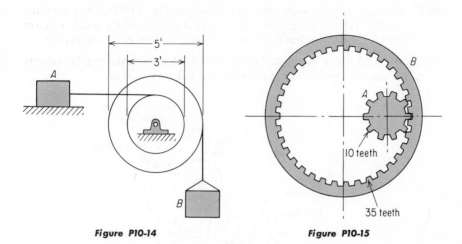

Figure P10-14   **Figure P10-15**

Gear *A* accelerates uniformly from rest to a speed of 1200 rpm in 20 sec. Find the angular displacement and angular acceleration of gear *B*.

10-16. In the cold rolling of steel, large back-up rolls keep the smaller "working" rolls from bending. If the velocity of the steel plate in the "four high" mill shown in Fig. P10-16 is 30 fps, find the angular velocity of roll *A* and of roll *B*.

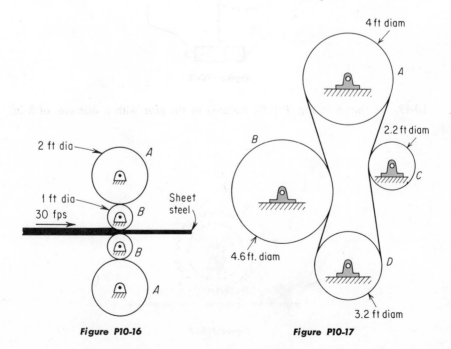

Figure P10-16   **Figure P10-17**

10-17. A chain and sprocket drive are shown in Fig. P10-17. Determine the angular velocity of sprockets *B*, *C*, and *D* and the chain speed in ft per min if the drive *A* has a clockwise angular velocity of 12 rad per sec.

10-18. A "clock train" is shown in Fig. P10-18. Determine the angular velocity of gear *E* if the weight *A* descends one inch in one hour.

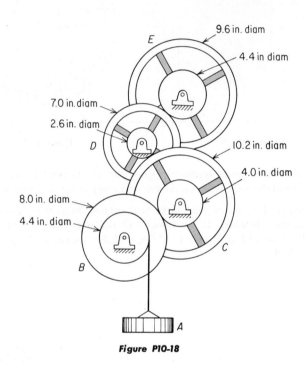

Figure P10-18

10-19. As shown in Fig. P10-19, rotation of the gear with a diameter of 8 in.

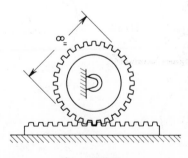

Figure P10-19

results in a vertical motion of the rack. If the gear turns clockwise through an angle of 75 deg, what is the displacement of the rack?

10-20. If the rack described in Prob. 10-19 moves 5 in. upwards, find the angular displacement of the gear.

10-21. If gear *A* of the system shown in Fig. P10-21 has an angular velocity of 30 rpm, what is the velocity of the rack?

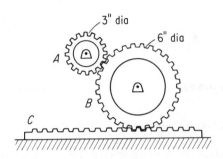

Figure P10-21

10-22. The driven gear *A* of the transmission shown in Fig. P10-22 has an angular velocity of 600 rpm. Determine the angular velocity of gears *B* and *C*.

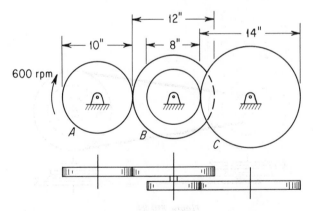

Figure P10-22

10-23. Gear *C*, in Prob. 10-22, increases its speed uniformly from a position of rest to 900 rpm in 10 sec. Determine the angular displacement of gears *A* and *B*.

10-24. Curved conic friction pulleys and an intermediate 2 in. diam swinging pulley are used to achieve variable angular motion in the mechanism shown in Fig. P10-24. Determine the angular velocity of shaft *B* if shaft *A* has a constant angular velocity of 60 rpm for the three positions of the swinging pulley *a-a*, *b-b*, and *c-c*.

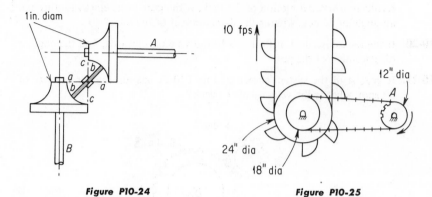

Figure P10-24   **Figure P10-25**

10-25. The bucket elevator illustrated in Fig. P10-25 is driven by a series of chains and sprockets. Determine the angular speed of the driving pulley A if the buckets are to move upward with a velocity of 10 fps.

10-26. Three possible velocities of pulley A can be obtained by shifting the belt on the paired step-pulleys shown in Fig. P10-26. Find these velocities if the motor pulley M turns at the rate of 1800 rpm.

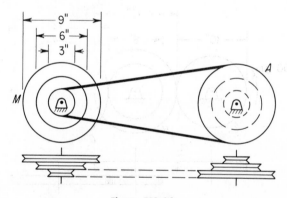

Figure P10-26

10-27. A tape recorder's drive mechanism is shown in Fig. P10-27. The motor pulley has a diameter of 0.625 in., while the diameters of the pressure wheel and magnetic pick-up drum are 1.720 in. and 1.50 in. respectively. If the tape is to travel at a speed of 10 in. per sec, determine the angular velocity of the (a) motor pulley; (b) pressure wheel; (c) pick-up drum.

10-28. The plane of rotation can be changed with the pulley arrangement shown

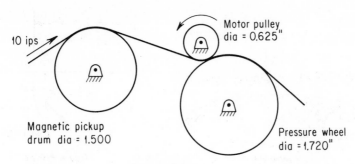

Figure P10-27

in Fig. P10-28. Find the belt speed in ft per min and the angular velocity of the driven pulley if the driving pulley has an angular velocity of 1800 rpm.

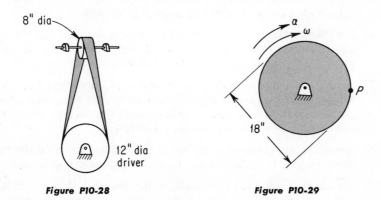

Figure P10-28　　　　　　　　　　　　**Figure P10-29**

10-29. The wheel shown in Fig. P10-29 has an angular velocity of 20 rad per sec and an angular acceleration of 25 rad per sec². Find the normal and tangential components of acceleration of a point P on the rim.

10-30. Find the normal component of acceleration of a point on the rim of a turbine wheel 12 in. in diameter which has an angular velocity of 10,000 rpm.

10-31. In Fig. P10-31 Vanguard III, an earth-orbiting satellite, has a velocity of 18,567 mph at the *perigee* (the closest approach to the earth), and a velocity of 12,631 mph at the *apogee* (the farthest distance from the earth). Determine the normal accelerations of the satellite at these two points if the perigee and apogee are 320 mi and 2329 mi respectively.

10-32. Find the angular velocity and the angular acceleration of the flywheel, if point P on the rim has a total acceleration of $25\sqrt{2}$ fps² directed as shown in Fig. P10-32.

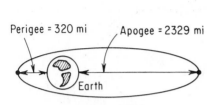

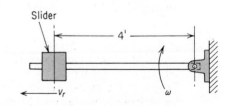

Figure P10-31　　　　　　　　　Figure P10-32

10-33. A propeller of 18 in. diam accelerates uniformly from rest to a speed of 900 rpm in 30 sec. Find the normal and tangential components of acceleration of a point on the periphery 10 sec after motion begins.

10-34. Find the normal acceleration that acts on an automobile as it rounds a curve with a radius of 1500 ft at a speed of 90 mph.

10-35. Find the normal acceleration of the earth (relative to the sun) if it makes one revolution about the sun every 365 days. The distance between the earth and the sun is approximately 93,000,000 mi.

10-36. A man is walking outward from the center of a merry-go-round with a velocity of 10 fps. Determine the Coriolis component of acceleration acting on the man if the merry-go-round has a clockwise angular velocity (when viewed from above) of (a) 20 rpm; (b) 40 rpm.

10-37. Determine the Coriolis component of acceleration acting on the man in Prob. 10-36 if he walks toward the center of the merry-go-round.

10-38. The slider is free to move radially in the slotted disk as shown in Fig. P10-38. Determine the Coriolis component of acceleration acting if the spring causes the slider to move inward with a velocity, relative to the disk, of 15 fps. The disk has a clockwise angular velocity of 50 rad per sec.

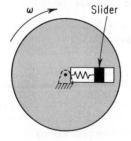

Figure P10-38　　　　　　　　　Figure P10-39

10-39. The slider shown in Fig. P10-39, which is free to move relative to the rod, has an outward velocity of 30 fps. Find the Coriolis component and the normal component of acceleration acting on the slider if the rod has a clockwise angular velocity of 10 rad per sec.

10-40. Find the velocity that the earth imparts, relative to its axis, to a satellite launched due east from New York City (north latitude 40°50′). Assume the radius of the earth to be 4000 mi.

10-41. An automobile is traveling due south in Alaska (north latitude 60°) at a speed of 90 mph. Find the Coriolis acceleration imparted to the car by the earth's rotation.

10-42. How many ft per mi, and in what direction, would the car described in Prob. 10-41 tend to drift?

10-43. Determine the two normal components of acceleration that act on the car described in Prob. 10-41.

10-44. The Mississippi River at a north latitude of 39° flows in a north-south direction with an approximate speed of 7.5 mph. Find the Coriolis component of acceleration acting on the water.

10-45. The wheel shown in Fig. P10-45 has a clockwise angular velocity of 20 rad per sec. Find the velocity of point P relative to point A.

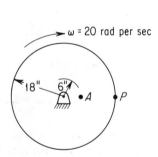

Figure P10-45

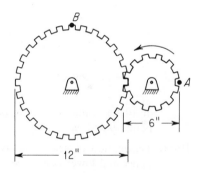

Figure P10-46

10-46. The smaller gear has a counterclockwise angular velocity of 600 rpm as shown in Fig. P10-46. Determine the velocity of point B relative to point A.

10-47. At the instant shown in Fig. P10-47, end B of the 15 ft ladder is moving to the right with a velocity of 10 fps. Use the *relative velocity method* to determine the angular velocity of the ladder and the velocity of end A.

10-48. Find the velocity of the midpoint m of the ladder described in Prob. 10-47.

10-49. Rotation of disk A, Fig. P10-49, causes wheel B to reciprocate. For the condition shown, determine the velocity and normal acceleration of points C, D, and E.

10-50. The top of the ladder in Fig. P10-50 is moving downward with a velocity

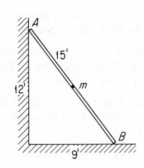

Figure P10-47

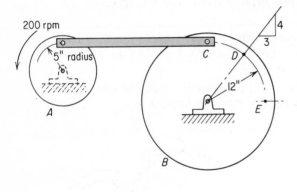

Figure P10-49

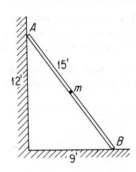

Figure P10-50

of 10 fps. Find, by the *method of instantaneous center*, the velocity of points B and m.

10-51. The motion of gear A is controlled by the independent motions of the upper and lower racks. Determine the angular velocity of the gear if the racks have the velocities shown in Fig. P10-51.

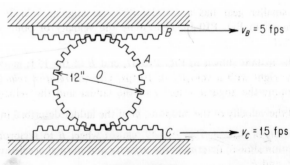

Figure P10-51

10-52. Solve Prob. 10-51 if rack *B* is moving to the right with a velocity of 5 fps and rack *C* to the left with a velocity of 20 fps.

10-53. The double disk rolls on the edge of the table as shown in Fig. P10-53. If the disk has an angular velocity of 5 rad per sec, determine the velocity of points *A*, *B*, and *C*.

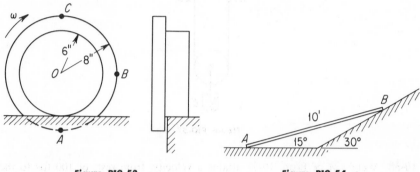

Figure P10-53   **Figure P10-54**

10-54. The ends *A* and *B* of the rod slide freely on the horizontal and inclined surfaces shown in Fig. P10-54. Locate the instant center of rotation and determine the velocity of end *B* if point *A* of the rod has a velocity of 5 fps to the right.

10-55. Determine the acceleration of weight *B* in Fig. P10-55 if weight *A* acquires a velocity of 30 fps to the left in 10 ft of travel.

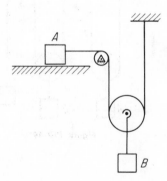

Figure P10-55

10-56. Find the velocity of weight *B* at the end of 2 sec in Prob. 10-55.

10-57. In Fig. P10-57, the displacement of weight *C* is to be 20 ft upward. Find the required displacement of weight *B* if (a) weight *A* does not move; (b) weight *A* moves 5 ft to the right; (c) weight *A* moves 5 ft to the left.

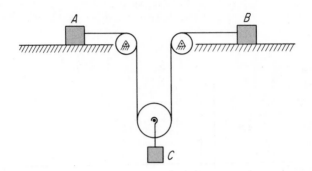

Figure P10-57

10-58. Weight *A* of Prob. 10-57 attains a velocity, from rest, of 100 fps to the right in 5 sec. Weight *B*, moving 7.5 ft to the right, increases its velocity from 5 fps to 10 fps. Find the acceleration of weight *C*.

10-59. Determine the velocity of body *C* in Fig. P10-59 if body *A* has a velocity of 4 fps upward and body *B* a velocity of 12 fps downward.

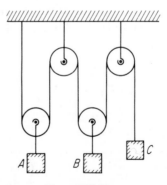

Figure P10-59

Chapter 11

KINETICS: THE LAWS OF FORCE AND MOTION

The fundamentals of mechanics were firmly established by two men: Galileo—the experimenter, and Newton—the theorist. By observing falling weights, oscillating pendulums, and rolling bodies, Galileo demonstrated the equations of motion which Newton later formally proposed.

So far as "ordinary" situations are concerned, these 300-year-old equations and laws adequately and correctly solve the problems of mechanics. Only when dealing with particles of sub-atomic size or with bodies having velocities which approach the velocity of light must the theory by modified.

11-1 The Second Law of Motion

The most important single statement of fact in mechanics is *the second law of motion*. It states that if an unbalanced force acts on a body: (1) the body will accelerate in the direction of the unbalanced force, and (2) the acceleration will be proportional to the unbalanced force and inversely

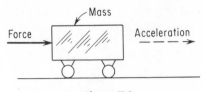

Force → [Mass] Acceleration - - →

Figure 11-1

proportional to the mass of the body. Correctness of this law can be demonstrated experimentally, as shown in Fig. 11-1.

The body, when it is acted upon by the force, is observed to accelerate in the direction of the force. If the force is doubled, the acceleration doubles; if the force is tripled, the acceleration triples; without exception the acceleration is *directly* proportional to the force:

$$a \propto F \tag{11-1}$$

A second set of observations will show how mass, the quantity of matter in the body, is related to acceleration. If the mass is doubled, with the force held constant, the acceleration is reduced by a factor of one-half, if the mass is tripled, the acceleration is reduced by a factor of one-third, and so on. The conclusion drawn from these observations is that acceleration is *inversely* proportional to the mass:

$$a \propto \frac{1}{m} \tag{11-2}$$

By the combination of measured data from the two sets of observations, a statement of the second law of motion can be written:

$$F = ma \tag{11-3}$$

Scientists and physicists look to this equation for a definition of the units of force. Mass in pounds and acceleration in ft per sec per sec gives force, called a *poundal*, the units of lb ft per sec^2

$$F = ma = [\text{lb}][\text{ft per sec}^2] = \text{lb ft per sec}^2$$

Engineers, on the other hand, use a slightly different approach to the system of units; mass in *slugs* is defined in terms of force and acceleration, the former in pounds and the latter in ft per sec per sec.

$$m = \frac{F}{a} = \frac{[\text{lb}]}{[\text{ft per sec}^2]} = \text{lb sec}^2 \text{ per ft}$$

In free fall, the unbalanced force acting on a body is its weight, and it reacts to this force with an acceleration equal to that of gravity. By Eq. (11-3):

$$F = ma$$

and

$$W = mg$$

Dividing the first equation by the second indicates that force and weight are in the same proportions as are acceleration and gravity.

$$\frac{F}{W} = \frac{a}{g}$$

$$F = \left(\frac{W}{g}\right)a \tag{11-4}$$

Thus, the mass of a body is equal to its weight divided by the acceleration of gravity.

EXAMPLE 1: Find the mass in slugs of a 200 lb weight. Assume a nominal value of 32.2 fps² for the acceleration of gravity.

Solution: The mass is the weight divided by gravity.

$$m = \frac{W}{g} = \frac{200\ \text{lb}}{32.2\ \text{ft/sec}^2} = 6.21\ \frac{\text{lb sec}^2}{\text{ft}} = 6.21\ \text{slugs}$$

It is important to note that mass, unlike weight, is independent of position in space. A force acting on a given mass on the surface of the earth would produce an acceleration exactly equal to that produced on the moon, on a far-off planet, or in outer space. Weight, on the other hand, is the force of attraction between two bodies and is dependent upon position. Thus, a man who weighs 180 lb on earth weighs only 30.6 lb on the moon, where the gravitational attraction is approximately one-fifth that of the earth.

EXAMPLE 2: An object, weighed on a spring scale in Portland, Oregon ($g = 32.173$ fps²), was found to weigh 200.000 lb. What would this same object weigh on a spring scale in Charleston, South Carolina ($g = 32.137$ fps²)?

Solution: The mass of the object is independent of location and is therefore the same in Portland, Oregon, as it is in Charleston, South Carolina.

$$m = \frac{200.000\ \text{lb}}{32.173\ \text{ft/sec}^2} = 6.216\ \text{slugs}$$

At the second weighing

$$W = mg = 6.216(32.137) = 199.764\ \text{lb}$$

The weight, therefore, differs in the two cities by

$$\Delta W = 200.000 - 199.764 = 0.236\ \text{lb}$$

or about $3\frac{3}{4}$ oz.

The second law of motion is very definite concerning the direction of acceleration: *"the body will accelerate in the direction of the unbalanced force ..."* The inference is that, if a system of unbalanced forces acts on a body, the acceleration will be in the same direction as the resultant unbalanced force. In some instances, when a system of forces acts on a body, the problem is best analyzed in terms of force components. Unbalanced force components in the orthogonal directions x, y, z, cause the mass to accelerate in the x, y, z directions. The second law, written for each of the orthogonal directions, is

$$\Sigma F_x = ma_x$$
$$\Sigma F_y = ma_y \qquad (11\text{-}5)$$
$$\Sigma F_z = ma_z$$

11-2 Particle Motion: Problem Analysis

The series of examples that follows illustrates a step by step procedure as a guide in setting up and solving the typical problem in kinetics. In each instance, a free-body diagram of the isolated mass is drawn with all forces properly labeled, and a sign convention that is consistent for all the masses in the problem is adopted. Finally, the equation of motion $F = ma$ is written for each mass or groups of masses. Obviously, to obtain a solution there should be as many independent equations as there are unknown quantities.

EXAMPLE 3: A 200 lb upward pull is transmitted through a cable to weight A which is in turn fastened to weight B by a second cable, as shown in Fig. 11-2. Find the acceleration of the weights and the tension in the cable.

Solution: A free-body diagram is drawn which treats the entire system as a single free-body as shown in Fig. 11-2(b). Since the cable joining weights A and B is not "cut," the force within this cable does not appear in the free-body diagram. Forces that affect the acceleration are the 200 lb upward pull and the two downward weights. With the upward direction assumed to be positive, the equation of motion is written

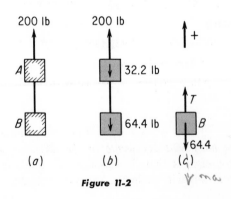

Figure 11-2

$$\Sigma F = ma$$

$$200 - 32.2 - 64.4 = \left(\frac{32.2}{32.2} + \frac{64.4}{32.2}\right)a$$

$$3a = 103.4$$

$$a = 34.5 \text{ fps}^2$$

Next, a free-body diagram of weight B is drawn. The unknown quantity in this instance is the tensile force in the cable that joins it to weight A. The equation of motion, written for this mass, is

$$F = ma$$

$$T - 64.4 = \frac{64.4}{32.2}(34.5)$$

Therefore $$T = 64.4 + 69.0 = 133 \text{ lb}$$

EXAMPLE 4: The coefficient of kinetic friction between the 100 lb block shown in Fig. 11-3 and the plane is $\mu_k = 0.20$. Find the velocity of the weight after it has moved 10 ft down the plane from an initial position of rest.

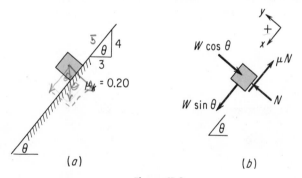

Figure 11-3

Solution: A system of x-y coordinates tangent and normal to the plane is selected as shown in Fig. 11-3(b). A free-body diagram of the block is then drawn with the weight force W in terms of its tangential component $W \sin \theta$, and its normal component $W \cos \theta$.

The y-components of force acting upon the body are balanced, and motion proceeds in the x-direction only:

$$\Sigma F_y = 0$$

$$N - W \cos \theta = 0$$

$$N = 100\left(\frac{3}{5}\right) = 60 \text{ lb}$$

The equation of motion is written for the x-direction:

$$\Sigma F_x = ma_x$$

$$W \sin \theta - \mu_k N = ma_x$$

$$100\left(\frac{4}{5}\right) - 0.20(60) = \frac{100}{32.2}a_x$$

$$80 - 12 = \frac{100}{32.2}a_x$$

Solving for the acceleration gives

$$a_x = \frac{68(32.2)}{100} = 21.9 \text{ fps}^2$$

The kinematic equation which relates distance, velocity, and acceleration is next used to find the desired velocity v_f.

$$v_f^2 - v_0^2 = 2as$$

where

$$v_f^2 - 0 = 2(21.9)10$$

and

$$v_f = \sqrt{2(21.9)10} = 20.9 \text{ fps}$$

EXAMPLE 5: Find the acceleration of the 20 lb block A shown in Fig. 11-4 if the coefficient of kinetic friction between A and the horizontal surface is $\mu_k = 0.30$. Block B weighs 30 lb. Assume both pulleys to be weightless and the cables inextensible.

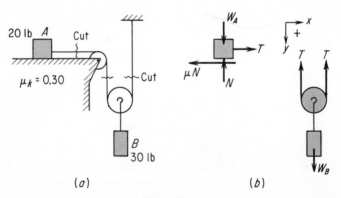

(a)   (b)

Figure 11-4

Solution: A consistent sign convention must be used for the motion of weights A and B. If "to the right" is assumed to be positive for weight A, then "down" must be assumed to be positive for weight B.

Two equations, one of equilibrium for the y-direction and one of motion for the x-direction, are written for body A.

$$\Sigma F_y = 0$$

$$N = 20 \text{ lb}$$

and
$$\Sigma F_x = ma_x$$

$$T - \mu N = \frac{W_A}{g}a$$

$$T = 0.30(20) + \frac{20}{32.2}a_A$$

The tension in the cord, in terms of the acceleration of body A, is

$$T = 6 + 0.621a_A \tag{a}$$

The weightless pulley requires no effort to turn it; this means that the tensions on either side of the pulley C must be equal and that the assembly, consisting of the pulley and weight B, can be treated as a single free-body. The equation of motion, written for this assembly, is

$$\Sigma F_y = am_y$$

Substituting data gives

$$30 - 2T = \frac{30}{g}a_B$$

where
$$T = 15 - 0.466a_B \tag{b}$$

Eqs. (a) and (b) are combined and the cable tension T eliminated:

$$6 + 0.621a_A = 15 - 0.466a_B$$

$$0.621a_A + 0.466a_B = 9 \tag{c}$$

A study of the geometry of the motion shows the displacement of B to be one-half that of A. The accelerations are, therefore, in the same ratio.

$$s_B = \frac{s_A}{2}$$

$$a_B = \frac{a_A}{2} \tag{d}$$

Eqs. (c) and (d) are solved simultaneously for the desired quantities a_A and a_B.

$$0.621a_A + 0.466\left(\frac{a_A}{2}\right) = 9$$

$$a_A = \frac{9}{0.854} = 10.5 \text{ fps}^2$$

and
$$a_B = \frac{a_A}{2} = \frac{10.5}{2} = 5.25 \text{ fps}^2$$

11-3 Dynamic Equilibrium: The Inertia-Force Method of Analysis

Newton's third law states that for every action there is an equal but opposite reaction. In the case of an unbalanced system of forces, the "reaction" mentioned in this law is *inertia force*, the product of the mass and the acceleration.

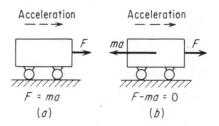

Figure 11-5

The object illustrated in Fig. 11-5(a) represents a body of mass m acted upon by a force F. The body will, of course, accelerate to the right, since the unbalanced force is directed to the right. When the free-body diagram is drawn, however, the *inertia force*, the product of the mass and the acceleration is represented vectorially as a force in a direction opposite to that of the acceleration—to the left in this case. A body represented in this way is said to be in *dynamic equilibrium*, and the analysis proceeds just as if the problem were one in statics.

EXAMPLE 6: A small 5 lb weight, suspended from a 5 ft cord of negligible mass, rotates in a horizontal circle with a radius of 3 ft as shown in Fig. 11-6. Determine the velocity of the weight and the tension in the cable.

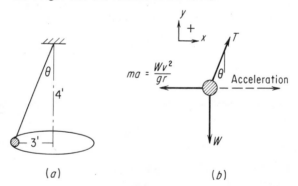

Figure 11-6

Solution: The body is placed in dynamic equilibrium by representing the product ma as a force, opposed to the direction of acceleration. The equations of statics $\Sigma F_x = 0$ and $\Sigma F_y = 0$ are then used to solve the problem.

$$\Sigma F_x = 0$$

$$T \sin \theta - \frac{W}{g} \frac{v^2}{r} = 0 \qquad (a)$$

and
$$\Sigma F_y = 0$$

$$T \cos \theta - W = 0 \qquad (b)$$

Dividing the first equation by the second eliminates the tension T:

$$\frac{\sin \theta}{\cos \theta} = \frac{v^2}{gr}$$

Thus
$$v = \sqrt{gr \tan \theta}$$

Substituting numerical values and solving gives

$$v = \sqrt{(32.2)3(0.75)} = 8.52 \text{ fps}$$

Eq. (b) is then used to determine the tension in the cord:

$$T = \frac{W}{\cos \theta} = \frac{5}{\frac{4}{5}} = 6.25 \text{ lb}$$

EXAMPLE 7: The rotating shaft shown in Fig. 11-7 has a small 2 oz weight eccentrically located at point C. Determine the bearing reactions at A and at B if the shaft rotates with an angular velocity of 1800 rpm.

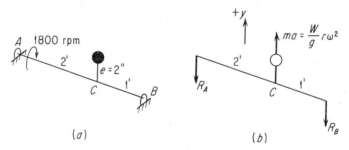

(a)   (b)

Figure 11-7

Solution: A free-body diagram is drawn showing the rod-mass assembly in dynamic equilibrium. The equations of statics, a force summation and a moment summation, are used to determine the unknown reactions at A and B.

$$\Sigma F_y = 0$$
$$mr\omega^2 - R_A - R_B = 0$$
$$R_A + R_B = \left[\frac{2}{32.2(16)}\right]\left(\frac{2}{12}\right)\left[1800\left(\frac{2\pi}{60}\right)\right]^2$$
$$R_A + R_B = 23 \tag{a}$$

and
$$\Sigma M_c = 0$$
$$2R_A = 1R_B \tag{b}$$

Eqs. (a) and (b) are solved simultaneously for R_A and R_B:

$$R_A + 2R_A = 23 \text{ lb}$$
$$R_A = \frac{23}{3} = 7.67 \text{ lb}$$
$$R_B = 2(7.67) = 15.3 \text{ lb}$$

In this and similar examples involving rotation of eccentric weights, the inertia force is dependent, in part, on the product of the weight and the eccentricity Wr. This factor is referred to as the *shaft unbalance*, and is usually expressed in units of oz in. Thus, a 1 oz weight located 4 in. from an axis of rotation is dynamically equivalent to a 4 oz weight located 1 in. from the axis of rotation.

11-4 Rigid Body Translation

The problem of rigid body translation is most effectively treated by the inertia-force method. One question that arises, however, concerns the proper location of the inertia-force vectors. To answer this question, the body shown in Fig. 11-8 has been divided into a number of strips or segments each having a mass Δm. The *inertia force* of each strip is a vector, directed opposite to the acceleration, having a magnitude of $(\Delta m)a$. Moments of each of these inertia forces about an arbitrary point O are

$$\sum \text{moments}_o = (\Delta m)ay_1 + (\Delta m)ay_2 + (\Delta m)ay_3 + \ldots$$
$$= a[(\Delta m)y_1 + (\Delta m)y_2 + (\Delta m)y_3 + \ldots]$$
$$= ma\bar{y} \qquad\qquad (11\text{-}6)$$

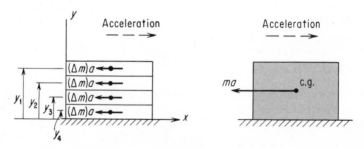

Figure 11-8

The bracketed term, by definition, is the product of the mass of the body and the distance from point O to the center of gravity. The conclusion, therefore, is that **when a rigid body has a translational acceleration, the inertia-force acts through the center of gravity and in a direction opposite to the acceleration.**

Everyday experiences serve to illustrate this principle. When the brakes are suddenly applied in a car, the driver, packages, and passengers are thrown forward—a direction opposed to the acceleration. When the car is accelerating forward, the same driver, packages, and passengers are forced backwards —again, in a direction opposed to the acceleration.

EXAMPLE 8: A 100 lb crate is placed on the bed of a truck as shown in Fig. 11-9. The coefficient of kinetic friction between the crate and the bed is $\mu_k = 0.50$. Determine the maximum permissible acceleration of the truck so that the crate will neither tip nor slip.

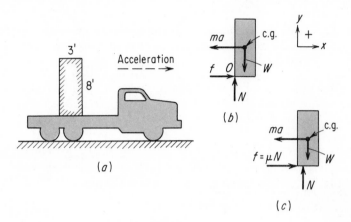

Figure 11-9

Solution: There are two critical accelerations of the truck: one, if exceeded, will cause the crate to tip, and the other, if exceeded, will cause the crate to slip. The smaller of these two accelerations is the correct answer.

The first assumption is that there is sufficient friction to prevent slipping, and that the crate will tip. If this is true, the entire weight of the crate will be concentrated at corner O, as seen in Fig. 11-9(b), and the moment of the inertia-force will just balance the moment of the weight force.

$$\sum M_o = 0$$
$$ma(4) = W(1.5)$$
$$\frac{a}{g} = \frac{1.5}{4}$$

$$a = \frac{1.5}{4}(32.2) = 12.1 \text{ fps}^2$$

To satisfy the second assumption, that involving slipping, the frictional force must be equal to its maximum value $\mu_k N$:

$$\sum F_y = 0$$
$$N - W = 0 \tag{a}$$

and
$$\sum F_x = 0$$
$$\mu N - ma = 0 \tag{b}$$

Combining Eqs. (a) and (b) gives

$$0.5W = \frac{Wa}{g}$$

$$a = 0.5(32.2) = 16.1 \text{ fps}^2$$

The maximum acceleration of the truck is, therefore, 12.1 fps². If this value is exceeded, the crate will tip.

EXAMPLE 9: At the instant shown in Fig. 11-10, the 300 lb swinging bar has a velocity of 20 fps. Determine the tension in each of the cables that support the bar.

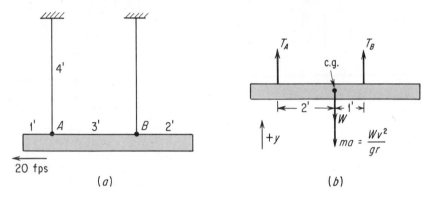

(a) (b)

Figure 11-10

Solution: The inertia-force acts at the center of gravity as shown; the effective weight is

$$W + ma = 300 + \frac{300}{32.2}\frac{(20)^2}{4} = 1232 \text{ lb}$$

Moments, taken first about A and then about B, complete the solution:

$$\sum M_A = 0$$
$$3T_B = 1232(2)$$
$$T_B = 821 \text{ lb}$$

and

$$\sum M_B = 0$$
$$3T_A = 1232(1)$$
$$T_A = 411 \text{ lb}$$

EXAMPLE 10: The 2500 lb jeep shown in Fig. 11-11 has four-wheel drive. Determine the maximum acceleration possible and the reactions at the front and at the rear wheels if the coefficient of friction between the tires and the pavement is $\mu_s = 0.80$. The center of gravity of the jeep is located as shown in the figure.

Solution: An x–y coordinate system is selected and the free-body diagram is drawn as shown in Fig. 11-11(b). Components of the weight force, the inertia

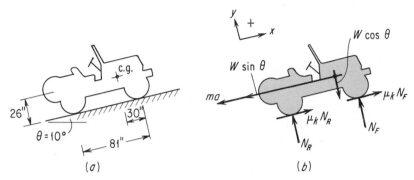

Figure 11-11

force, and the reactions at the wheels comprise the system of forces which act on the jeep.

A force summation for the y-direction gives

$$\Sigma F_y = 0$$

$$N_R + N_F = W \cos 10° \qquad \text{(a)}$$

In a similar manner, the x-components of force must balance:

$$\Sigma F_x = 0$$

$$ma + W \sin 10° = \mu(N_R + N_F) \qquad \text{(b)}$$

Combining (a) and (b) gives

$$a = (0.8 \cos 10° - \sin 10°)32.2 = [0.8(0.9848) - 0.1736]\,32.2$$
$$= 19.8 \text{ fps}^2$$

To find the reactions N_F and N_R, moments are balanced about the center of gravity

$$\Sigma M_{cg} = 0$$

$$26(\mu N_R + \mu N_F) + 30N_F - 51N_R = 0$$

Combining with Eq. (a) and rewriting gives

$$51N_R - 30N_F = 26(0.8)2500 \cos 10°$$

$$51N_R - 30N_F = 73,860 \qquad \text{(c)}$$

Eqs. (a) and (c) solved simultaneously for N_F and N_R give

$$N_F = 918 \text{ lb} \quad \text{and} \quad N_R = 1544 \text{ lb}$$

11-5 Angular Motion

Newton's second law can easily be interpreted in terms of rotational motion. Consider the body, shown in Fig. 11-12, which is comprised of particles of mass Δm and is rotating about a fixed axis with an angular ac-

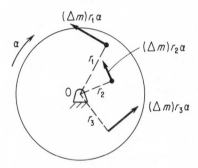

Figure 11-12

celeration α. Each particle has its own distinct inertia force $(\Delta m)r\alpha$, and each of these inertia forces exerts an *internal* moment $(\Delta m)r^2\alpha$ about the axis of rotation. To be in dynamic equilibrium, the moments created within the body must be equal and opposite to the external action—the torque.

$$\sum \text{external torques}_o = \sum \text{internal moments}_o$$
$$T_o = (\Delta m)r_1^2\alpha + (\Delta m)r_2^2\alpha + (\Delta m)r_3^2\alpha + \cdots$$
$$= \alpha[(\Delta m)r_1^2 + (\Delta m)r_2^2 + (\Delta m)r_3^2 + \cdots]$$

The term in the brackets is, by definition, the moment of inertia of the mass about the axis of rotation; thus, the equation of motion for rotation becomes

$$\sum T_o = I_o\alpha \qquad\qquad (11\text{-}7)$$

The algebraic statement $\sum T_o = I_o\alpha$ for rotation is analogous to $\sum F = ma$ for translation. Verbally, the equation states: *an angular acceleration results when an unbalanced torque acts on a body; the acceleration is in the direction of the torque, proportional to the torque, and inversely proportional to the moment of inertia.*

EXAMPLE 11: A cord is wrapped around each of the two identical 64.4 lb solid cylinders as shown in Fig. 11-13. A force of 20 lb is exerted on the first cord and a weight of 20 lb is suspended from the second. Determine the angular acceleration of each cylinder if the bearings in each case offer no resistance to the motion.

Solution: Both cylinders are acted upon by an unbalanced torque; therefore, both have an angular acceleration. In the first case, the torque results from the action of a 20 lb force, and in the second case, from the action of a cable tension T. First case:

$$\sum T_o = I_o\alpha$$
$$20(2) = \frac{1}{2}\frac{64.4}{32.2}(2)^2\alpha$$

and $\alpha = 10$ rad per sec^2

Second case:

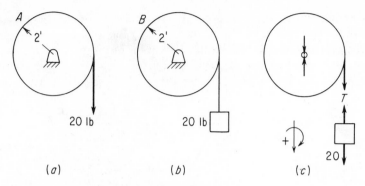

Figure 11-13

Two equations are required: $\sum T_o = I_o \alpha$ for the cylinder and $\sum F = ma$ for the weight.

Cylinder:

$$\sum T_o = I_o \alpha$$

$$2T = \frac{1}{2}\frac{64.4}{32.2}(2)^2 \alpha \qquad 2T = 4 \alpha$$

$$T = 2\alpha \qquad\qquad (a)$$

Weight:

$$\sum F = ma$$

$$20 - T = \frac{20}{32.2}a \qquad\qquad (b)$$

The accelerations of the weight and the cylinder are related by geometry, where

$$a = r\alpha = 2\alpha \qquad\qquad (c)$$

Eqs. (a), (b), and (c) are combined and a and T, eliminated:

$$20 - T = \frac{20}{32.2}(2\alpha) = 1.24\alpha$$

$$20 - 2\alpha = 1.24\alpha$$

Therefore

$$\alpha = \frac{20}{3.24} = 6.17 \text{ rad per sec}^2$$

The difference in the two answers, 10 rad per sec² and 6.17 rad per sec², illustrates an important point—the 20 lb of force has only to accelerate the cylinder, while the 20 lb of weight has also to accelerate itself.

11-6 Inertia Forces in Gear Trains and Belt Drives

The determination of inertia force plays an important part in the design of machines. As is quite often the case, a large portion of the energy that is put into a machine in the form of fuel is used to accelerate the individual components and is, therefore, lost as far as the output of the machine is concerned. This loss is, in a way, analogous to friction losses.

Of special concern is the determination of the torque required to accelerate a train of gears. To illustrate, consider the two-gear speed reducer shown in Fig. 11-14, in which gear A is the driver. The couple C_A, acting on the

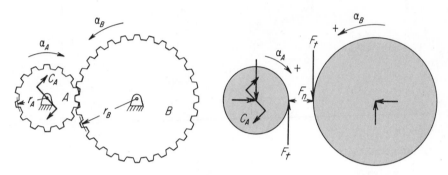

Figure 11-14

driving gear, accelerates both gear A and gear B, but at different rates. The force F_t that appears in the free-body diagram is a component of the pressure force between mating gear teeth; this force, prompted by the couple, accelerates the second gear. The equation of motion for gear A is

$$\Sigma T_o = I_o \alpha$$

where

$$C_A - F_t r_A = I_A \alpha_A \qquad (a)$$

and for gear B

$$\Sigma T_o = I_o \alpha \qquad (b)$$

$$F_t r_B = I_B \alpha_B$$

where I_A and I_B are the mass moment of inertias of the two gears.

Eliminating F_t between these two equations gives

$$C_A = F_t r_A + I_A \alpha_A = \frac{r_A}{r_B} I_B \alpha_B + I_A \alpha_B$$

From the geometry of the motion

$$\alpha_B = \frac{r_A}{r_B} \alpha_A$$

The torque C_A can then be written

$$C_A = \left[I_A + \left(\frac{r_A}{r_B} \right)^2 I_B \right] \alpha_A \qquad (11\text{-}8)$$

The fraction r_A/r_B is actually the *acceleration* ratio α_B/α_A, because

$$r_A \alpha_A = r_B \alpha_B$$

$$\frac{r_A}{r_B} = \frac{\alpha_B}{\alpha_A}$$

Eq. (11-8) can be extended to cover a train consisting of more than two gears. For the system shown in Fig. 11-15, the accelerating torque C_A becomes

$$C_A = \left[I_A + \left(\frac{r_A}{r_B}\right)^2 I_B + \left(\frac{r_A}{r_B}\right)^2 \left(\frac{r_B}{r_C}\right)^2 I_C \right] \alpha_A \qquad (11\text{-}9)$$

This equation is also valid for belt-driven pulleys; the driving force is belt tension rather than pressure.

EXAMPLE 12: Gear C of the three-gear trains shown in Fig. 11-15 is to acquire a speed of 100 rad per sec from rest in 5 sec. Determine the torque C_A that must be supplied to gear A. The following data apply to the gears.

$$r_A = 6 \text{ in.,} \qquad I_A = 0.05 \text{ slug ft}^2$$
$$r_B = 18 \text{ in.,} \qquad I_B = 0.15 \text{ slug ft}^2$$
$$r_C = 12 \text{ in.,} \qquad I_C = 0.10 \text{ slug ft}^2$$

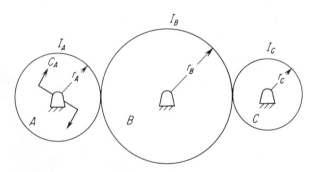

Figure 11-15

Solution: The acceleration of gear C is first found:

$$\alpha_C = \frac{\omega_f - \omega_0}{t} = \frac{100 - 0}{5} = 20 \text{ rad per sec}^2$$

Since the torque desired is that which acts on gear A, the acceleration of this gear must be determined.

$$\alpha_A = \frac{r_B}{r_A} \alpha_B = \left(\frac{r_B}{r_A}\right)\left(\frac{r_C}{r_B}\right) \alpha_C$$

$$= \left(\frac{12}{6}\right) \alpha_C = 2(20) = 40 \text{ rad per sec}^2$$

Substitution of data into Eq. (11-9) gives

$$C_A = \left[I_A + \left(\frac{r_A}{r_B}\right)^2 I_B + \left(\frac{r_A}{r_B}\right)^2 \left(\frac{r_B}{r_C}\right)^2 I_C \right] \alpha_A$$

$$= \left[0.05 + \left(\frac{6}{18}\right)^2 (0.15) + \left(\frac{6}{12}\right)^2 (0.1) \right] 40$$

$$= \left[0.05 + \frac{0.15}{9} + \frac{0.1}{4} \right] 40 = 3.67 \text{ lb ft}$$

Although Eq. (11-9) will adequately solve a given problem, in many instances an analysis of the actual free-body diagram provides a more understandable solution. This is the case in the example that follows.

EXAMPLE 13: The 20 lb weight shown in Fig. 11-16 is fastened to a cord which is wrapped around the drum portion of pulley A. Pulley B is driven by pulley A by means of a belt. Determine the acceleration of the weight if the moments of inertia of A and B are 1.5 slug ft^2 and 2.0 slug ft^2 respectively.

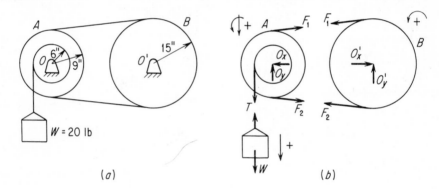

Figure 11-16

Solution: The free-body diagrams for the three members are drawn and the equations of the motion that apply to each are written.

For the weight: $\Sigma F = ma$

$$20 - T = \frac{20}{32.2} a = 0.621a \qquad\qquad (a)$$

For pulley A: $\Sigma T_o = I_o \alpha$

$$\frac{6}{12} T - \frac{9}{12}(F_1 - F_2) = 1.5\alpha_A$$

Since $\alpha_A = 2a$

The equations of motion, simplified, become

$$T - 1.5(F_1 - F_2) = 6a \qquad\qquad (b)$$

For pulley B: $\Sigma T_o = I_o \alpha$

$$\frac{15}{12}(F_1 - F_2) = 2\alpha_B$$

$$\alpha = \frac{a}{r}$$

and
$$\alpha_B = \frac{9}{15}\alpha_A = \frac{6}{5}a$$

Thus
$$(F_1 - F_2) = 1.92a \qquad\qquad (c)$$

Combining Eqs. (a), (b), and (c) gives

$$[0.621 + 6 + (1.5 \times 1.92)]a = 20$$

$$a = 2.11 \text{ fps}^2$$

11-7 Center of Percussion

Almost everyone has experienced the "sting" that occurs when a baseball is struck too close to or too far from the grip of the bat. The sting, which in machinery is a destructive force, can be eliminated by striking the ball at just the proper point on the bat. This proper point, which eliminates the reactive shock at the axis of rotation, is called the *center of percussion*.

Consider the body, shown in Fig. 11-17, which is free to rotate about an axis at O and which is subjected to a force F applied at a distance d from the axis. The product Fd is a torque, and the body reacts by accelerating.

$$\Sigma T_o = I_o \alpha$$

$$\alpha = \frac{T_o}{I_o} = \frac{Fd}{mk_o^2} \qquad\qquad (a)$$

where k_o is the radius of gyration of the mass about O. Newton's second law, $\Sigma F = ma$, governs the relationship between the acceleration of the mass center $\bar{r}\alpha$ and the force

$$\Sigma F = ma = m\bar{r}\alpha \qquad\qquad (b)$$

Substituting the value of F into equation (a) gives

$$\alpha = \frac{m\bar{r}\alpha d}{mk_o^2}$$

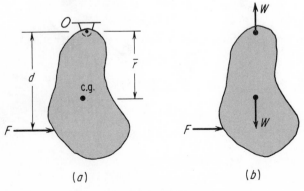

Figure 11-17

Where d, the distance from the axis O to the center of percussion, is

$$d = \frac{k_o^2}{\bar{r}} \qquad (11\text{-}10)$$

If d is less than $k_o^2/\bar{r}$, there will be a horizontal bearing reaction acting toward the left at O; if d is greater than $k_o^2/\bar{r}$, the reaction at O will be toward the right.

EXAMPLE 14: A long, slender rod weighing 32.2 lb is free to rotate about point O as shown in Fig. 11-18. Determine the horizontal component of the bearing reaction if the 20 lb force acts at (a) $y = 2$ ft; (b) $y = 10$ ft; (c) at the center of percussion.

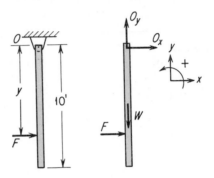

Figure 11-18

Solution: A sign convention is selected and the free-body diagram is drawn with the bearing reaction O_x assumed to be positive. The equation of motion for rotation is written with y as a variable quantity.

$$\Sigma T_o = I_o \alpha$$

$$20y = \frac{1}{3}\frac{32.2}{32.2}(10)^2 \alpha$$

$$\alpha = 0.6y \qquad (a)$$

$120 = 100t$

$40 = \frac{100}{3}\alpha$

$\alpha = 1.2$

Next, the equation of motion for the translation is written, noting that $\bar{a} = 5\alpha$:

$$\Sigma F = m\bar{a}$$

$$20 + O_x = \frac{32.2}{32.2}(5)\alpha$$

$$O_x = 5\alpha - 20 \qquad (b)$$

$20 + O_x = 5(1.2)$

$20 +$ 6.0

A simultaneous solution of Eqs. (a) and (b) gives the reaction O_x as a function of y.

$$O_x = 5(0.6)y - 20 = 3y - 20 \qquad (c)$$

For $y = 2$ ft

$$O_x = 3(2) - 20 = -14 \, \text{lb}$$

where the minus sign indicates that O_x acts toward the left.
For $y = 10 \, \text{ft}$

$$O_x = 3(10) - 20 = 10 \, \text{lb}$$

where O_x is toward the right as assumed.
For the center of percussion $y = d$, where

$$d = \frac{k_o^2}{\bar{r}} = \frac{(10)^2}{3(5)} = \frac{20}{3}$$

then
$$O_x = 3\left(\frac{20}{3}\right) - 20 = 0$$

Thus, the horizontal bearing reaction is zero when the force is applied at the center of percussion.

11-8 Plane Motion

The equations of motion $T = I\alpha$ and $F = m\bar{a}$ can be applied to bodies moving with plane motion. Fig. 11-19 shows three identical masses acted upon by three separate force systems. The first mass is translating with an acceleration equivalent to that of the mass center $\bar{a}_x$, produced by force components in the x-direction. The second mass is acted upon by forces in the y-direction and it therefore has an acceleration $\bar{a}_y$. The third mass illustrated, subjected to torques, has an angular acceleration with an axis at the center of gravity. These three bodies, when superimposed, form a single body whose plane motion is governed by

$$\sum F_x = m\bar{a}_x$$
$$\sum F_y = m\bar{a}_y \qquad (11\text{-}11)$$
and
$$\sum T_{cg} = \bar{I}\alpha$$

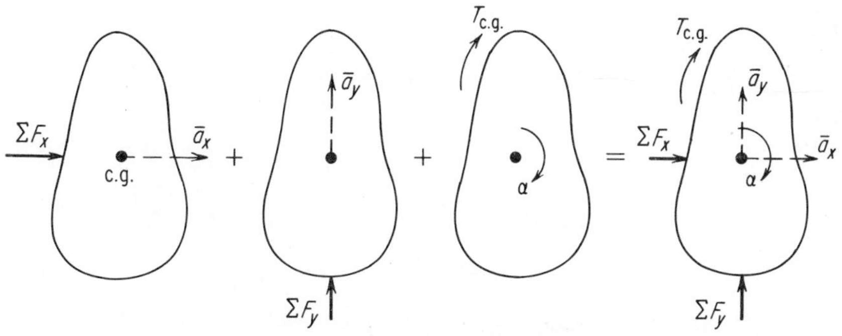

Figure 11-19

EXAMPLE 15: A solid cylindrical 64.4 lb wheel rolls on the horizontal plane when acted upon by a horizontal force $F = 20$ lb as shown in Fig. 11-20. Determine (a) the angular acceleration of the wheel, and (b) the minimum coefficient of friction that is required to prevent slipping.

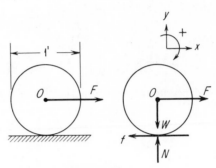

Figure 11-20

Solution: The free-body diagram is drawn as shown in Fig. 11-20(b). Since slipping does not occur, the friction force f must be some value less than μN. An equation of equilibrium is written for the y-direction and an equation of motion for the x-direction:

$$\Sigma F_y = 0$$

$$N = W \tag{a}$$

and

$$\Sigma F_x = m\bar{a}_x$$

$$20 - f = \frac{64.4}{32.2}a_x$$

$$20 - f = 2a_x \tag{b}$$

To find f in terms of the variables, moments are taken about the center of gravity:

$$\Sigma T_{cg} = \bar{I}\alpha$$

where $\bar{I} = mr^2/2$

$$\frac{1}{2}f = \frac{1}{2}\frac{64.4}{32.2}\left(\frac{1}{2}\right)^2\alpha$$

Thus,

$$f = \frac{\alpha}{2} \tag{c}$$

From the geometry of the motion

$$\bar{a}_x = \frac{1}{2}\alpha \tag{d}$$

Eqs. (b), (c), and (d) are combined and the angular acceleration α is determined.

$$20 - \frac{\alpha}{2} = \alpha$$

$\alpha = 13.3$ rad per sec^2 clockwise

To prevent slipping, the frictional force, at most, is equal to μN:

$$f = \mu N$$

where from Eq. (c) $f = \alpha/2 = 6.7$ lb. Thus

$$\mu = \frac{6.7}{64.4} = 0.104$$

PROBLEMS

11-1. Find the mass in slugs of a weight of (a) 32.2 lb; (b) 1288 lb; (c) 3 tons.

11-2. Determine the weight of an object that has a mass of (a) 3 slugs; (b) 5.2 slugs; (c) 9.8 lb sec^2 per ft.

11-3. If an object weighs 200 lb on earth ($g = 32.2$ fps^2), what would it weigh on (a) the moon ($g = 5.47$ fps^2); (b) the planet Jupiter ($g = 86.8$ fps^2)?

11-4. What is the weight of 10 slugs of mass on (a) the moon ($g = 5.47$ fps^2); (b) the planet Mars ($g = 12.9$ fps^2); and (c) the planet Jupiter ($g = 86.8$ fps^2)?

11-5–11-10. The system of forces acts on the body as shown in Figs. P11-5–P11-10. Find the acceleration of the mass by (a) determining the resultant acceleration from the components of acceleration, and (b) determining the acceleration from the resultant force. In each instance give the direction of the acceleration in terms of direction cosines.

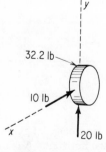

Figure P11-5

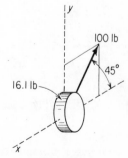

Figure P11-6

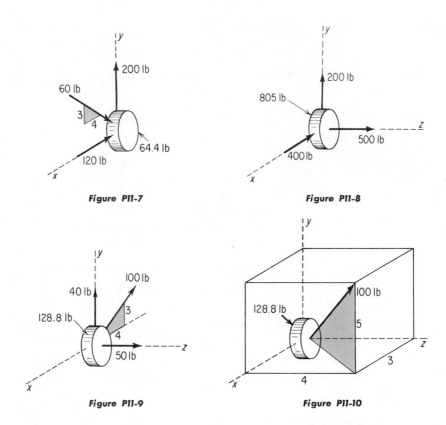

Figure P11-7   Figure P11-8

Figure P11-9   Figure P11-10

11-11. A weight of 16.1 lb is acted upon by the 10 lb horizontal force shown in Fig. P11-11. Find the acceleration of the weight if (a) the plane is perfectly smooth; (b) the coefficient of kinetic friction between the block and the plane is $\mu_k = 0.20$; (c) the coefficient of kinetic friction between the block and the plane is $\mu_k = 0.40$.

Figure P11-11   Figure P11-12

11-12. The 64.4 lb block in Fig. P11-12 acquires a velocity of 30 fps in 5 sec from rest with uniform acceleration. Find the horizontal force F required to cause acceleration if the coefficient of kinetic friction between the block and plane is $\mu_k = 0.25$.

11-13. Two bodies, coupled by an inextensible cable, are acted upon by a force $F = 100$ lb, as shown in Fig. P11-13. If the coefficient of kinetic friction at each contact surface is $\mu_k = 0.15$, find the acceleration of the bodies and the tension in the cable between them.

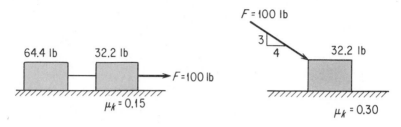

Figure P11-13   Figure P11-14

11-14. A force $F = 100$ lb acts on the 32.2 lb body shown in Fig. P11-14. Find the acceleration of the body if the coefficient of kinetic friction between it and the plane is $\mu_k = 0.30$.

11-15. A passenger on an elevator weighs 180 lb. What is the force between him and the elevator if the elevator is (a) accelerating upward at the rate of 4 fps²; (b) accelerating downward at the rate of 4 fps²; (c) moving downward with a constant velocity; (d) moving upward with a constant velocity?

11-16. In Fig. P11-16, find the tension in the cable and the acceleration of the two weights if the coefficient of kinetic friction between the 300 lb weight and the horizontal surface is $\mu_k = 0.30$. Neglect the weight of the pulley.

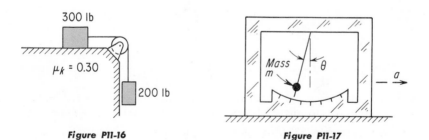

Figure P11-16   Figure P11-17

11-17. The device shown in Fig. P11-17, used to measure accelerations, consists of a mass suspended by a very light thread from a frame, which, in turn, is placed on an accelerating object. The scale reading in degrees is a measure of the acceleration. Find the acceleration equivalent to a scale reading of (a) 15 deg; (b) 25 deg; (c) 36 deg.

11-18. What is the "apparent" weight of a 200 lb man subjected to an upward acceleration of 5 g's?

11-19. What weight W would be required to cause the 60 lb weight in Fig. P11-19 to move up the plane with an acceleration of 5 fps^2? Assume the coefficient of kinetic friction to be $\mu_k = 0.20$, and neglect the weight of the pulley.

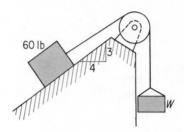

Figure P11-19

11-20. Find the weight W in Prob. 11-19 if the 60 lb weight moves downward with an acceleration of 5 fps^2.

11-21. Bodies A and B weigh 100 lb and 200 lb respectively. Determine the acceleration of each weight and the tension in the cable joining them if the system is released in the position shown in Fig. P11-21. Assume the pulley to have negligible mass.

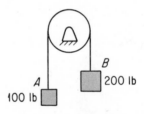

Figure P11-21

11-22. A man standing on the ground can lift 200 lb. What weight could he lift in an elevator that is descending with a downward acceleration of 6 fps^2?

11-23. What weight could the man in Prob. 11-22 lift if the elevator were descending with an upward acceleration of 6 fps^2?

11-24. A 10 lb weight, fastened to a 2 ft cord, is whirled in a vertical circle with an angular velocity of 100 rpm. Determine the tension in the cord when (a) the weight is at the top of the circle; (b) when the weight is at the bottom of the circle.

11-25. Determine, in Prob. 11-24, the minimum angular velocity that the weight can have and still completely travel the circular path.

11-26. An airplane which properly maneuvers a turn will bank at an angle θ so that the resultant of the weight force and inertia force is normal to the wings. In this way the plane will neither tend to drift upward or downward. Determine the proper angle of bank if the plane has a velocity of 100 mph while making a turn of 2000 ft radius as shown in Fig. P11-26.

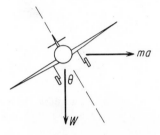

Figure P11-26

11-27. Determine the proper angle of bank in Prob. 11-26, if the speed of the plane doubles.

11-28. To balance out the force of gravity and study the effects of "weightlessness," an aircraft pilot maneuvers his plane in a vertical circle. Determine the proper speed of the aircraft if, at the top of the circle of 1 mi radius shown in Fig. P11-28, the inertia force and the weight force are just equal.

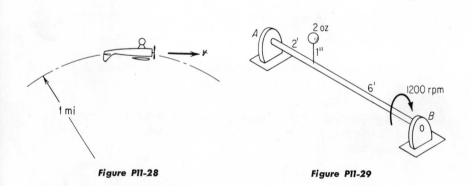

Figure P11-28   **Figure P11-29**

11-29. Find the bearing reactions at A and B caused by the dynamic unbalance in the rotating shaft shown in Fig. P11-29.

11-30. In Fig. P11-30, find the distance d from the axis of the shaft to the 4 oz weight so that the dynamic unbalance of the system will be zero.

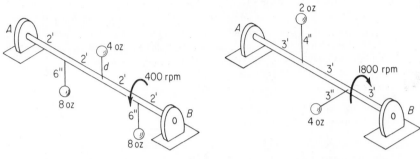

Figure 11-30   Figure P11-31

11-31. Find the bearing reaction at *A* and at *B* caused by the two-dimensional dynamic unbalance in the shaft shown in Fig. P11-31.

11-32. In Fig. P11-32, where on the shaft and at what distance from the axis should 4 oz weights be placed so that the system is in dynamic balance?

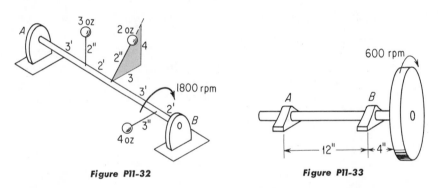

Figure P11-32   Figure P11-33

11-33. The large flywheel shown in Fig. P11-33 has an unbalance of 2.5 oz-in. Determine the bearing reaction at *A* and at *B* if the flywheel rotates at 600 rpm.

11-34. A high-speed gas turbine has an unbalance of 0.4 oz in. in its runner blades. In Fig. P11-34, determine the bearing reaction at *A* and at *B* at an operating speed of 10,000 rpm.

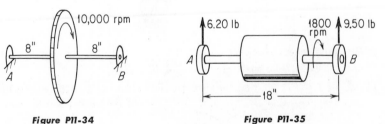

Figure P11-34   Figure P11-35

11-35. The armature of a 20 hp motor was tested in a specially instrumented set of bearings that were capable of recording the force due to dynamic unbalance. At the operating speed, 1800 rpm, bearing A registered a force of 6.20 lb and bearing B, 9.50 lb in the directions shown in Fig. P11-35. Determine (a) the unbalance of the armature in oz-in., and (b) the position of the unbalance on the shaft of the armature measured with respect to bearing A.

11-36. What would the bearing reactions be in Prob. 11-35 if the angular velocity of the armature was doubled?

11-37. Determine whether the 128.8 lb uniform crate in Fig. P11-37 will either tip or slip when the 50 lb force is applied. The coefficient of kinetic friction between the contact surfaces is $\mu_k = 0.40$. If the crate slips, find its acceleration.

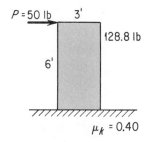

Figure P11-37

11-38. Solve Prob. 11-37 if the coefficient of kinetic friction is reduced to $\mu_k = 0.20$.

11-39. Determine the maximum possible acceleration of the automobile shown in Fig. P11-39 if the coefficient of static friction between the tires and the pavement is $\mu_s = 0.80$ and the car has (a) a conventional rear wheel drive; (b) front wheel drive.

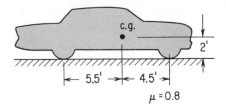

Figure P11-39

11-40. If the brakes lock on all four wheels, how far will the car of Prob. 11-39 slide in coming to rest? Assume that the car is initially traveling with a velocity of 45 mph and that the coefficient of kinetic friction between the tires and pavement is reduced to $\mu_k = 0.40$.

11-41. A cyclist leans toward the center of curvature when maneuvering a turn. In this way, the moment of the weight force just equals the moment of inertia force about a point of contact between the wheels and the ground. Determine the banking angle θ, measured from the vertical, if the radius of the turn is 30 ft and the velocity of the cycle is 10 fps. Assume that there is sufficient friction to prevent slipping.

11-42. Determine the minimum coefficient of friction between the tires and the pavement for the conditions stated in Prob. 11-41.

11-43. A 128.8 lb uniform weight is suspended by means of two parallel cables, each having a length of 6 ft. At the instant shown in Fig. P11-43, the weight has a velocity of 30 fps directed toward the right. Determine the tension in each cable.

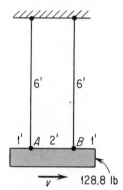

Figure P11-43

11-44. Find the tension in each cable if the center of gravity of the weight in Prob. 11-43 is 0.5 ft to the right of point A.

11-45. Find the maximum speed at which the 3220 lb car shown in Fig. P11-45 can maneuver a turn of 130 ft radius on a horizontal pavement. The coefficient of friction between the tires and the pavement is $\mu_s = 0.7$. Consider the possibility of both slipping and overturning.

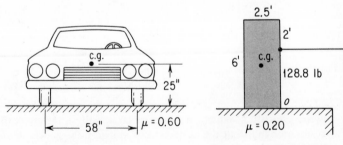

Figure P11-45   *Figure P11-46*

11-46. Find the maximum weight of body B in Fig. P11-46 if the uniform 128.8 lb block A is to slip rather than tip. The coefficient of friction between the block and the plane is $\mu_s = 0.20$.

11-47. A large flywheel weighing 6440 lb coasts to rest in 4 min from an initial velocity of 300 rpm. The flywheel has a radius of gyration of $k_o = 1.5$ ft. Find the frictional moment acting in the axle bearing.

11-48. Determine the torque required to accelerate the flywheel of Prob. 11-47 from rest to its original speed of 300 rpm in 20 sec if the frictional moment in the bearings is 20 lb ft. How many revolutions will the flywheel turn during the 20 sec period?

11-49. A grinding wheel weighs 32.2 lb and may be assumed to be a solid homogeneous cylinder 8 in. in diameter. After the power is turned off, a piece of metal is pushed against the wheel with a force of 5 lb. Determine the number of revolutions the wheel will turn before coming to rest from a speed of 1200 rpm. The coefficient of kinetic friction between the metal and the wheel is $\mu_k = 0.85$.

11-50. Determine the angular acceleration of the 32.2 lb solid homogeneous cylinder shown in Fig. P11-50 if no slipping occurs between the cylinder and the flexible cord that connects weights A and B.

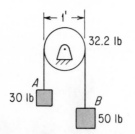

Figure P11-50

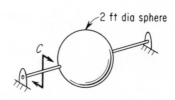

Figure P11-51

11-51. In Fig. P11-51 find the moment of the couple C required to accelerate the 644 lb homogeneous sphere from rest to 600 rpm in 10 sec.

11-52. The band-brake shown in Fig. P11-52 consists of a length of heavy leather belting pulled against the rotating flywheel. Friction between the belt and the flywheel causes a reduction in angular velocity. If the flywheel weighs 128.8 lb and has a radius of gyration $k_o = 9$ in., find the number of revolutions it will turn before coming to rest from a speed of 1200 rpm.

11-53. The 2000 lb elevator is lifted by means of a cable wrapped around the drum shown in Fig. P11-53. Find the moment of the couple C if the elevator is to have an acceleration of 4 fps² upward. The drum weighs 644 lb and has a radius of gyration of $k_o = 9$ in.

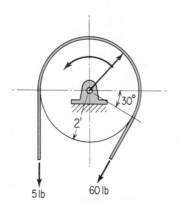

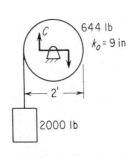

Figure PII-52

Figure PII-53

11-54. Force is applied to the brake shoe through the lever OA as shown in Fig. P11-54. Determine the force P if the 64.4 lb solid homogeneous cylinder comes to rest in 5 sec from an initial clockwise angular velocity of 1200 rpm. The coefficient of kinetic friction between the shoe and the cylinder is $\mu_k = 0.30$.

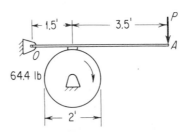

Figure PII-54

11-55. If the force P in Prob. 11-54 is 10 lb, through how many revolutions will the wheel turn in coming to rest from an initial angular velocity of 1200 rpm? Is the direction of rotation of any concern in this problem?

11-56. The magnitude of the couple C changes, as shown in the graph, Fig. P11-56, throughout the course of motion of the cylinder. Determine the angular displacement of the cylinder 2 ft in diameter if it weighs 64.4 lb and it starts from rest.

11-57. A clockwise couple of 10 lb ft acts on a solid homogeneous disk having a radius of 10 in. and a mass of 2 slugs. The disk has an initial counterclockwise angular velocity of 50 rad per sec. Determine the angular velocity of the disk after (a) 1 sec; (b) 2 sec; (c) 5 sec.

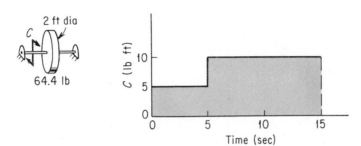

Figure P11-56

11-58. The velocity-time curve is shown in Fig. P11-58 for a disk having a centroidal moment of inertia of 2 slug ft^2. Find the moment of the couple acting during the 10 sec time interval.

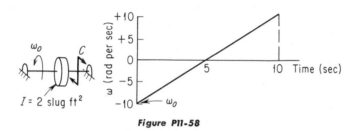

Figure P11-58

11-59. The velocity of the 64.4 lb solid cylinder, having a centroidal moment of inertia of 3 slug ft^2, varies according to the curve, as shown in Fig. P11-59. If the bearings offer no resistance to the motion, find the moment of the couple C which acts on the body (a) for the first 10 sec of motion; (b) for the last 15 sec of motion.

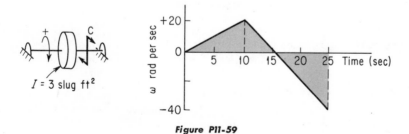

Figure P11-59

11-60. Find the magnitude of the couple C in Fig. P11-60 required to accelerate gear A at the rate of 20 rad per sec^2. Gears A and B may be assumed to be solid homogeneous cylinders with weights of 32.2 lb and 64.4 lb respectively.

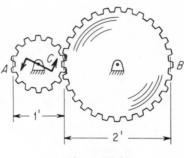

Figure P11-60

11-61. Solve Prob. 11-60 if gear *B*, instead of gear *A*, is to be accelerated at the rate of 20 rad per sec².

11-62. How much torque would have to be supplied to gear *A* in Prob. 11-60 if the axle bearings of both gears were in poor alignment and afforded a frictional moment of 1.5 lb ft each?

11-63. The 5 lb ft couple *C* acts on the 128.8 lb gear *A* as shown in Fig. P11-63. Find the acceleration of gear *B* if it weighs 32.2 lb. Assume both gears to be solid homogeneous cylinders.

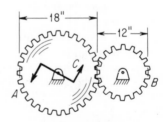

Figure P11-63

11-64. A three gear speed reducer is shown in Fig. P11-64. Find the magnitude of the couple *M* that is required to accelerate gear *C* from rest to 900 rpm in 10 sec.

11-65. In Fig. P11-65, the cord that supports the 200 lb weight *A* is wrapped around the drum fastened to gear *B*. Determine the acceleration of the weight if the mass moments of inertia of gears *B* and *C* are 1.0 slug ft² each.

11-66. Find the magnitude of the couple that would have to be applied to gear *C* of Prob. 11-65, if the weight is to accelerate upward at the rate of 10 fps².

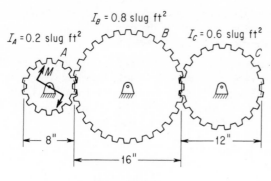

$I_B = 0.8$ slug ft²

$I_A = 0.2$ slug ft²

$I_C = 0.6$ slug ft²

Figure P11-64

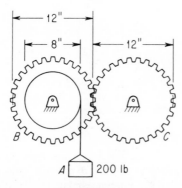

Figure P11-65

11-67. Determine the moment of the couple C that must be supplied to pulley A in Fig. P11-67 in order to accelerate pulley B at the rate of 15 rad per sec². Pulleys A and B weigh 32.2 and 128.8 lb respectively and may be assumed to be solid homogeneous cylinders.

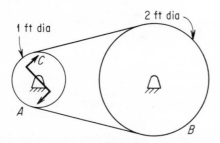

Figure P11-67

11-68. A large inertia of 5 slug ft^2 is coupled directly to pulley B of Prob. 11-67. Determine the moment of the couple C required for the accelerations if all other data remain the same.

11-69. A 3 pulley speed reducer is shown in Fig. P11-69. The driving pulley A reaches a speed of 1800 rpm in 4 sec from rest. Determine the torque that must be supplied by the motor coupled to pulley A. The armature of the motor has a moment of inertia of 10 slug ft^2 and $I_A = 0.5$ slug ft^2, $I_B = 1.0$ slug ft^2, and $I_C = 1.5$ slug ft^2.

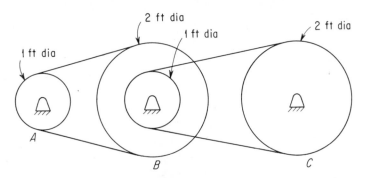

Figure P11-69

11-70. Three identical pulleys are belt driven as shown in Fig. P11-70. The angular acceleration of pulley A is 10 rad per sec^2 counterclockwise. Find the driving couple C and the difference in belt tensions $(T_1 - T_2)$ and $(T_3 - T_2)$. Assume each pulley to have a moment of inertia of 2 slug ft^2.

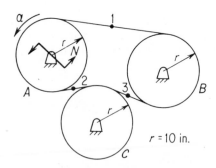

Figure P11-70

11-71. Determine the center of percussion of the slender rod, the solid cylinder, and the hoop, all of which are suspended from an axis O as shown in Fig. P11-71.

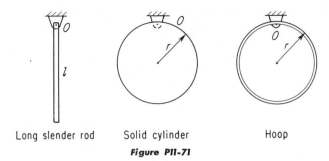

Long slender rod　　　Solid cylinder　　　　　Hoop

Figure P11-71

11-72. Find the reaction at the bearing O, if a 100 lb force F acts on the 64.4 lb solid cylinder as shown in Fig. P11-72.

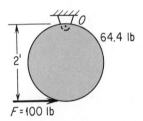

Figure P11-72

11-73. Find the bearing reaction in Prob. 11-72 if the 100 lb force acts at a point 6 in. below the axis; all other data remains the same.

11-74. The 128.8 lb solid cylinder rolls without slipping under the action of the 100 lb horizontal force shown in Fig. P11-74. Determine the minimum coefficient of friction necessary to prevent slipping.

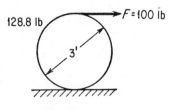

Figure P11-74

11-75. Solve Prob. 11-74 if the rolling mass is a sphere instead of a cylinder.

11-76. A 20 lb weight is suspended from a cord which is fastened to the axis of the 32.2 lb homogeneous cylinder as shown in Fig. P11-76. If the cylinder rolls without slipping, find its acceleration and the tension in the cord. Neglect the weight of the small pulley.

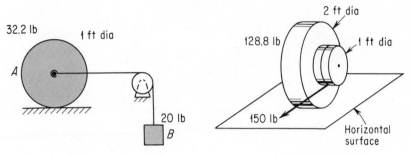

Figure P11-76   Figure P11-77

11-77. The wheel-drum assembly in Fig. P11-77 has a weight of 128.8 lb and a centroidal radius of gyration of $\bar{k} = 1.5$ ft. A force of $F = 150$ lb, applied through a cord wrapped around the smaller drum, causes the wheel to roll on the plane without slipping. Determine (a) the angular acceleration of the wheel, and (b) the frictional force developed at the plane.

11-78. A disk, a sphere, and a hoop of similar radius and weight are released from rest and allowed to roll down a plane inclined at 20 deg with the horizontal. Determine the acceleration of the mass center of each object if they roll without slipping.

11-79. At what distance d above the plane should the force F act on the solid cylinder in Fig. P11-79 if the force of friction is to be zero?

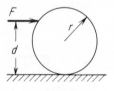

Figure P11-79

Chapter **12**

WORK, ENERGY, AND POWER

Certain mathematical difficulties arise when one attempts to apply the second law of motion, $F = ma$, to problems in which the accelerating force is a variable. Even such relatively simple problems involving a determination of the velocity of a pendulum at various points along its path or dealing with the variable force exerted by a spring on a mass are difficult to solve directly by the second law. The concepts of work and energy which will be discussed in this chapter, however, provide a simple and direct approach to this type of dynamics problem.

12-1 The Concept of Work

When a force F acts on a body and the body moves through a distance s in the direction of the force, then, by definition, work has been done on the body. The quantity of this work U, is equal to the product of the force F and the distance s.

The definition does not imply that a force doing work is necessarily the one that causes the body to move. The force of friction retards motion, yet it does work on the body. The only restriction placed on the force is that it must be directed along the line of action of the motion.

Three situations in which a force F acts on a moving body are illustrated in Fig. 12-1. In Case I, the force is collinear with the displacement, and the work, therefore, is simply

$$U = Fs \qquad\qquad (12\text{-}1)$$

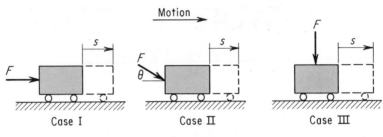

Figure 12-1

In Case II, however, the vertical component of the force, $F \sin \theta$, is perpendicular to the action line of the displacement and therefore does no work. Only the horizontal component does work and the amount is equal to

$$U = (F \cos \theta)s$$

No work is done on the body by the force F in Case III since its line of action is normal to the displacement.

Work is a scalar quantity with dimensions of [distance] $\times$ [force]; it is considered to be positive when the force has the same sense as the displacement, and to be negative when its sense is opposite to the displacement.

To illustrate, imagine the weight in Fig. 12-2 to be moving upward a distance s. The tensile force T in the cord does positive work on the weight, while the gravity force W opposes the motion and, therefore, does negative work. The total, or net, work on the system is

$$U = Ts - Ws = (T - W)s$$

If the situation is reversed and the weight moves downward a distance s, the gravity force W now has the same sense as the displacement and, therefore, contributes positive work to the system, while the tensile force T does negative work. Thus, for motion downward, the total work is

$$U = Ws - Ts = (W - T)s$$

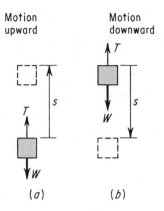

Motion   Motion
upward   downward

(a)   (b)

Figure 12-2

EXAMPLE 1: A 20 lb weight moves 5 ft up a plane, inclined as shown in Fig. 12-3, due to the action of the 100 lb force. If the coefficient of kinetic friction between the weight and the plane is $\mu_k = 0.20$, determine the total work done on the block.

Solution: The 100 lb force has the same sense as the displacement, so it does positive work on the system.

$$U_1 = Fs = 100(5) = +500 \text{ ft lb}$$

The weight force is resolved into components parallel and normal to the plane. The component parallel to the plane does negative work on the system, since it opposes the motion, and the component normal to the plane does no work.

$$U_2 = -W(\sin\theta)s = -20(\sin 30°)(5) = -50 \text{ ft lb}$$

The frictional force $\mu_k N$ contributes negative work to the system, since its sense is opposite to that of the motion:

$$U_3 = \mu_k Ns = -(0.20)20 \cos 30°(5) = -17.32 \text{ ft lb}$$

The net work on the system is

$$U_{\text{total}} = U_1 + U_2 + U_3 = 500 - 50 - 17.32 = +432.68 \text{ ft lb}$$

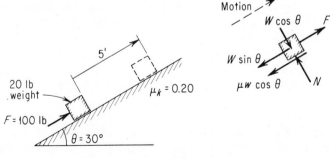

Figure 12-3

12-2 Work of a Variable Force

It is common in mechanics to encounter forces which undergo continual changes in magnitude while they act on a moving body. The pressure of the air on the moving piston of a compressor and the pull on a spring that is being stretched are two examples of forces which vary with the position of the body on which they act.

Work, by definition, is the product of force and distance: $U = Fs$; an area of a rectangle is the product of its height and its width: $A = hw$. The similarity between these two statements leads to the conclusion that work can be expressed as the area of a rectangle whose height is F and whose width is s. These areas appear graphically whenever force is plotted against displacement. Thus, the shaded area $ABCD$ shown in Fig. 12-4(b) represents the work done by the force F as it acts on the body.

$$U = \text{area } ABCD = F(s_f - s_o)$$

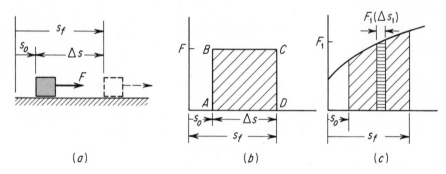

Figure 12-4

Now suppose that the force continually changes in value as the body moves. A graph of this force plotted against its displacement may appear as shown in Fig. 12-4(c). These *work diagrams*, as they are called, are usually the result of experimental force measurements. The area under the curve, which represents the work done, is not a single rectangle, but actually the sum of many rectangles $F_1(\Delta s_1)$. In fact, one way of approximating the area is to divide it into strips and add the areas of the strips. If the plot is made on cross-sectioned paper, a count of the number of squares under the curve may be a more convenient method of finding the area; when the curves consist of straight lines, simple area formulas can be used.

EXAMPLE 2: The magnitude of a force that acts on a moving piston is measured experimentally and found to vary as shown in the graph in Fig. 12-5. Determine the total work done by this force as the piston moves 10 in. to the right.

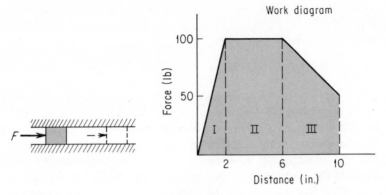

Figure 12-5

Solution: The area under the diagram is equal to the work done by the force. In this case, the areas of three geometric figures are involved: a triangle, a rectangle, and a trapezoid.

(a) triangle: area $= \dfrac{\text{[base]} \times \text{[height]}}{2}$

$$U_1 = \frac{2(100)}{2} = 100 \text{ in. lb}$$

(b) rectangle: area $=$ [base] $\times$ [height]

$$U_2 = 4(100) = 400 \text{ in. lb}$$

(c) trapezoid: area $=$ [base] $\times$ [mean height]

$$U_3 = 4\left(\frac{100 + 50}{2}\right) = 300 \text{ in. lb}$$

The total work done is the sum of the areas of these three figures

$$U = U_1 + U_2 + U_3 = 100 + 400 + 300 = 800 \text{ in. lb}$$

12-3 Elastic Springs

A spring can store work just as a tank can store water. When a clock is wound, for example, work is done on the main spring. The stored work turns the hands, rings bells, and ticks away the hours.

Springs are *elastic;* when a force is applied, they stretch or contract, depending upon the direction of the force. When the force is removed, they return to their original length. Theoretically, this means that a spring can return all the work that has been put into it.

A spring is characterized by the fact that the force required to stretch it or to compress it is proportional to its change in length. If 10 lb of force will increase the length of a spring by one inch, then 20 lb will increase the

length by two inches, 30 lb by three inches, and so on. The constant of proportionality, called the *spring constant* or *spring modulus*, has the dimensions
of [force]/[distance] and units of lb per in. or lb per ft.

$$k = \frac{F}{s} \tag{12-2}$$

Suppose a force of 100 lb causes a certain spring to stretch 4 in.; the spring
constant k is F/s, or 25 lb per in. If any two of the three variables in Eq. (12-2)
are known, the third can be found by simple multiplication or division.

The work diagram for a typical spring which has been stretched by an
amount s is shown in Fig. 12-6. Since the force is proportional to distance,
the diagram will always be bounded by a sloping straight line. The triangular
area under this curve represents the work done on the spring by the force F.

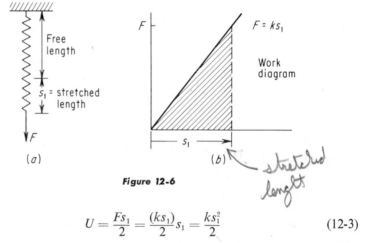

(a)

(b)

Figure 12-6

$$U = \frac{Fs_1}{2} = \frac{(ks_1)}{2}s_1 = \frac{ks_1^2}{2} \tag{12-3}$$

Additional work done on the spring is represented by a trapezoidal area
in the diagram. This area, illustrated in Fig. 12-7, is equal to the product of

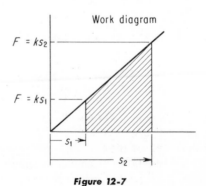

Figure 12-7

the mean height and the base. In this case

$$U = \frac{(ks_1 + ks_2)}{2}(s_2 - s_1) = \frac{k(s_2^2 - s_1^2)}{2} \tag{12-4}$$

EXAMPLE 3: A spring with a free length of 4 in. is stretched between a fixed support and a wheel, as shown in Fig. 12-8(a). Determine the amount of work done on the spring if the wheel is turned 90 deg clockwise. The constant of the spring is $k = 10$ lb per in.

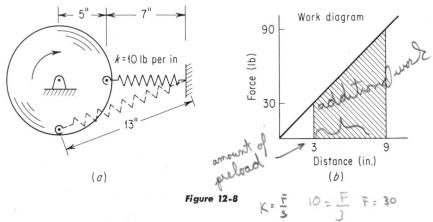

Figure 12-8

$K = \frac{F}{s}$ $10 = \frac{F}{3}$ $F = 30$

Solution: A work diagram is drawn for the spring. Since the free length of the spring is 4 in., some initial work had to be done on it to fasten it to the wheel. This is represented by the triangular area in the work diagram. When the wheel is rotated a quarter turn, the spring, now 13 in. long, has stretched an additional 6 in. and the force acting on it is 90 lb. The shaded trapezoidal area represents the additional work done on the spring.

$$U = [\text{mean height}] \times [\text{base}] = \left(\frac{90 + 30}{2}\right)6 = 360 \text{ in. lb}$$

12-4 Work Done by Torques and Couples

The equation for work $U = Fs$ applies to bodies which are rotating as well as those which are translating. Consider, for example, the constant force F, shown in Fig. 12-9, which is applied to the disk by means of a cord wrapped around its periphery. As the disk rotates through an angle θ, the force moves downward a distance s, where

$$s = r\theta$$

The work done is the product of the force and the distance through which it moves:

$$U = Fs = Fr\theta$$

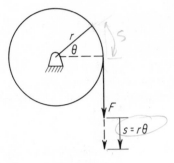

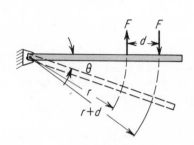

Figure 12-9   **Figure 12-10**

Since the product Fr is equal to the torque T_o acting on the disk, the equation for work can be written:

$$U = T_o\theta \qquad (12\text{-}5)$$

The dimensions of this equation are [lb ft] × [ft/ft] or, simply, ft lb, the same as that for the work done by a translating force.

A couple, too, is capable of doing work. In Fig. 12-10, the outermost force that acts on the rotating body moves in the direction of the body's displacement and the force, therefore, does positive work. The force closest to the axis of rotation opposes the displacement and does negative work. The net work on the body is the algebraic sum of the work done by each force.

$$U = F(r + d)\theta - Fr\theta = Fd\theta$$

The product of the force and the distance, Fd, is equal to the moment of the couple, therefore

$$U = C\theta \qquad (12\text{-}6)$$

Experimental measurements of torque variation with respect to rotation are used to plot diagrams which represent the work done by the torque. The areas under these curves can be found by any of the methods employed for force-displacement diagrams.

EXAMPLE 4: A brake, in the form of a block pressed against a rotating wheel, causes the wheel shown in Fig. 12-11 to slow down and finally stop after turning through 30 revolutions. Determine the amount of work done by the brake on the wheel if a force $F = 100$ lb is applied as shown in Fig. 12-11. Assume that the coefficient of kinetic friction between the block and the wheel is $\mu_k = 0.25$.

Solution: A frictional force $\mu_k F$ results when the brake is pressed against the rotating wheel. The moment of the frictional force is opposed to the motion of

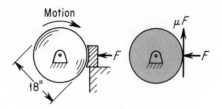

Motion

μF

F

F

18"

Figure 12-11

the wheel; therefore, it does negative work. Eq. (12-5) is used to compute the amount of this work:

$$U = T_o \theta = -\mu F r \theta$$
$$U = -0.25(100)\tfrac{9}{12}(30)2\pi = -3,530 \text{ ft lb}$$

12-5 Energy

Energy is defined as the ability or capacity to do work. Mechanical energy, electrical energy, heat energy, and nuclear energy are a few of its many forms.

Mechanical energy exists in two distinctly different ways: one is dependent upon position, the other upon motion. A compressed spring has energy by virtue of position, as does a weight suspended above a plane. Energy in this form is called *potential energy*.

Energy of motion, *kinetic energy*, is a measure of the amount of work that a moving object is capable of doing if it is brought to rest. It can also be viewed as the amount of work that must be done on an object to impart to it a given velocity.

The relationship between work done on a translating body and the kinetic energy the body thus acquires can be obtained from Newton's second law, $F = ma$. The work done by the force is the product of force and distance, Fs; therefore

$$U = Fs = mas \qquad\qquad\qquad\text{(a)}$$

The kinematic equation of Chap. 9 gives the relationship for the product *as:*

$$as = \frac{v_f^2 - v_o^2}{2} \qquad\qquad\qquad\text{(b)}$$

When (a) and (b) are combined, the equation for work becomes

$$U = \frac{m}{2}(v_f^2 - v_o^2) \qquad\qquad\qquad\text{(12-7)}$$

Verbally, the equation states: **when work is done on a translating body, the kinetic energy, $mv^2/2$, changes. If positive work is done, the kinetic energy will increase; if negative work is done, the kinetic energy will decrease.**

Eq. (12-7) is written symbolically as

$$U = \Delta T \tag{12-8}$$

The symbol T is used to designate kinetic energy, and ΔT a change in kinetic energy. The dimensions of energy are the same as the dimensions of work: [force] × [distance].

$$mv^2 = \frac{\text{lb sec}^2}{\text{ft}} \times \frac{\text{ft}^2}{\text{sec}^2} = \text{ft lb}$$

A freely falling weight does work on itself and thereby increases its kinetic energy; energy of position is transformed into energy of motion. If it falls a distance h from rest, the work done on itself is Wh; since $U = \Delta T$

$$Wh = \frac{1}{2}\frac{W}{g}(v_f^2 - O^2)$$

Thus, the velocity it acquires on falling is

$$v_f = \sqrt{2gh} \tag{12-9}$$

The principle of conservation of energy states that, while the form of the energy may change in a system, the quantity remains constant. Potential energy may be transformed into kinetic energy—kinetic energy can be transformed into potential energy—kinetic energy lost in friction is in reality transformed into heat energy; there are scores of possible conversions.

EXAMPLE 5: A 5 lb weight falls a distance of 3 ft onto a spring, as shown in Fig. 12-12. Determine the constant of the spring if it is compressed 6 in. as it brings the weight momentarily to rest.

1) K is in in." ÷ by 12

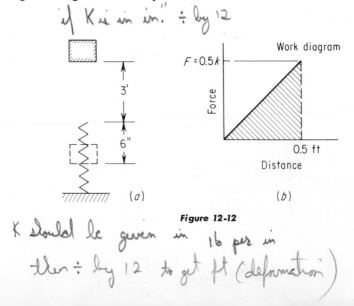

Figure 12-12

K should be given in lb per in
then ÷ by 12 to get ft (deformation)

Solution: The velocity that the weight acquires in 3 ft of free fall is found by substitution into Eq. (12-9).

$$v_f = \sqrt{2gh} = \sqrt{2(32.2)3} = 13.9 \text{ fps}$$

After contacting the spring, the weight continues to do positive work on itself as it moves downward the additional 6 in. The spring, in the meantime, is being compressed 6 in., and it does negative work on the weight. This negative quantity is equal to the area under the work diagram of the spring shown in Fig. 12-12(b). The two values of work are substituted into Eq. (12-8) and the spring constant computed: *elastic pot.*

$$U = \Delta T$$

$$Ws + \frac{1}{2}ks^2 = \frac{1}{2}m(v_f^2 - v_0^2)$$

$$5\left(\frac{6}{12}\right) - \frac{1}{2}k\left(\frac{6}{12}\right)^2 = \frac{1}{2}\frac{5}{32.2}[0^2 - (13.9)^2]$$

$$\frac{5}{2} - \frac{1}{2}k\left(\frac{1}{2}\right)^2 = \frac{1}{2}\frac{5}{32.2}[-(13.9)^2]$$

$$5 - \frac{k}{4} = -30$$

$$\frac{k}{4} = 35$$

$$k = 140 \text{ lb per ft}$$

An alternate solution: It is simpler and more direct to consider the entire sequence in one step. The weight starts from rest and ends, momentarily, at rest. The change in kinetic energy is zero. By falling a total of 3.5 ft, the weight does positive work on itself, and, as before, the spring does negative work on the weight. The loss of potential energy of the weight equals the gain in potential energy of the spring.

$$U = \Delta T = 0$$

$$5(3.5) - \frac{1}{2}k\left(\frac{6}{12}\right)^2 = 0$$

$$k = 8(5)3.5 = 140 \text{ lb per ft}$$

EXAMPLE 6: A 20 lb weight is pushed up an inclined plane by a force of $F = 50$ lb as shown in Fig. 12-13. Determine the velocity that the weight acquires if it moves 10 ft from an initial position of rest. The coefficient of kinetic friction between the weight and the plane is $\mu_k = 0.20$.

Solution: The free-body diagram indicates that both the friction force, $\mu_k N$, and the weight force, $W \sin \theta$, do negative work on the body, since they oppose its direction of motion. The force F, however, moves with the body and thereby does positive work.

The frictional force is equal to

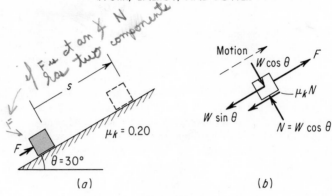

Figure 12-13

$$\mu_k N = \mu_k W \cos 30°$$

Substitution into Eq. (12-8) gives the desired velocity.

$$U = \Delta T$$

$$Fs - (W \sin \theta + \mu_k W \cos \theta)s = \frac{1}{2} m(v_f^2 - O^2)$$

$$50(10) - [20(0.5) + 0.2(20)(0.866)]10 = \frac{1}{2} \frac{20}{32.2} v_f^2$$

$$500 - 134.6 = 0.31 \, v_f^2$$

$$v_f = \sqrt{1176} = 34.3 \text{ fps}$$

EXAMPLE 7: A weight $W_A = 20$ lb is suspended by means of a cord that is passed over a small pulley of negligible mass and then fastened to a second weight $W_B = 40$ lb as shown in Fig. 12-14. The coefficient of kinetic friction between weight W_B and the plane is $\mu_k = 0.30$. If the system is released from rest, determine the velocity of W_A after it has moved downward a distance of 5 ft.

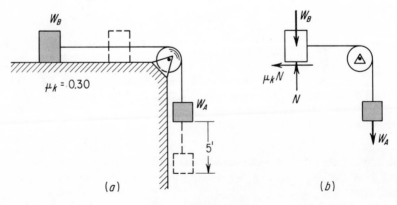

Figure 12-14

Solution: Positive work is done on the system by W_A as it moves downward, while the frictional force acting on W_B opposes the motion and does negative work. Weight B does no work on itself or on the system, since its motion is horizontal. The kinetic energy T of the system is the sum of the kinetic energy of each weight. Both weights move with the same velocity.

The data are substituted into Eq. (12-8).

$$U = \Delta T$$

$$W_A s - fs = \frac{1}{2} \frac{(W_A + W_B)}{g}(v_f^2 - 0)$$

$$20(5) - 0.30(40)5 = \frac{1}{2} \frac{(20 + 40)}{32.2} v_f^2$$

$$100 - 60 = 0.932 v_f^2$$

Solving this equation for the velocity gives

$$v_f = \sqrt{\frac{40}{0.932}} = 6.55 \text{ fps}$$

12-6 Rotation and Plane Motion

The rotating body shown in Fig. 12-15 is composed of an infinite number of particles, each with a mass Δm and a kinetic energy of $(\Delta m)v^2/2$. The velocity v of each particle is equal to the product of the distance r to the axis of rotation and the angular velocity ω. The kinetic energy of the body is the sum of the kinetic energies of its particles

$$T = \Sigma \frac{1}{2}mr^2\omega^2 = \frac{\omega^2}{2} \Sigma mr^2$$

The term Σmr^2 is the moment of inertia of the body about the axis of rotation. The kinetic energy of the rotating body, in terms of moment of inertia, is

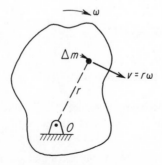

Figure 12-15

$$T = \frac{1}{2}I_o\omega^2 \qquad (12\text{-}10)$$

Newton's second law, $T_o = I_o\alpha$, when combined with the kinematic equation $2\alpha\theta = \omega_f^2 - \omega_o^2$, gives a relationship for the work done by a torque and the corresponding change in rotational kinetic energy.

$$T_o = I_o\alpha = I_o\frac{\omega_f^2 - \omega_o^2}{2\theta}$$

$$T_o\theta = \frac{1}{2}I_o(\omega_f^2 - \omega_o^2) \qquad (12\text{-}11)$$

In plane motion, a body rotates about its instantaneous center. The kinetic energy of each particle of mass, Δm, in the body is

$$\frac{1}{2}(\Delta m)v^2 = \frac{1}{2}(\Delta m)(r\omega)^2$$

where r is the distance of the particle from the instantaneous center. The kinetic energy of the body is the sum of the kinetic energies of its particles:

$$T = \frac{\sum (\Delta m)(r\omega)^2}{2} = \frac{\omega^2}{2}\sum (\Delta m)r^2$$

where $\sum (\Delta m)r^2$ is the moment of inertia of the body about its instantaneous center. Therefore

$$T = \frac{1}{2}I_{ic}\omega^2$$

As in translation and rotation, the work done on a body having plane motion either increases or decreases its kinetic energy.

$$U = \Delta T = \frac{1}{2}I_{ic}(\omega_f^2 - \omega_o^2) \qquad (12\text{-}13)$$

It was shown in Chapter 10 that the instantaneous center of rotation of a rolling wheel is the point of contact between it and the plane, provided, of course, that the wheel does not slip. The kinetic energy of the wheel at any instant is, therefore

$$T = \frac{1}{2}I_{ic}\omega^2 = \frac{1}{2}\left[\frac{1}{2}mr^2 + mr^2\right]\omega^2$$

The bracketed term is the moment of inertia of the wheel with reference to an axis through the instantaneous center.

EXAMPLE 8: A torsional resistance M_f in the bearings of the 644 lb solid homogeneous flywheel in Fig. 12-16 amounts to 12 lb ft. Through how many revolutions will the flywheel turn before coming to rest from a speed of 600 rpm?

Solution: The moment of inertia is computed and the initial angular velocity is expressed in units of rad per sec.

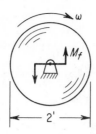

Figure 12-16

$$I_o = \frac{1}{2}mr^2 = \frac{1}{2}\frac{644}{32.2}(1)^2 = 10 \text{ slug ft}^2$$

and
$$\omega_o = 600\left(\frac{2\pi}{60}\right) = 20\pi = 62.8 \text{ rad per sec}$$

Substituting the computed values and the given data into Eq. (12-11) gives

$$T_o\theta = \frac{1}{2}I_o(\omega_f^2 - \omega_o^2)$$

$$-12\theta = \frac{1}{2}(10)[0^2 - (62.8)^2]$$

$$\theta = \frac{5}{12}(62.8)^2 = 1645 \text{ rad}$$

where
$$1645 \text{ rad}\left(\frac{1 \text{ rev}}{2\pi \text{ rad}}\right) = 262 \text{ revolutions}$$

EXAMPLE 9: A spring, whose constant is $k = 120$ lb per ft, is fastened to a solid homogeneous disk weighing 32.2 lb as shown in Fig. 12-17. The unstretched length of the spring is 4 in. If the system is released in the position shown, determine the velocity of the disk after it has turned 90 deg counterclockwise.

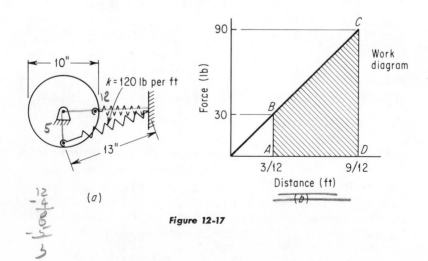

Figure 12-17

Solution: The shaded area of the work diagram represents the potential energy which is transferred from the spring to the disk. This potential energy is converted into rotational kinetic energy. The problem illustrates the principle of *conservation of energy*. (Note: the disk does no work on itself, since its center of gravity is fixed in position.) The work transferred by the spring is computed by the area method.

$$U = \text{area } ABCD = \left(\frac{90 + 30}{2}\right)\frac{6}{12} = 30 \text{ ft lb}$$

The change in kinetic energy of the disk is set equal to U:

$$U = \Delta T = \frac{1}{2}I_o(\omega_f^2 - \omega_0^2)$$

$$30 = \frac{1}{2}\left[\frac{1}{2}\frac{32.2}{32.2}\left(\frac{5}{12}\right)^2\right](\omega_f^2 - O^2)$$

$$30 = 0.0434\omega_f^2$$

$$\omega_f = \sqrt{691.2}$$

Solving for ω_f gives

$$\omega_f = 26.3 \text{ rad per sec}$$

12-7 Power and Efficiency

Power, a term frequently used to evaluate and compare electrical and mechanical machines, is defined as *the rate of doing work*. If the rate is constant, power can be expressed mathematically as

$$P = \frac{U}{t} \tag{12-14}$$

Since work is force times distance, the power may also be expressed as the product of force and velocity:

$$P = \frac{Fs}{t} = Fv \tag{12-15}$$

In terms of angular motion, power is the product of the torque and the angular velocity

$$P = \frac{T\theta}{t} = T\omega \tag{12-16}$$

When the rate of doing work varies with velocity or position, the power relationship must be expressed in terms of an average value:

$$P_{\text{avg}} = \frac{\Delta U}{\Delta t} \tag{12-17}$$

The dimensions of power are those of work divided by time: [ft lb]/[sec]. Industry, however, has adopted several units of power more convenient to their specific needs. For instance, electrical power is measured in units of *watts* or *kilowatts* (*kw*), mechanical power in units of *horsepower* (*hp*), and thermal power in units of *British thermal units per sec* (*Btu per sec*). The conversion from one system of units to another is accomplished through the definitions of these units.

$$1 \text{ hp} = 550 \text{ ft lb/sec} = 33,000 \text{ ft lb/min}$$
$$1 \text{ watt} = 0.738 \text{ ft lb/sec}$$
$$1 \text{ kw} = 738 \text{ ft lb/sec}$$
$$1 \text{ Btu/sec} = 778 \text{ ft lb/sec}$$
$$1 \text{ hp} = 0.746 \text{ kw}$$

The product of power and time is work. Some of the industrial units for this are the *horsepower hour* (*hp hr*) and the *kilowatt hour* (*kw hr*), where

$$1 \text{ hp hr} = 1.98 \times 10^6 \text{ ft lb}$$
$$1 \text{ kw hr} = 2.65 \times 10^6 \text{ ft lb}$$

Mechanical efficiency, another term that is frequently used in industry, is defined as the ratio of power output to power input. The Greek letter η (eta) is the symbol generally used for efficiency.

$$\eta = \frac{\text{output power}}{\text{input power}} = \frac{P_o}{P_i} \tag{12-18}$$

The efficiency of any mechanical device can never equal or exceed 1. Some power is always used in overcoming friction.

EXAMPLE 10: A truck weighing 10 tons climbs a 2 per cent grade (2 ft rise in 100 ft of travel), at a speed of 30 mph. How much power must the truck develop if the overall mechanical efficiency of the engine and transmission is 0.80?

Solution: The potential energy of the truck is increasing at a constant rate as it moves up the plane; therefore, work must be done on it. The force that moves the truck up the plane acts at the tires and is just equal to the component of the weight force down the plane, $W \sin \theta$. The theoretical power required is

$$P = Fv = (W \sin \theta)v$$
$$= 10 \text{ ton}\left(\frac{2000 \text{ lb}}{\text{ton}}\right)\frac{2}{100}\left(\frac{30 \text{ mi}}{\text{hr}}\right)\left(\frac{5280 \text{ ft}}{\text{mi}}\right)\left(\frac{\text{hr}}{3600 \text{ sec}}\right)$$
$$= 17,600 \frac{\text{ft lb}}{\text{sec}}$$

The answer in units of horsepower is

$$\text{hp} = 17,600 \frac{\text{ft lb}}{\text{sec}} \frac{1 \text{ hp}}{550 \frac{\text{ft lb}}{\text{sec}}} = 32 \text{ hp}$$

This is the output power at the wheels of the truck. The engine must develop more power because of the friction losses that occur between it and the tires. From Eq. (12-17)

$$\eta = \frac{\text{output power}}{\text{input power}}$$
$$P_i = \frac{P_o}{\eta} = \frac{32}{0.80} = 40 \text{ hp}$$

PROBLEMS

12-1. A weight of 100 lb falls freely for a distance of 50 ft. Determine the work done by the weight on itself. Use the methods of the last chapter to find the velocity at the 50 ft mark.

12-2. An object is acted upon by a force of 10 lb directed in each of the three ways shown in Fig. P12-2. Determine the work done by the force for each case if the object moves 10 ft to the right.

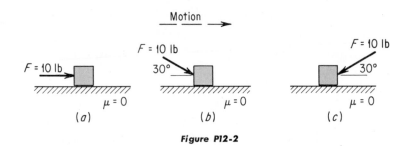

Figure P12-2

12-3. The object in Prob. 12-2 weighs 20 lb, and the coefficient of kinetic friction between the surfaces is $\mu_k = 0.25$. Determine the work done by the frictional force for each of the three situations if the object moves 10 ft to the right.

12-4. When the brakes are applied on a 3000 lb automobile, the wheels lock and the car slides 60 ft as it comes to rest. If the coefficient of kinetic friction between the tires and the pavement is $\mu_k = 0.80$, determine the work done by friction. $F = \mu N \qquad U = Fs$

12-5. A 30 lb body slides 5 ft down a plane inclined as shown in Fig. P12-5. Determine the net work done by all the forces that act on the system. The coefficient of kinetic friction between the block and the plane is $\mu_k = 0.11$.

$$U = (100 \times \cos\theta)10 - \left[.15(20 \times \cos\theta + 100 \sin\theta)\right]10 - (20 \times \sin\theta)$$

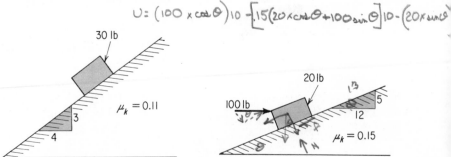

Figure P12-5   **Figure P12-6**

12-6. Determine the net work done by all the forces involved if the 20 lb block shown in Fig. P12-6 moves 10 ft up the incline. The coefficient of kinetic friction between the block and the plane is $\mu_k = 0.15$.

12-7. Determine the net work done on the block in Prob. 12-6 if it moves 10 ft down the incline.

12-8. The weight W in Fig. P12-8 moves 10 ft upward due to the action of the force $F = 20$ lb. How much work is done by this force?

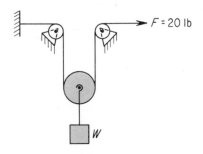

$F = 20$ lb

W

Figure P12-8

12-9–12-11. Determine the amount of work done by the variable force during the course of its motion as represented by the work diagram in Figs. P12-9–P12-11.

12-12–12-14. Estimate the amount of work done by the variable force between the limits of motion s_1 and s_2 in Figs. P12-12–P12-14.

12-15. Determine the constant k of a spring if 50 lb of force will change its length by 2 in.

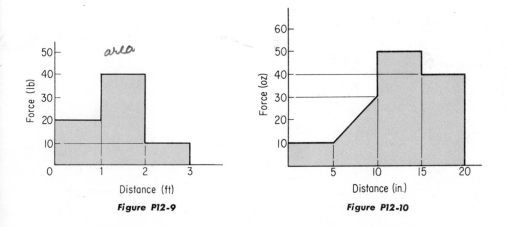

Figure P12-9

Figure P12-10

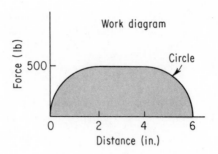

Figure P12-11

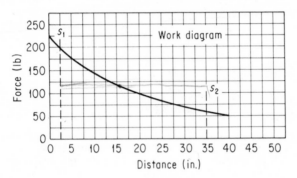

Figure P12-12

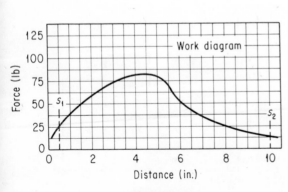

Figure P12-13

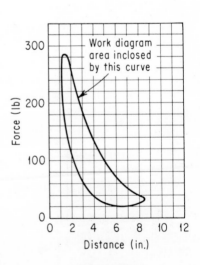

Figure P12-14

12-16. The constant of a certain spring is known to be 100 lb per ft. How much force is acting on the spring when it is compressed 3 in.? Stretched 3 in.?

12-17. A force of 200 lb is applied to a spring whose constant is $k = 200$ lb per in. By how much will the length of the spring change?

12-18. A spring has a free length of 6 in. and a constant of $k = 30$ lb per in. When a force is applied to it, the spring stretches to a length of 9 in. How much work is done on the spring by this force?

12-19. How much additional work would have to be done on the spring of Prob. 12-18 to stretch it to a length of 15 in.?

12-20. How much work is done on the spring in Fig. P12-20 if the crank rotates 90 deg clockwise? The spring has a constant of 20 lb per in. and an unstretched length of 15 inches.

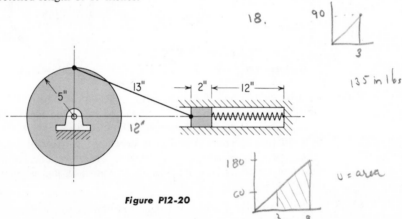

Figure P12-20

12-21. The motor shown in Fig. P12-21 weighs 1000 lb. It is supported by four springs, each with a constant of 250 lb per in. How much additional work is done on each spring if a static force of 2000 lb acts downward at the centroid of the motor?

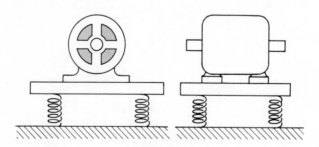

Figure P12-21

12-22. A 20 lb weight, when suspended from a spring, causes it to stretch an amount h. When an additional weight of 60 lb is added, the spring stretches an additional 2 in. Determine the spring constant k and the value of h.

12-23. How much work is done by the couple shown in Fig. P12-23 if it turns the steering wheel through one-quarter of a revolution?

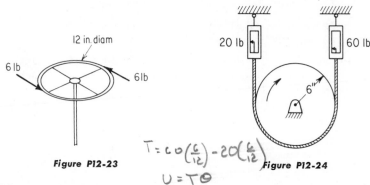

Figure P12-23

$$T = 60\left(\frac{6}{12}\right) - 20\left(\frac{6}{12}\right)$$
$$U = T\theta$$

Figure P12-24

12-24. A leather belt is pulled against a rotating disk, as shown in Fig. P12-24, and the tension on either side is measured by spring scales. This device, called a *prony brake*, is used to measure the rate at which work is done by a rotating machine. Friction is developed between the belt and the wheel, and this causes the belt tensions on either side to be different. How much work is done per second on the wheel if it is rotating at 500 rpm?

12-25. A torque-angular displacement curve is obtained from experimental data on a certain machine and appears as shown in Fig. P12-25. Estimate the amount of work done by the machine.

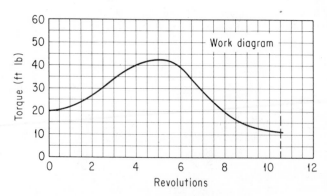

Figure P12-25

12-26. The spring brake shown in Fig. P12-26 is used to stop a rotating disk. Determine the amount of work done by the brake if the disk turns through 20 revolutions while coming to rest. The coefficient of kinetic friction between the brake shoe and the wheel is 0.20 and the spring is compressed 2 in.

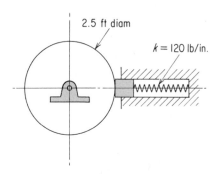

2.5 ft diam

$k = 120$ lb/in.

Figure P12-26

12-27. How much kinetic energy does a 3220 lb automobile possess if it is traveling at (a) 20 mph; (b) 60 mph; (c) 100 mph?

12-28. A truck and its cargo weigh 10 tons. How much kinetic energy does it possess if it is traveling at a speed of 70 mph? $KE = \frac{1}{2}mv^2$

12-29. How much work is done by the brakes of a 3220 lb automobile in bringing it to rest from a speed of 80 mph?

12-30. A cubic foot of natural gas as it is delivered to the home contains a potential to do work that is equivalent to approximately 800,000 ft lb. What velocity would a 100 lb weight have to acquire to contain this much energy?

12-31. How much kinetic energy does a cubic foot of water acquire in falling 100 ft? (Water weighs approximately 62.4 lb per cu ft.)

12-32. What velocity will a weight attain if it falls a distance of 100 ft on the moon ($g = 5.47$ fps^2)?

$v_P = \sqrt{2gh}$

12-33. Compare the kinetic energy, on the earth and on the moon, of a 100 lb weight (earth weight) that is moving with a velocity of 20 fps.

12-34. A 10 lb weight is held just above a spring whose constant is $k = 100$ lb per ft. If the weight is suddenly released, by how much will the spring deform?

12-35. The 25 lb car in Fig. P12-35 rolls without friction down the left incline, then up the right incline to the horizontal surface. Determine its velocity as it moves along this horizontal plane.

34. $10x = \frac{1}{2}\left(\frac{100}{12}\right)x^2$

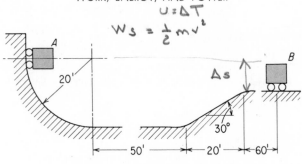

$U = \Delta T$

$W_s = \frac{1}{2} m v^2$

Figure P12-35

12-36. The three "bumper" springs are used to stop the motion of the 50,000 lb railroad tank car shown in Fig. P12-36. By how much will their length change if they bring the car to rest from an initial speed of 5 mph?

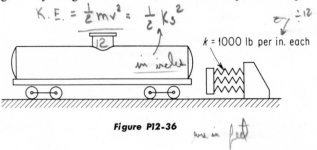

$K.E. = \frac{1}{2} m v^2 = \frac{1}{2} k s^2$

$k = 1000$ lb per in. each

Figure P12-36

12-37. The free length of each of the identical springs shown in Fig. P12-37 is 5 in. The springs are stretched and fastened to the 10 lb weight; the weight is moved 4 in. to the right and released. If it slides without friction on the horizontal surface, determine the velocity of the weight as it passes the center position. The constant of each spring is $k = 15$ lb per in.

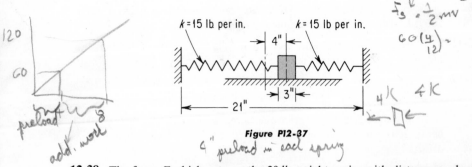

$k = 15$ lb per in. $k = 15$ lb per in.

4"

21"

3"

Figure P12-37

12-38. The force F which acts on the 20 lb weight varies with distance as shown in the graph in Fig. P12-38. Determine the velocity of the weight after it moves 10 ft from rest if the coefficient of kinetic friction between the weight and the plane is (a) $\mu_k = 0$; (b) $\mu_k = 0.2$; (c) $\mu_k = 0.9$.

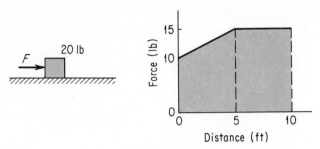

Figure P12-38

12-39. A 32.2 lb weight is released at a height of 25 ft above a horizontal plane. Determine the total energy (the sum of the potential energy and the kinetic energy) relative to the plane after it has fallen (a) zero ft; (b) 5 ft; (c) 10 ft; (d) 24.39 ft.

12-40. An airplane, traveling in a horizontal plane at a speed of 700 mph and an elevation of 5000 ft, releases a bomb that weighs 1200 lb. With what velocity does it strike the ground? Use methods of work and energy.

12-41. Solve Prob. 12-40 if the airplane is diving at an angle of 60 deg with the horizontal.

12-42. A large flywheel, weighing 1288 lb, has a radius of gyration of 12 in. Determine its kinetic energy if it is rotating with an angular velocity of (a) 60 rpm; (b) 120 rpm; (c) 600 rpm. $K = \frac{1}{2} I_o \omega^2$

12-43. The flywheel described in Prob. 12-42 is used in press-forming steel plate. How much work is it capable of doing if during an operation its speed is reduced from 120 rpm to 80 rpm? How much work must be done by a motor to restore the lost energy? $U = \Delta T = \frac{1}{2} I \left(\omega_f^2 - \omega_o^2 \right)$

12-44. As shown in Fig. P12-44, a weight of 20 lb is suspended from a cord which in turn is wrapped around a solid homogeneous cylinder that weighs 64.4 lb. Determine the angular velocity of the cylinder if the weight descends 10 ft after being released.

$$W_s = \frac{1}{2} m v^2 + \frac{1}{2} I_o \omega^2$$

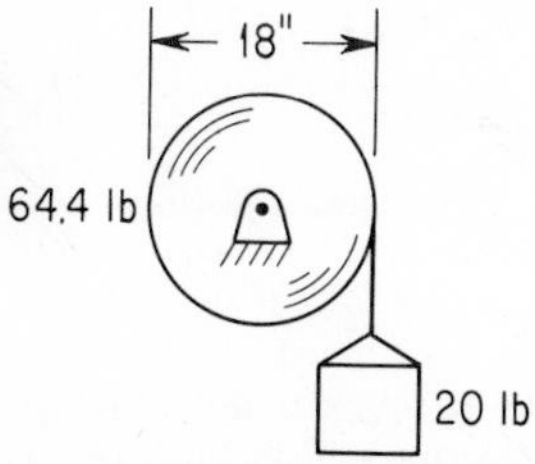

$$\omega^2 = \frac{v^2}{r^2}$$

├─ 18" ─┤

64.4 lb

20 lb

Figure P12-44

12-45. If the cord is suddenly cut after the weight described in Prob. 12-44 has descended the 10 ft, what velocity will it acquire in an additional 10 ft of free-fall?

12-46. A 64.4 lb long, slender rod with an axis at one end is held in the horizontal position by a small support as shown in Fig. P12-46. Determine the angular velocity of the rod as it passes through the vertical position if the support is suddenly removed.

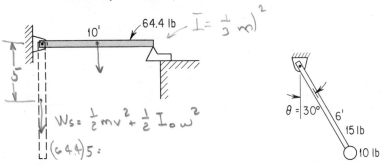

Figure P12-46   Figure P12-47

12-47. The pendulum consists of a small 10 lb weight fastened to a 6 ft rod that weighs 15 lb. Determine the velocity of the weight as the pendulum passes through the vertical position, if it is released in the position shown in Fig. P12-47.

12-48. Solve Prob. 12-47 if the angle θ is increased to 60 deg.

12-49. Determine the total kinetic energy of the gear train shown in Fig. P12-49 if gear A has a velocity of 240 rev per min. Assume both gears to be solid homogeneous cylinders. Gears A and B weigh 32.2 lb and 8.05 lb respectively.

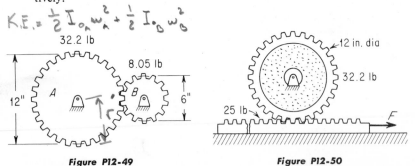

Figure P12-49   Figure P12-50

12-50. The 25 lb rack shown in Fig. P12-50 is being pulled by a force $F = 100$ lb, and it, in turn, rotates the 32.2 lb gear. Determine the angular velocity of the gear if the rack moves 2 ft to the right from an initial rest position.

Assume the radius of gyration of the gear to be 4 in. and the coefficient of friction between the rack and the plane to be zero.

12-51. Determine the angular velocity of the gear, if the force F acting on the rack of Prob. 12-50 is replaced by a compressed spring having a constant $k = 240$ lb per in. The spring, which is compressed 6 in. when the system is released, transmits all of its energy to the rack and gear assembly; it is at this instant that the angular velocity is to be found.

12-52. The torque which acts on the rotating 32.2 lb solid homogeneous disk varies with the angular displacement as shown in the graph in Fig. P12-52. If the disk starts from a rest position, determine its angular velocity after it has turned through 20 rev.

$$\text{area } (2\pi)$$

$$T_0 \, \theta = \frac{1}{2} I_0 \left(w_f^2 - w_0^2 \right)$$

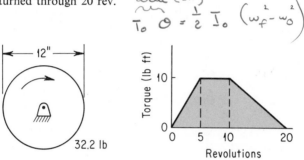

Figure P12-52

12-53. Solve Prob. 12-52 if the disk has an initial counterclockwise angular velocity of 600 rpm.

12-54. Determine the kinetic energy of the wheel shown in Fig. P12-54 if it weighs 96.6 lb and rolls on the plane without slipping. The velocity of the center is $v_0 = 10$ fps, and the wheel has a centroidal radius of gyration of $k_0 = 6$ in.

$$K.E. = \frac{1}{2} mv^2 + \frac{1}{2} I_0 \, w^2$$

$$V = r w$$

$$10 = (1) w$$

$$w = 10$$

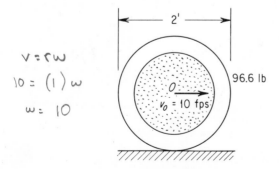

Figure P12-54

12-55. The wheel-drum assembly illustrated in Fig. 12-55 weighs 64.4 lb and has a centroidal radius of gyration of $k_0 = 4$ in. Determine its kinetic energy if the velocity of the center is $v_0 = 10$ fps and if the assembly rolls without slipping.

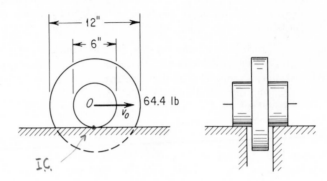

Figure P12-55

12-56. At the instant shown in Fig. P12-56, point A on the 64.4 lb slender rod has a downward velocity of 20 fps. Determine the kinetic energy of the rod.

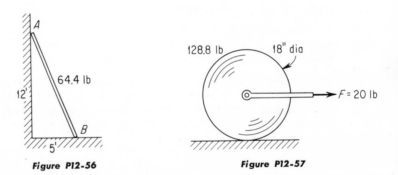

Figure P12-56   *Figure P12-57*

12-57. Determine the velocity of the center of the wheel in Fig. P12-57 if it moves 10 ft to the right from a position of rest under the action of the horizontal 20 lb force. The wheel, a solid homogeneous disk, weighs 128.8 lb and rolls without slipping.

12-58. The weight W_A in Fig. P12-58 is suspended by means of a light cord which passes over a small pulley of negligible mass and is then fastened to the axle of a 64.4 lb wheel. The centroidal radius of gyration of the wheel is 3 in., and it rolls without slipping. Determine the value of the weight W_A if the wheel acquires an angular velocity of 30 rad per sec while moving 10 ft to the right.

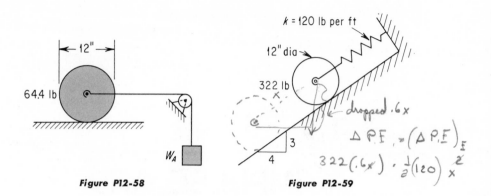

Figure P12-58   Figure P12-59

12-59. The 322 lb solid homogeneous disk is released from rest on the inclined plane as shown in Fig. P12-59. If there is no initial tension in the spring determine the maximum distance that the disk will roll down the plane. The spring has a constant $k = 120$ lb per ft.

12-60. What is the output torque of a 50 hp motor running at (a) 600 rpm; (b) 1200 rpm; (c) 1800 rpm? $550 \times 50 = \longrightarrow P : T \omega \leftarrow$ rad

12-61. How many kilowatts of electricity must be supplied to run a motor that is rated at 20 hp if electrical energy is transformed into mechanical energy with an efficiency of (a) 100 per cent; (b) 80 per cent? $20 \times .746$

12-62. To overcome rolling resistance, a locomotive exerts a force of 20,000 lb while pulling a train of cars over a level road at 20 mph. Determine the horsepower that is developed by the engine.

12-63. The locomotive described in Prob. 12-62 burns Diesel fuel with a theoretical energy content of 140,000 Btu per gallon. How many gallons of fuel would be consumed per hour if the conversion of chemical energy to mechanical energy is 25 per cent efficient?

12-64. How many ft lb of work can be done in a 24 hr day by a kilowatt of electricity?

12-65. An automobile weighing 3220 lb is brought to rest from a speed of 60 mph in a distance of 200 ft. Determine the horsepower hours of work expended by the brakes.

12-66. What does it cost per 8 hr day to operate a 20 hp motor under full load? Assume that electricity costs 2.2 cents per kilowatt hour, and that the conversion of electrical energy to mechanical energy is 83 per cent efficient.

$$\frac{8 \times 20 \times .746}{.83} \times 2.2$$

Chapter 13

IMPULSE AND
MOMENTUM

Forces which change suddenly in magnitude and direction are frequently encountered in mechanics. This chapter will consider these forces, which sometimes act for only a fraction of a second, and their effects on the motion of bodies.

13-1 Linear Impulse and Linear Momentum

If one could measure with very sensitive instruments the force that is exerted on a baseball as it is struck with a bat, he would find the force to vary in a very short interval of time from zero to some maximum value and then back to zero again. The baseball would react to this *impulsive force* by undergoing a drastic acceleration which would consist of a change in both the magnitude and direction of its velocity. Since the force which acts changes with time, the acceleration cannot be found by direct substitution into the inertia equation, $F = ma$. The same situation was encountered in the chapter on work and energy: Newton's second law of motion must be modified to accommodate a variable force.

The definition of acceleration $a = \Delta v/\Delta t$, substituted into $\sum F = ma$, gives an expression equating the products $F\Delta t$ and $m\Delta v$:

$$\sum F = ma = m\frac{\Delta v}{\Delta t}$$

$$\sum F(\Delta t) = \dot{m}(\Delta v) \tag{13-1}$$

If the force F is expressed in terms of an average value F_{avg}, Eq. (13-1) can be written

$$F_{avg}(\Delta t) = m(v_f - v_o) \tag{13-2}$$

The product of force and time is called an *impulse* and the product of mass and velocity, *momentum*. Equation (13-2), therefore, states simply that **the momentum of a body changes when the body is acted upon by an impulse.** It is important to note that both terms are vector quantities, and direction as well as magnitude must be considered in the application of Eq. (13-2). The dimensions of implulse, as well as those of momentum, are [force] × [time] (lb sec).

Experimental measurements of force versus time, when plotted, are frequently employed in computing a change in momentum; the area under the resulting curve is equivalent to an average impulse. Often these areas are found by approximation, as illustrated in the example that follows.

EXAMPLE 1: An 8.05 lb body, initially at rest, is acted upon by a force which varies with time, as shown in Fig. 13-1(b). Determine the velocity that the body acquires.

Solution: The area under the force-time diagram, which is equivalent to the average impulse on the body, is approximately that of a triangle.

$$F_{avg}(\Delta t) = m(v_f - v_o)$$

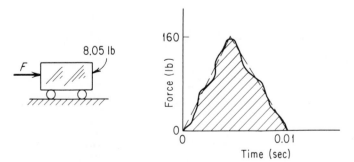

Figure 13-1

where $\qquad\qquad F_{avg}(\Delta t) =$ [area under $F\text{-}t$ diagram]

therefore $\qquad\qquad \dfrac{1}{2}(0.01)160 = \dfrac{8.05}{32.2}(v_f - 0)$

Solving for v_f gives

$$v_f = 3.2 \text{ fps to the right}$$

EXAMPLE 2: In Fig. 13-2 the action of the brakes causes the wheels to lock on an automobile that is traveling at a speed of 60 mph. Determine the time required for the car to come to rest if the coefficient of kinetic friction between the tires and the pavement is $\mu_k = 0.75$.

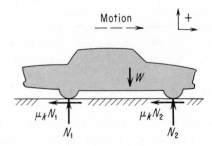

Figure 13-2

Solution: Since the motion of the car is confined to the x-direction, the sum of the y-components of force is zero.

$$\Sigma F_y = 0$$
$$N_1 + N_2 = W \qquad\qquad\qquad \text{(a)}$$

The x-components of force, when multiplied by the time, are equal to the change of momentum of the automobile:

$$\Sigma F(\Delta t) = m(v_f - v_o)$$
$$(-\mu N_1 - \mu N_2)t = \frac{W}{g}(0 - v_o) \qquad\qquad \text{(b)}$$

Since the sum of the normal reactions $(N_1 + N_2)$ is equal to the weight W, Eq. (b) reduces to

$$-\mu W t = \frac{W}{g}(0 - v_o)$$

Substitution of data gives

$$0.75 W t = \frac{W}{32.2}(88)$$

Solving for t:

$$t = \frac{88}{32.2(0.75)} = 3.64 \text{ sec}$$

It is interesting to note that, since the weight of the car appears on both sides of the impulse-momentum equation, it cancels out of the computation. A light car and a heavy car would come to rest in the same length of time.

13-2 Angular Impulse and Angular Momentum

An impulsive force that acts on a lever arm is equivalent to an *angular impulse*. Just as a linear impulse produces a change in linear momentum, an angular impulse produces a change in angular momentum. The defining equation which relates the two angular quantities is developed by combining the second law of motion for rotation $\sum T_o = I_o \alpha$ with the kinematic relationship $\alpha = \Delta\omega/\Delta t$.

$$\sum T_o = I_o \alpha = I_o \frac{\Delta\omega}{\Delta t}$$

$$\sum T_o(\Delta t) = I_o \Delta\omega$$

In terms of average torques, the defining equation becomes

$$(T_o)_{avg} \Delta t = I_o(\omega_f - \omega_o) \tag{13-3}$$

The units of both angular impulse and angular momentum are [torque] $\times$ [time], (lb ft sec).

Equation (13-3) is valid for bodies which have plane motion as well as those whose motion is pure rotation. Care must be exercised, however, in selecting the reference point O; for plane motion, point O must be located at the center of gravity of the body.

$$\sum T_{avg}(\Delta t) = \bar{I}(\omega_f - \omega_o) \tag{13-4}$$

where $\bar{I}$ is the moment of inertia of the body with reference to the mass center.

As will be illustrated in the examples that follow, a second equation, the relationship between linear impulse and linear momentum, is necessary in problems involving plane motion. The velocity used in the writing of these impluse-momentum equations must be that of the mass center; thus

$$\sum F(\Delta t) = m(\bar{v}_f - \bar{v}_o) \tag{13-5}$$

EXAMPLE 3: A torque of 10 lb ft acts on a 128.8 lb flywheel that is supported in frictionless bearings. Determine the velocity that the pulley acquires in 2 sec from an initial state of rest. The radius of gyration of the flywheel about its axis of rotation is $k_o = 6$ in.

Solution: This is an example of pure rotation, and data can be substituted directly into Eq. (13-3):

$$\Sigma T_o(\Delta t) = I_o(\omega_f - \omega_o)$$

$$10(2) = \frac{128.8}{32.2}\left(\frac{1}{2}\right)^2(\omega_f - 0)$$

and $\omega_f = 20$ rad per sec

EXAMPLE 4: A 10 lb weight W_A is suspended from a cord which passes over a small pulley of negligible mass, as shown in Fig. 13-3. The cord is fastened to the axle of a pair of disks which are free to roll without slipping on the horizontal plane. If the disks have a combined weight of $W_B = 64.4$ lb, find the velocity of weight W_A five sec after it is released and the tension in the cord.

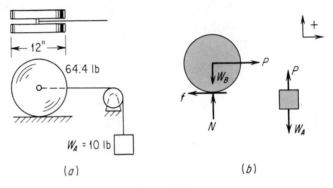

Figure 13-3

Solution: The disks and the weight are separated and free-body diagrams are drawn for each. One equation, the linear impulse-momentum relationship, is written for weight W_A; two equations are required for the paired disks, since they have plane motion. *direction of motion is +*

For the weight W_A:

$$\Sigma F\Delta t = m(v_f - v_o)$$

$$(10 - P)5 = \frac{10}{32.2}(v_f - 0)$$

$$10 - P = 0.062v_f \qquad\qquad (a)$$

For the disks:

$$I = \frac{1}{2}mr^2 = \frac{1}{2}\frac{64.4}{32.2}\left(\frac{6}{12}\right)^2 = 0.25 \text{ slug ft}^2$$

Rotation: $$\Sigma T_{cg}\Delta t = I(\omega_f - \omega_o)$$

$$\frac{6}{12}f(5) = 0.25(\omega_f - 0)$$

$$f = 0.10\omega_f \qquad\qquad (b)$$

Translation: $$\Sigma F\Delta t = m(\bar{v}_f - \bar{v}_o)$$

$$(P - f)5 = \frac{64.4}{32.2}(\bar{v}_f - 0)$$

$$5P - 5f = 2v_P$$

$$P - f = 0.4\bar{v}_f \qquad \text{(c)}$$

A fourth relationship is required, one of geometry, which relates the velocity of the mass-center of the disk $\bar{v}_f$ to its angular velocity ω. It should be noted that the velocity $\bar{v}_f$ is also the velocity of the weight:

$$\bar{v}_f = r\omega_f = 0.5\omega_f \qquad \text{(d)}$$

The four equations are rewritten

$$10 - P = 0.062v_f \qquad \text{(a)}$$

$$f = 0.10\omega_f \qquad \text{(b)}$$

$$P - f = 0.4\bar{v}_f \qquad \text{(c)}$$

$$v_f = \bar{v}_f = 0.5\omega_f \qquad \text{(d)}$$

Equations (b), (c), and (d) are combined to give a relationship between P and v_f:

$$P - 0.10\omega_f = 0.4\bar{v}_f$$

$$P = \frac{0.10}{0.5}v_f + 0.4v_f = 0.6v_f \qquad \text{(e)}$$

Combining Eqs. (a) and (e) gives the desired velocity:

$$10 - 0.6v_f = 0.062v_f$$

$$v_f = \frac{10}{0.662} = 15.1 \text{ fps}$$

The tension P is found by substitution of the velocity, just determined, into Eq. (a):

$$P = 10 - 0.062(15.1) = 9.06 \text{ lb}$$

13-3 Conservation of Linear Momentum

So far, little emphasis has been placed on Newton's third law of motion: *for every action there is an equal opposite reaction.* One of the most important concepts of mechanics, however, has the third law as its basis. To illustrate, consider the two platforms shown in Fig. 13-4 to be perfectly free

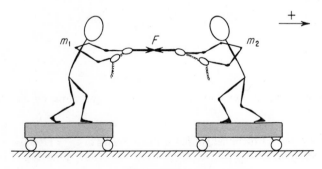

Figure 13-4

to move but for the moment to be at rest. Each man on each of the platforms holds an end of the rope. The mechanical system, consisting of the platforms, the men, and the rope, is in equilibrium with the surroundings. The forces exerted are merely those necessary to support the two masses m_1 and m_2. Now let the men pull on the rope; each exerts a force upon the other, and the platforms move. As far as the surroundings are concerned, the forces on the system are still only those required to support the two masses. The platforms move because of forces within the system. The motion can be analyzed by separating the masses into two free-bodies and writing the impulse-momentum equation for each.

Platform I: $$F(\Delta t) = m_1[(v_1)_f - 0]$$ (a)

Platform II: $$-F(\Delta t) = m_2[(v_2)_f - 0]$$ (b)

The left hand sides of these equations differ only in sign; each body exerts an equal but opposite impulse on the other.

Combined, these equations give

$$m_1[(v_1)_f - 0] = - m_2[(v_2)_f - 0]$$

or

$$m_1(v_1)_f + m_2(v_2)_f = 0$$

The conclusion drawn from the experiment is that *internal forces* acting within a system neither increase nor decrease the total momenta of the system. This conclusion, restated in terms of external forces, is the law of *conservation of momentum*: **If the external forces which act on a system are in static balance, the momentum of the system cannot change.**

EXAMPLE 5: A bullet weighing 0.5 oz is fired from a rifle weighing 9 lb. Find the recoil velocity of the rifle if the bullet leaves the muzzle with a velocity of 1800 fps.

Solution: The rifle and the bullet form a *system* in which momenta are conserved.

$$\text{initial momenta} = \text{final momenta}$$

$$0 = m_1(v_1)_f + m_2(v_2)_f$$

$$0 = \frac{9}{32.2}(v_1)_f + \frac{0.5}{16(32.2)}1800$$

$$9(v_1)_f = -\frac{900}{16}$$

$$(v_1)_f = -6.25 \text{ fps}$$

The negative sign indicates that the rifle is moving in a direction opposite to that of the bullet.

EXAMPLE 6: A 1 oz bullet is fired with a velocity of $v_1 = 1200$ fps into a block of wood weighing 10 lb. Prior to being struck, the wood is moving at right angles

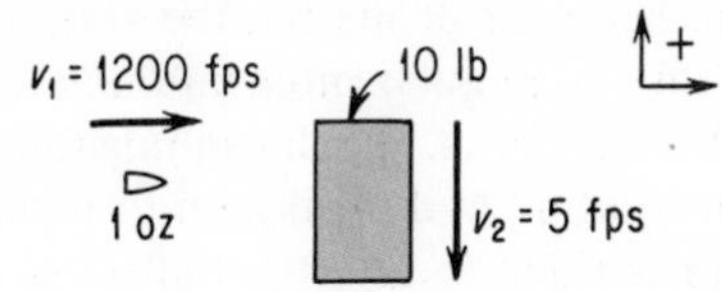

Figure 13-5

to the bullet with a velocity of $v_2 = 5$ fps as shown in Fig. 13-5. Determine the velocity of the block after the bullet becomes lodged.

Solution: Momentum, a vector quantity, is conserved in both the x- and y-directions.

$$\text{(initial momenta)}_x = \text{(final momenta)}_x$$

$$(m_1 v_1)_x + (m_2 v_2)_x = (m_1 + m_2)v_x$$

$$\frac{1}{16(32.2)}1200 + 0 = \frac{10.063}{32.2}v_x$$

$$v_x = \frac{1200}{16(10.063)} = 7.45 \text{ fps}$$

and

$$\text{(initial momenta)}_y = \text{(final momenta)}_y$$

$$(m_1 v_1)_y + (m_2 v_2)_y = (m_1 + m_2)v_y$$

$$0 - \frac{10(5)}{32.2} = \frac{10.063}{32.2}v_y$$

$$v_y = \frac{10(5)}{10.063} = -4.97 \text{ fps}$$

The final velocity of the block is the vector sum of v_x and v_y:

$$v = \sqrt{v_x^2 + v_y^2} = \sqrt{(7.45)^2 + (-4.94)^2} = 8.96 \text{ fps}$$

$$\theta = \text{arc tan } \frac{v_y}{v_x} = \text{arc tan } \frac{4.97}{7.45}$$

$$\theta = 33.7 \text{ deg } \triangleleft$$

13-4 Conservation of Angular Momentum

The law of *conservation of angular momentum* can be demonstrated by performing an experiment analogous to that performed for linear systems. In effect, the conclusion drawn from the experiment would be a statement of the law: **If the external torques which act an a system are in static balance, the angular momentum of the system cannot change.**

An example of this law in action is the whirling figure skater who has complete control over his angular velocity. When his arms are extended, his angular velocity is low; when his arms are drawn close to his body, his angular velocity is high. Moment of inertia, the variable that changes, does so from within the system and angular momentum is conserved.

The principle of conservation of angular momentum applies to direction as well as magnitude; a rotating body will tend to maintain a constant axis. Gun barrels are sometimes rifled to give the bullet "spin", which helps it to maintain a straight path. Stabilizers in ships and missiles are principally nothing more than large rotating inertias whch resist, forcibly, any change in the direction of their axes.

A translating particle of mass m can possess angular momentum with respect to a point. This angular momentum, called *moment of momentum*, is the product *mvr;* r is the perpendicular distance between the velocity vector and the reference point. The bullet which strikes the pivoted bar shown in Fig. 13-6 illustrates this situation. By the law of conservation of angular momentum *mvr*, the bullet's initial moment of mementum must equal the angular momentum $\sum I\omega$ of the rod and imbedded bullet after impact.

EXAMPLE 7: Assume the pivoted rod shown in Fig. 13-6 to have a length of 6 ft, to weigh 50 lb, and to be at rest. A bullet weighing 1 oz is fired with a velocity of 2000 fps at the rod and becomes embedded in it. Find the angular velocity after impact.

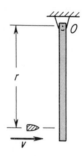

Figure 13-6

Solution: Angular momentum is conserved; the moment of momentum of the bullet prior to impact must equal the angular momentum of the bar after impact. The mass of the lodged bullet will be neglected as too small to consider in computing the moment of inertia of the 50 lb bar.

$$I_o = \frac{1}{3}ml^2 = \frac{1}{3}\frac{50}{g}(6)^2 = \frac{600}{g} \text{ slug ft}^2$$

By the law of conservation of angular momentum

$$mvr = I_o\omega$$

$$\frac{1}{16g}2000(6) = \frac{600}{g}\omega$$

$$\omega = \frac{20}{16} = 1.25 \text{ rad per sec}$$

EXAMPLE 8: The spin of the satellite shown in Fig. 13-7 may be controlled, as it travels through space, by weights fastened to cords which can be extended or retracted from within the satellite. Assume the satellite to have a moment of inertia of 0.5 slug ft² and each of the four 0.25 lb weights to be initially extended to $r = 1$ ft. In this position, the angular velocity of the body is 10 rad per sec. Determine the angular velocity of the satellite if an internal mechanism extends the weights to $r = 3$ ft.

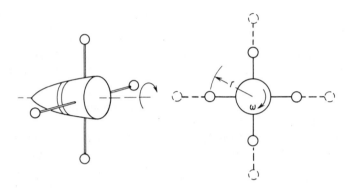

Figure 13-7

Solution: The law of conservation of angular momentum is used.

[angular momentum]$_o$ = [angular momentum]$_f$

$$I_o \omega_o = I_f \omega_f$$

$$\left[0.5 + \frac{4(0.25)}{32.2} (1)^2 \right] 10 = \left[0.5 + \frac{4(0.25)}{32.2} (3)^2 \right] \omega_f$$

Where the moment of inertia of each weight is mr^2

$$5.3 = 0.78 \omega_f$$

$$\omega_f = \frac{5.3}{0.78} = 6.8 \text{ rad per sec}$$

Thus, the angular velocity is reduced from 10 rad per sec to 6.8 rad per sec. If the weights are drawn inward to $r = 1$ ft, the initial angular velocity will be restored.

13-5 Elastic Impact

Up to this point in the discussion, only *inelastic* types of impact have been considered. The bullet that struck the block of wood always managed to become embedded. What happens when colliding objects rebound? The experience of countless observations has shown that, when two bodies collide, the negative ratio of their relative velocities after impact to their relative

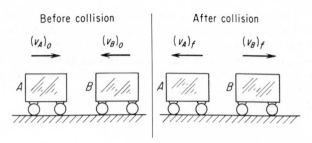

Figure 13-8

velocities before impact is a constant. If A and B shown in Fig. 13-8 have initial velocities $(v_A)_o$ and $(v_B)_o$ and final velocities $(v_A)_f$ and $(v_B)_f$ respectively, then

$$-\frac{(v_{A/B})_f}{(v_{A/B})_o} = -\frac{(v_A)_f - (v_B)_f}{(v_A)_o - (v_B)_o} = \text{constant} = e \qquad (13\text{-}6)$$

The constant of proportionality e, called the *coefficient of restitution*, is a positive number which lies between zero and one. When objects collide and stick together, their relative velocity after impact is zero and, therefore, $e = 0$; if their relative velocity after impact is exactly equal to their relative velocity before impact (this could happen only in theory), $e = 1$. The former case illustrates a *perfectly inelastic collision*, the latter, a *perfectly elastic collision*.

Physical properties of the two bodies involved in the collision determine the value of e. In terms of approximate values, the coefficient is 0.9 for steel on steel, 0.2 for wood on wood, and 0.4 for steel on concrete.

In the analysis of impact and rebound, the data given generally consists of the initial velocity of each body and the coefficient of restitution that applies. The final velocity of each body must be determined. Therefore, two algebraic equations are necessary for a solution: one obtained through use of the law of conservation of momentum and the other obtained through use of the defining relationship for the coefficient of restitution:

(1) initial linear momenta = final linear momenta

(2) $e = -\dfrac{(v_A)_f - (v_B)_f}{(v_A)_o - (v_B)_o}$

EXAMPLE 9: Determine the rebound velocities of the two bodies similar to those shown in Fig. 13-8. Body A is moving to the right with a velocity of 20 fps and body B to the left with a velocity of 40 fps. The weights of bodies A and B are 50 lb and 100 lb respectively, and the coefficient of restitution is $e = 0.60$.

Solution: By the conservation of linear momentum

[linear momenta]$_o$ = [linear momenta]$_f$

$$\frac{50}{g}(20) + \frac{100}{g}(-40) = \frac{50}{g}(v_A)_f + \frac{100}{g}(v_B)_f$$

$$(v_A)_f + 2(v_B)_f = -60 \tag{a}$$

The velocity data are substituted in the equation which defines the coefficient of restitution.

$$e = -\frac{(v_A)_f - (v_B)_f}{(v_A)_o - (v_B)_o}$$

$$(v_A)_f - (v_B)_f = -(0.60)[(v_A)_o - (v_B)_o] = -0.60\,[20 - (-40)]$$

$$(v_A)_f - (v_B)_f = -36 \tag{b}$$

Simultaneous solution of Eqs. (a) and (b) gives the desired final velocities:

$$(v_A)_f = -44 \text{ fps}$$

$$(v_B)_f = -8 \text{ fps}$$

Both bodies have negative velocities, indicating that they are moving to the left, with body A "running away" from body B.

EXAMPLE 10: A golf ball, dropped from a height of 25 ft onto the pavement, rebounds to a height of 16 ft. Determine the coefficient of restitution between the ball and the pavement.

Solution: The pavement, body B in this case, can be assumed to be unaffected by the impact; its velocity before and after collision is zero. The velocity of the golf ball just prior to striking the pavement is found by work and energy methods:

$$U = \Delta T$$

$$Wh = \frac{1}{2}\frac{W}{g}(v_f^2 - v_o^2)$$

$$(v_A)_o = \sqrt{2gh} = \sqrt{(2g)25}, \text{ downward}$$

Since the ball rises to a height of 16 ft, its velocity after impact must be

$$(v_A)_f = \sqrt{2gh} = \sqrt{(2g)16}, \text{ upward}$$

Assuming "upward" to be positive, the coefficient of restitution is

$$e = -\frac{(v_A)_f - (v_B)_f}{(v_A)_o - (v_B)_o} = \frac{\sqrt{(2g)16}}{\sqrt{(2g)25}} = 0.8$$

PROBLEMS

13-1. Determine the impulse in units of lb sec that is equivalent to (a) 10 lb acting for 2 sec; (b) 50 lb acting for 0.3 minutes; (c) 3 tons acting for 500 microseconds; (d) 500 lb acting for 20 milliseconds.

Note: 1 microsecond = 10^{-6} seconds
1 millisecond = 10^{-3} seconds

13-2. The 128.8 lb body is acted upon by a force that varies with time as shown in Fig. P13-2. If the body is initially at rest, determine the velocity after (a) 2 sec; (b) 4 sec; (c) 6 sec.

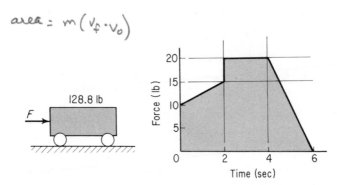

$$area = m\left(v_f - v_0\right)$$

128.8 lb

F

Figure P13-2

13-3. Solve Prob. 13-2 for an elapsed time of 6 sec if the body has an initial velocity of (a) 20 fps to the right; (b) 30 fps to the left.

13-4. An airplane traveling horizontally with a speed of 300 mph uses two rocket assist engines to increase its speed. Each engine exerts a constant thrust of 5000 lb on the plane. Determine the velocity of the plane if it weighs 15,000 lb and if the engines are fired for 4 sec.

13-5. A golf ball weighing 1.62 oz acquires a velocity of 200 fps after it is struck. If the ball is in contact with the club for 0.04 sec, determine the average impulsive force acting during the impact. $F\,\Delta T = m\left(v_f - v_0\right)$

13-6. A rifle bullet weighing 0.5 oz acquires a velocity of 2000 fps in the 2 milliseconds it is in the barrel. Find the average impulsive force acting on the bullet.

13-7. A rocket, used to decrease the speed of a 322 lb satellite, exerts an opposing thrust of 40,000 lb for a period of 5 sec. Determine the velocity of the satellite after the 5 sec period if it is initially traveling at a speed of 70,000 mph.

13-8. A particle of mass weighs 8.05 lb. Although it is initially at rest, it is free to move in the x–y plane shown in Fig. P13-8. If two forces, F_x and F_y, act on the particle, find the velocity it acquires after 5 sec.

13-9. Compare the momentum and the kinetic energy of a 2000 lb automobile traveling with a velocity of 10 fps to a 10 lb shell traveling with a velocity of 2000 fps. $M = m\,\Delta v$

13-10. A 2 oz bullet, fired through a plank, has a velocity of 1800 fps when it is approaching the plank. Find the impulse acting on the bullet if it leaves the plank with a velocity of 600 fps. no time given

$$F\,\Delta T = m\left(v_f - v_0\right)$$

answer = 16 sec

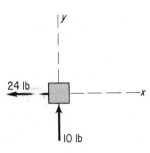

Figure P13-8

13-11. A 50 lb block is released on the inclined plane in Fig. P13-11 and allowed to slide for 3 sec. Determine the velocity that the block acquires if the coefficient of kinetic friction between it and the plane is $\mu_k = 0.20$.

50 lb

5

12

Figure P13-11

13-12. Find the angular momentum of a 644 lb flywheel which is rotating about a centroidal axis with an angular velocity of 1200 rpm. The radius of gyration of the flywheel is $\bar{k} = 12$ in. $\Sigma T_o (\Delta t) = I_o (\omega_f \cdot \omega_i)$ *lb ft sec .*

13-13. If the bearings of the flywheel described in Prob. 13-12 were poorly aligned and produced a retarding frictional moment of 10 lb ft, how long would it take the flywheel to come to rest? $-10 (\Delta t) = 20 (0 - 125.6)$

13-14. When the armature of a generator, weighing 6440 lb, was driven by a torque 250 lb ft, it increased its speed from 10 rad per sec to 40 rad per sec in 12 sec. Find the radius of gyration of the armature.

13-15. A horizontal force $F = 10$ lb acts as shown in Fig. P13-15 on the axle of a 64.4 lb solid disk. The disk is free to roll without slipping and is initially at rest. Determine the velocity v_o after an elapsed time of 15 sec.

trans: $\Sigma F (\Delta t) = m (v_f - v_o)$
$(10-f) 15 = \frac{64.4}{g} (v_f - 0)$

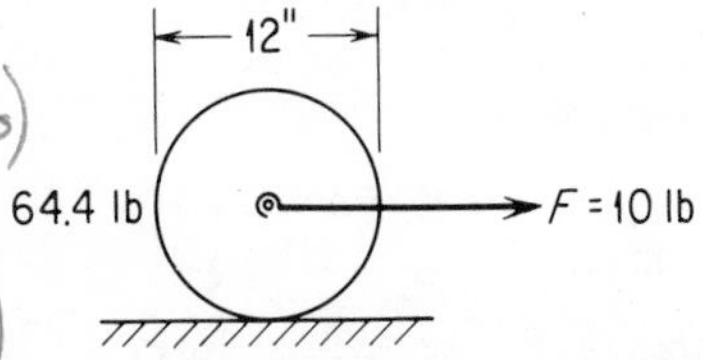

Rota: $\Sigma T(\Delta t) = I (\omega_f - \omega_o)$
$\frac{6}{12} f (15) = .25 (\omega_f - 0)$

Mo: $v_f = r\omega_f = .5 \omega_f$

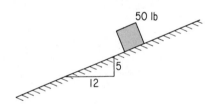

12"

64.4 lb

$F = 10$ lb

Figure P13-15

$f = .03 \omega_f$

13-16. Solve Prob. 13-15 if the initial velocity of the center of the disk is (a) 10 fps to the right; (b) 10 fps to the left.

13-17. A solid homogeneous sphere of weight W is released on a plane inclined at an angle of 45 deg with the horizontal. Determine the velocity of the center of the sphere 2 sec later. Assume the sphere to roll without slipping.

13-18. A 10 lb weight W_A is suspended from a cord which is wrapped around a 64.4 lb disk as shown in Fig. P13-18. If the radius of gyration of the disk is $k_o = 4$ in., find the velocity of the weight 2 sec after motion impends.

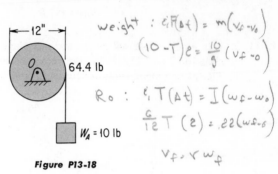

weight : $\xi F(\Delta t) = m(v_f - v_o)$

$(10 - T)\ell = \frac{10}{g}(v_f - o)$

R_o : $\xi_i T(\Delta t) = I(w_f - w_o)$

$\frac{c}{12} T (2) = .22(w_f - 6)$

$v_f = r\, w_f$

Figure P13-18

13-19. Solve Prob. 13-18 if the bearings impose a resisting frictional moment of 1.5 lb ft on the disk.

13-20. Determine the couple which must be applied to the disk shown in Fig. P13-20 if the 50 lb weight is to acquire a velocity of 20 fps in 5 sec from rest. The moment of inertia of the disk is 4 slug ft², and the coefficient of kinetic friction between the weight and the plane is $\mu_k = 0.20$.

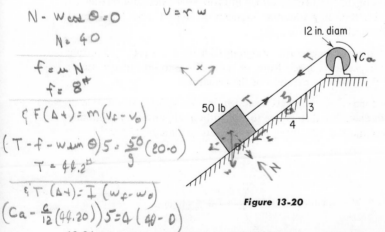

$N - W\cos\theta = 0$

$V = r\, w$

$N = 40$

$f = \mu N$

$f = 8^{\#}$

$\xi F(\Delta t) = m(v_f - v_o)$

$(T - f - w\sin\theta)5 = \frac{50}{g}(20 - 0)$

$T = 44.2^{b}$

$\xi T (\Delta t) = I (w_f - w_o)$

$\left(C_a - \frac{c}{12}(44.20)\right)5 = 4\left(40 - 0\right)$

12 in. diam

$\downarrow C_a$

50 lb

$\begin{smallmatrix}3\\4\end{smallmatrix}$

Figure 13-20

13-21. A bullet weighing 0.5 oz is fired from a 6 lb rifle. Determine the recoil velocity of the rifle if the muzzle velocity of the bullet is 1800 fps.

13-22. Find the recoil velocity of a gun weighing 50 tons if it fires a shell weighing 250 lb with a muzzle velocity of 1200 fps. $= m_1 (v_1)_a + m_e (v_e)_a$

13-23. A bullet weighs 1 oz. When it is fired into a block of wood weighing 6 lb, it becomes embedded. If the block is initially at rest on a horizontal plane, determine its velocity after the impact. Assume the velocity of the bullet to be 1800 fps before striking the block. $(m_1 v_1) + (m_2 v_2) = (m_1 + m_2) v$

13-24. If the coefficient of kinetic friction between the block and the plane in Prob. 13-23 is $\mu_k = 0.40$, determine how far the block will move before coming to rest.

13-25. Determine the velocity of the 80 lb cart in Fig. P13-25 if, prior to receiving a 200 lb load, it is traveling with a velocity of 30 fps.

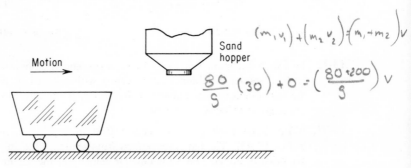

Motion

Sand hopper

$(m_1 v_1) + (m_2 v_2) = (m_1 + m_2) v$

$\dfrac{80}{g} (30) + 0 = \left(\dfrac{80 + 200}{g}\right) v$

Figure P13-25

13-26. A railroad boxcar weighing 80 tons is coupled to a second boxcar weighing 50 tons. Just prior to coupling, the first car is traveling with a speed of 2 mph and the second car is stationary. Find the velocity of the two boxcars after coupling.

13-27. How much energy is lost in the coupling of the two boxcars described in Prob. 13-26? Account for this loss.

13-28. A man weighing 180 lb jumps off a dock onto a stationary boat weighing 400 lb. The horizontal velocity component of the man as he leaves the dock is 10 fps. Assuming that he does not fall out of the boat, find his velocity after landing. $(m_1 v_1) + (m_2 v_2) = (m_1 + m_2) v$

13-29. A bullet weighing 2 oz is fired with a velocity of 2000 fps into a 10 lb block of wood that is moving with a velocity of 40 fps perpendicular to the path of the bullet. Find the velocity of the combination after impact.

13-30. A 2 oz bullet is fired with a velocity of 2400 fps into a 15 lb sandbox mounted on wheels as shown in Fig. P13-30. After impact the box strikes a spring and is brought to rest in a distance of 6 in. Find the constant of the spring.

orig K.E + chang in K.E.

U = ΔT

find v

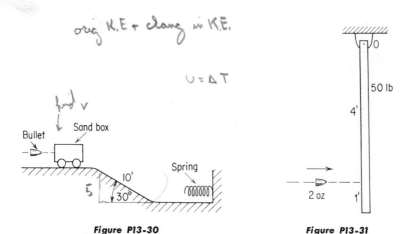

Figure P13-30   **Figure P13-31**

13-31. The 50 lb bar shown in Fig. P13-31 is suspended from a smooth bearing at O. A bullet weighing 2 oz traveling with a speed of 2500 fps strikes the bar and becomes embedded. If the bar is initially at rest, determine the angular velocity after impact.   *m vr = I_o ω*   *r=4 I=5*

13-32. A 2 oz bullet traveling at a speed of 2500 fps strikes a 25 lb bar as shown in Fig. P13-32. The bar is suspended from a smooth bearing and is stationary prior to impact. Find the angular velocity of the bar just after impact.

I = $\frac{1}{3} m l^2$

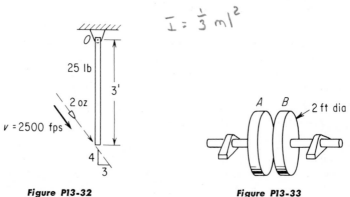

Figure P13-32   **Figure P13-33**

13-33. The "clutch" shown in Fig. P13-33 consists of two identical 128.8 lb solid homogeneous disks which are engaged by sliding the axle of disk B towards disk A. Disk A has an initial angular velocity of 1800 rpm; prior to contact, disk B is stationary. Find (a) the final angular velocity of the system after the disks reach a common speed, and (b) the energy lost during slippage.

13-34. Determine, in Prob. 13-33, the angular impulse that disk A exerts on disk B during slippage.

$$\left(I_o\right) \omega_o = \left(I_1 + I_c\right) \omega_f$$

$$KE = \frac{1}{2} I_o \omega^2 \qquad \text{take difference}$$

13-35. In Fig. P13-35, the 50 lb block fastened to a slack cord is dropped from a height of 4 ft. Find the angular velocity of the disk at the instant the cord becomes taut. The disk, a solid homogeneous cylinder, weighs 64.4 lb and is supported in smooth bearings.

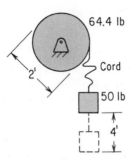

64.4 lb

2'

Cord

50 lb

4'

Figure P13-35

13-36. A stack of 12 in. LP records is rotating freely on a turntable at $33\frac{1}{3}$ rpm when a group of six more records is dropped suddenly on the stack. Determine the angular velocity of the system when slipping ceases. Assume the moment of inertia of the original system to be 0.40 slug ft², and the moment of inertia of the six records to be 0.05 slug ft².

13-37. Explain what would happen to the length of a day if the earth were to expand slightly at its equator.

13-38. A small 1 lb weight is fastened to a length of cord which in turn passes through a small hole in the horizontal table as shown in Fig. P13-38. When the weight is set in motion, it whirls about in a 2 ft diameter orbit maintained by a force F acting on the free end of the cord. The tangential velocity of the weight in this position is 15 fps. Find (a) the velocity of the weight if 3 in. of cord are drawn through the hole; (b) the work done

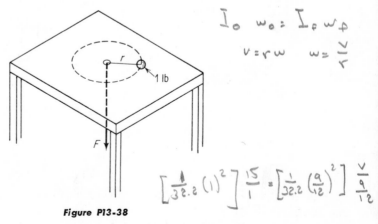

$I_o \, w_o = I_p \, w_p$

$v = r w \qquad w = \frac{v}{r}$

$\left[\frac{1}{32.2} (1)^2 \right] \frac{15}{1} = \left[\frac{1}{32.2} \left(\frac{9}{12} \right)^2 \right] \frac{v}{\frac{9}{12}}$

1 lb

F

Figure P13-38

by the force in Part (a). Hint: *Relate the work done to the change in kinetic energy.*

13-39. A 1.6 oz golf ball dropped from a height of 25 ft rebounds to a height of 16 ft. Determine the value of the coefficient of restitution.

13-40. How much kinetic energy does the golf ball lose in Prob. 13-39? Account for the loss.

13-41. Determine the height of the second bounce of the golf ball in Prob. 13-39.

13-42. An automobile weighing 3220 lb and traveling with a velocity of 30 mph collides with a second car, of equal weight, but stationary. Determine the velocity of each car after impact if the coefficient of restitution is $e = 0.30$.

13-43. Determine the loss in kinetic energy in the collision described in Prob. 13-42.

13-44. Body A, traveling to the right with a velocity of 30 fps, collides with body B, which is traveling to the left with a velocity of 10 fps. Determine the velocity of each body after impact if $W_A = 300$ lb, $W_B = 150$ lb, and $e = 0.80$.

$-10 fps$ $+\longrightarrow$

---

39. $(v_A)_0 = \sqrt{2gh} = \sqrt{2g}\,25$

     $(v_A)_f = \sqrt{2gh} = \sqrt{2g}\,16$

     $c = -\dfrac{(v_A)_f (v_B)_f}{(v_A)_0 - (v_B)_0} = \dfrac{\sqrt{2g}\,16}{\sqrt{2g}\,25} = \dfrac{4}{5} = 0.8$

41      $e = -\dfrac{(v_{A_f}) - (v_B)_f}{(v_{A_0}) - (v_A)_0}$

     $.8 = \dfrac{\sqrt{2g}\,(5)}{\sqrt{2g}\,(10)} = \dfrac{\sqrt{5}}{4}$

42. $(m_A v_{A_0}) + (m_B v_{B_0}) = (m_A v_{A_f}) + (m_B v_{B_f})$ cancel g's

     $e = -\dfrac{(v_A)_f - (v_B)_f}{(v_A)_0 - (v_B)_0}$

     $v_A + v_0 = ?$

     $(v_A)_f - (v_B)_f = -(0.30)\left[(v_A)_0 - (v_B)_0\right]$

Chapter 14

MECHANICAL
VIBRATIONS

Designers and operators of mechanical equipment are aware of the importance of an understanding of mechanical vibrations. Machines have destroyed themselves, bridges have collapsed, and aircraft have exploded in mid-air because of undesirable vibrations. A few aspects of the vibration problem will be introduced in this chapter.

14-1 Periodic Motion

Any motion that repeats itself after a given time interval is called *periodic motion*. The swinging pendulum, the bobbing boat, and the daily tides are examples of periodic motion. Each repetition of motion is called a *cycle*, and the time interval required to repeat one cycle is termed the *period*. The number of cycles of motion that are completed in a unit of time is referred to as the *frequency*. Mathematically, the frequency is the reciprocal of the period.

$$f = \frac{1}{T} \tag{14-1}$$

14-2 Harmonic Motion

Some types of mechanical vibrations are closely related, mathematically, to rotational motion; these are referred to as harmonic vibrations. For example, the mechanism illustrated in Fig. 14-1, called a *scotch yoke*, converts rotational motion into periodic vertical motion. The pin which extends outward from the face of the disk engages in the slotted frame; the frame moves repeatedly, up and down, as the disk rotates. The frame undergoes one complete cycle of motion for every revolution of the disk. The period of the motion, then, is the time interval required for 1 revolution, or

$$T = \frac{\theta}{\omega} = \frac{2\pi \; rad}{\omega \; \text{rad/sec}} = \frac{2\pi}{\omega} \sec$$

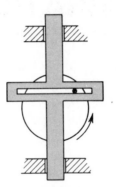

Figure 14-1

where ω is the angular velocity of the disk in rad per sec. The frequency of the motion is the reciprocal of the period.

$$f = \frac{1}{T} = \frac{\omega}{2\pi} \text{cps (cycles per sec)} \tag{14-2}$$

The vertical motion of the frame is controlled by the revolving pin; therefore the frame and the pin have the same vertical displacement y, the same vertical velocity v_y, and the same vertical acceleration a_y. These three components of motion are shown in Fig. 14-2. A, the distance of the pin from the center of the circle, is called the *amplitude* of the vibration. The angular displacement θ of the pin can be expressed in terms of the angular velocity and the time, thus

$$\theta = \omega t$$

The displacement, velocity, and acceleration of the frame, in terms of ωt and A, is

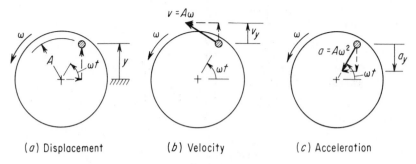

(a) Displacement   (b) Velocity   (c) Acceleration

Figure 14-2

$$y = A \sin \theta = A \sin (\omega t) \tag{14-3}$$

$$v_y = A\omega \cos \theta = A\omega \cos (\omega t) \tag{14-4}$$

$$a_y = -A\omega^2 \sin \theta = -A\omega^2 \sin (\omega t) \tag{14-5}$$

The combination of Eqs. (14-3) and (14-5) gives the defining equation of harmonic motion:

$$a_y = -\omega^2 y \tag{14-6}$$

Verbally, Eq. (14-6) states: *in harmonic motion, the magnitude of the acceleration is proportional to the magnitude of the displacement and is directed opposite to that of the displacement.*

Equation (14-2) defines the frequency of the motion in terms of the angular velocity ω.

$$f = \frac{\omega}{2\pi}$$

Solving for ω and squaring gives

$$\omega^2 = 4\pi^2 f^2$$

Substitution of this value into Eq. (14-6) gives the acceleration a_y in terms of the frequency:

$$a_y = (4\pi^2 f^2)y \tag{14-7}$$

14-3 The Mass and Spring System

Elastic forces can cause harmonic motion. As an illustration, consider the weight W, which is suspended from a spring whose constant is k. The system is shown in Fig. 14-3. The spring is statically stretched an amount y_o; the spring force which results is in equilibrium with the weight force of

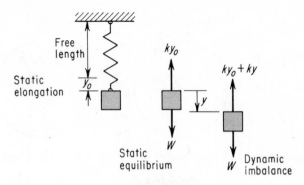

Figure 14-3

the body:

$$W = ky_0$$

Suppose that the weight is pulled down an additional distance y and released. The system is no longer in equilibrium; motion begins, and with it an acceleration. The acceleration is found through the use of the second law of motion:

$$\Sigma F = ma$$

$$W - ky_0 - ky = \frac{W}{g}a_y \qquad \text{(a)}$$

Since $W = ky_0$, Eq. (a) becomes

$$a_y = -\left(\frac{kg}{W}\right)y$$

This equation has the same mathematical form as the defining equation for harmonic motion, $a_y = (4\pi^2 f^2)y$. Therefore

$$4\pi^2 f^2 = \frac{kg}{W}$$

Solving for the frequency gives

$$f = \frac{1}{2\pi}\sqrt{\frac{kg}{W}} \qquad \text{(14-8)}$$

EXAMPLE 1: A weight of 16.1 lb is suspended from a spring whose constant is $k = 1200$ lb per ft. Determine the frequency and period of the vibration.

Solution: Equation (14-8) is used to find the frequency.

$$f = \frac{1}{2\pi}\sqrt{\frac{kg}{W}} = \frac{1}{2\pi}\sqrt{\frac{1200(32.2)}{16.1}} = 7.8 \text{ cps}$$

cps

or

$$f_n = 3.13\sqrt{\frac{1}{\delta_{ST}}} \quad \text{in inches}$$

The period is

$$T = \frac{1}{f} = \frac{1}{7.8} = 0.13 \text{ sec per cycle}$$

EXAMPLE 2: Determine the maximum velocity and maximum acceleration of the weight in Example 1 if the amplitude of the vibration is 1.5 in.

Solution: The velocity of a body undergoing harmonic motion is given by Eq. (14-4):

$$v_y = A\omega \cos(\omega t) = A(2\pi f)\cos(\omega t)$$

The velocity assumes a maximum value when $\cos(\omega t) \doteq 1$

therefore
$$(v_y)_{\max} = A(2\pi f) = \frac{1.5}{12}(2\pi)7.8$$

$$= 6.13 \text{ fps}$$

The maximum acceleration is found by replacing the displacement y by the amplitude A in Eq. (14-7). The minus sign is disregarded, since only a magnitude is required.

must be in feet $\frac{1.5}{12}$

accel
$$(a_y)_{\max} = 4\pi^2 f^2 A = 4\pi^2(7.8)^2\frac{1.5}{12}$$

$$= 300 \text{ fps}^2$$

Large accelerations, like the one just computed, are always accompanied by tremendous periodic forces. It is this type of force which so often causes disastrous mechanical damage.

14-4 Oscillating Pendulums

Pendulums which oscillate with small amplitudes execute harmonic motion. Consider the system, shown in Fig. 14-4, which consists of small weight W fastened to a light cord of length l. The pendulum is oscillating; at the

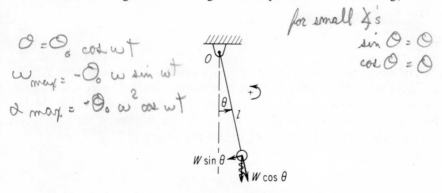

for small θ's

$\sin \theta = \theta$

$\cos \theta = \theta$

$\theta = \theta_0 \cos \omega t$

$\omega_{\max} = -\theta_0 \omega \sin \omega t$

$\alpha_{\max} = -\theta_0 \omega^2 \cos \omega t$

Figure 14-4

instant shown it has an angular displacement of θ measured from the equilibrium position. A torque, equal to the product of the weight component $W \sin \theta$ and the lever arm l, tends to return the body to the equilibrium position.

The second law of motion is used to find the angular acceleration α.

$$\Sigma T_o = I_o \alpha$$

Substitution of the data gives

$$-W(\sin \theta)l = \frac{W}{g} l^2 \alpha$$

The sine of a small angle is approximately equal to the magnitude of the angle expressed in radians.

$$\sin \theta = \theta$$

Therefore

$$-Wl\theta = \frac{W}{g} l^2 \alpha$$

$$\alpha = -\frac{g}{l}\theta$$

This equation obeys the definition of harmonic motion: the acceleration is proportional to the displacement and in a direction opposed to the displacement. The constant of proportionality g/l, is equal, then, to the square of ω.

$$\omega^2 = \frac{g}{l}$$

The frequency, defined by Eq. (14-2), is

$$f = \frac{\omega}{2\pi} = \frac{1}{2\pi}\sqrt{\frac{g}{l}} \tag{14-9}$$

where the period, T, is

$$T = \frac{1}{f} = 2\pi\sqrt{\frac{l}{g}} \quad \text{sec.}$$

The mechanical system just described is called a *simple pendulum*. When the mass of an oscillating body is distributed, rather than concentrated, the system is called a *compound pendulum*. This is illustrated in Fig. 14-5. Newton's second law of motion is applied to the distributed mass by taking moments about the point of suspension O.

$$\Sigma T_o = I_o \alpha$$

$$-W(\sin \theta)c = I_o \alpha$$

where c is the distance from the point of suspension to the center of gravity of the body.

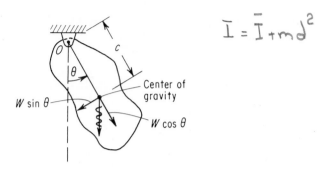

$$I = \bar{I} + md^2$$

Figure 14-5

For small angles, $\sin \theta = \theta$; this reduces the equation of motion to

$$\alpha = -\frac{Wc}{I_o}\theta$$

The frequency of the motion, therefore, is

$$f = \frac{1}{2\pi}\sqrt{\frac{Wc}{I_o}} \qquad \text{use transfer} \qquad (14\text{-}10)$$

EXAMPLE 3: Determine the length of a simple pendulum which has a frequency of 1 cps.

Solution: Equation (14-9) is used to compute the frequency.

$$f = \frac{1}{2\pi}\sqrt{\frac{g}{l}}$$

$$1 = \frac{1}{2\pi}\sqrt{\frac{32.2}{l}}$$

$$l = \frac{32.2}{4\pi^2} = 0.816 \text{ ft or } 9.79 \text{ in.}$$

EXAMPLE 4: An automotive connecting rod weighing 4 lb is suspended from a knife edge as shown in Fig. 14-6. The center of gravity is 5 in. below the knife edge. Determine the radius of gyration about the point of suspension if the connecting rod oscillates with a frequency of 2 cps.

Solution: The moment of inertia about the point of suspension, in terms of the radius of gyration k_o, is

$$I_o = \frac{W}{g}k_o^2$$

The data are substituted into Eq. (14-10):

$$f = \frac{1}{2\pi}\sqrt{\frac{Wc}{I_o}}$$

$$2 = \frac{1}{2\pi}\sqrt{\frac{W5/12}{Wk_o^2/g}}$$

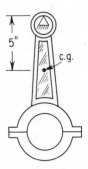

Figure 14-6

The frequency of the connecting rod does not depend upon its weight, since W appears in both the numerator and the denominator of the fraction.

$$(4\pi^2) = \frac{32.2(5)}{k_o^2(12)}$$

$$k_o^2 = \frac{32.2(5)}{12(4\pi)^2} = 0.085$$

$$k_o = \sqrt{0.085} = 0.292 \text{ ft or } 3.5 \text{ in.}$$

PROBLEMS

14-1. Determine the period of a mechanical vibration which has a frequency of 120 cps. $T = \frac{1}{f}$

14-2. A particular harmonic vibration has a period of 0.005 sec. Determine the frequency in (a) cycles per second; (b) cycles per minute; (c) radians per second.

14-3. A machine part that is vibrating with harmonic motion has a frequency of 150 cps and an amplitude of 0.05 in. Determine the maximum acceleration due to the vibration. $a = 4\pi^2 f^2 A$

14-4. An 8.05 lb weight is suspended from a spring which has a constant of 40 lb per in. Determine the frequency of vibration of the system.

14-5. A 1 lb weight attached to a light spring elongates it 0.50 in. Determine the natural frequency of vibration of the system. $f = kx$ $f_n = 3.13\sqrt{\frac{1}{\delta_{st}}}$

14-6. When a 4 lb weight is attached to a spring, it vibrates with a frequency of 120 cpm. Determine the constant of the spring.

14-7. The 6000 lb platform shown in Fig. P14-7 is suspended from four identical springs. If the static deflection of the platform is 1 in., determine the constant of each spring and the frequency of vibration of the platform.

$F = kx$

$f_n = 3.13\sqrt{\frac{1}{\delta_{st}}}$

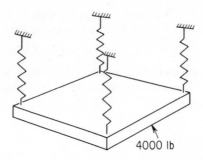

Figure P14-7

14-8. By what per cent will the frequency change if an additional 1000 lb is placed on the platform of Prob. 14-7?

14-9. Determine the frequency of vibration of the 4 lb weight shown in Fig. P14-9. The springs are unstretched when the weight is in the equilibrium position.

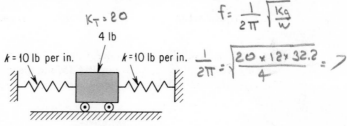

$K_T = 20$

4 lb

$k = 10$ lb per in. $k = 10$ lb per in.

$$f = \frac{1}{2\pi}\sqrt{\frac{kg}{w}}$$

$$\frac{1}{2\pi} = \sqrt{\frac{20 \times 12 \times 32.2}{4}} = 7$$

Figure P14-9

14-10. Determine the natural frequency of the weight in Prob. 14-9 if the springs are each initially stretched 2 in.

14-11. The small weight shown in Fig. P14-11 is supported by a 4 ft rod of negligible mass. Determine the period of this *simple pendulum*.

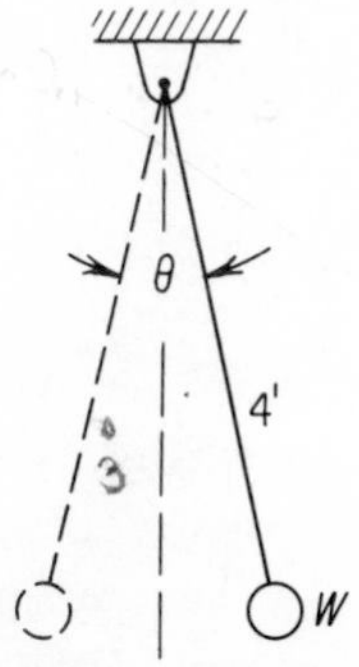

$$T = 2\pi\sqrt{\frac{\ell}{g}} = 2\pi\sqrt{\frac{4}{32.2}}$$

θ

4'

3

W

Figure P14-11

14-12. If the weight of Prob. 14-11 swings through an arc of 6 deg, determine its maximum velocity and maximum acceleration.

14-13. Determine the length of a simple pendulum if it has a period of 4 sec.

14-14. A thin homogeneous disk, weighing 16.1 lb, is supported as shown in Fig. P14-14. Determine the frequency of oscillation if it swings through a very small arc.

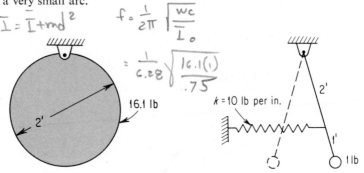

$$I = \bar{I} + md^2 \qquad f = \frac{1}{2\pi}\sqrt{\frac{wc}{I_o}}$$

$$= \frac{1}{6.28}\sqrt{\frac{16.1(1)}{.75}}$$

16.1 lb $k = 10$ lb per in.

Figure P14-14   **Figure P14-15**

14-15. A small 1 lb weight is suspended from a 3 ft rod of negligible mass. A spring is fastened as shown in Fig. P14-15, and the system oscillates through a very small arc. Determine the frequency of the resulting vibration.

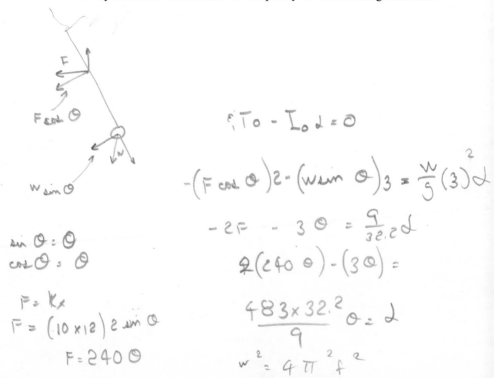

$$\Sigma T_o - I_o \ddot{\alpha} = 0$$

$$-(F\cos\theta)2 - (w\sin\theta)3 = \frac{w}{g}(3)^2\ddot{\alpha}$$

$$-2F - 3\theta = \frac{9}{32.2}\ddot{\alpha}$$

$$2(240\,\theta) - (3\theta) =$$

$$\frac{483 \times 32.2}{9}\theta = \ddot{\alpha}$$

$$w^2 = 4\pi^2 f^2$$

$F\cos\theta$

$w\sin\theta$

$\sin\theta = \theta$

$\cos\theta = \theta$

$F = kx$

$F = (.10 \times 12)\,2\sin\theta$

$F = 240\,\theta$

APPENDIX

Table 1. Natural Trigonometric Functions

sin

	.0	.1	.2	.3	.4	.5	.6	.7	.8	.9		
0°	.0000	.0017	.0035	.0052	.0070	.0087	.0105	.0122	.0140	.0157	.0175	89°
1°	.0175	.0192	.0209	.0227	.0244	.0262	.0279	.0297	.0314	.0332	.0349	88°
2°	.0349	.0366	.0384	.0401	.0419	.0436	.0454	.0471	.0488	.0506	.0523	87°
3°	.0523	.0541	.0558	.0576	.0593	.0610	.0628	.0645	.0663	.0680	.0698	86°
4°	.0698	.0715	.0732	.0750	.0767	.0785	.0802	.0819	.0837	.0854	.0872	85°
5°	.0872	.0889	.0906	.0924	.0941	.0958	.0976	.0993	.1011	.1028	.1045	84°
6°	.1045	.1063	.1080	.1097	.1115	.1132	.1149	.1167	.1184	.1201	.1219	83°
7°	.1219	.1236	.1253	.1271	.1288	.1305	.1323	.1340	.1357	.1374	.1392	82°
8°	.1392	.1409	.1426	.1444	.1461	.1478	.1495	.1513	.1530	.1547	.1564	81°
9°	.1564	.1582	.1599	.1616	.1633	.1650	.1668	.1685	.1702	.1719	.1736	80°
10°	.1736	.1754	.1771	.1788	.1805	.1822	.1840	.1857	.1874	.1891	.1908	79°
11°	.1908	.1925	.1942	.1959	.1977	.1994	.2011	.2028	.2045	.2062	.2079	78°
12°	.2079	.2096	.2113	.2130	.2147	.2164	.2181	.2198	.2215	.2233	.2250	77°
13°	.2250	.2267	.2284	.2300	.2317	.2334	.2351	.2368	.2385	.2402	.2419	76°
14°	.2419	.2436	.2453	.2470	.2487	.2504	.2521	.2538	.2554	.2571	.2588	75°
15°	.2588	.2605	.2622	.2639	.2656	.2672	.2689	.2706	.2723	.2740	.2756	74°
16°	.2756	.2773	.2790	.2807	.2823	.2840	.2857	.2874	.2890	.2907	.2924	73°
17°	.2924	.2940	.2957	.2974	.2990	.3007	.3024	.3040	.3057	.3074	.3090	72°
18°	.3090	.3107	.3123	.3140	.3156	.3173	.3190	.3206	.3223	.3239	.3256	71°
19°	.3256	.3272	.3289	.3305	.3322	.3338	.3355	.3371	.3387	.3404	.3420	70°
20°	.3420	.3437	.3453	.3469	.3486	.3502	.3518	.3535	.3551	.3567	.3584	69°
21°	.3584	.3600	.3616	.3633	.3649	.3665	.3681	.3697	.3714	.3730	.3746	68°
22°	.3746	.3762	.3778	.3795	.3811	.3827	.3843	.3859	.3875	.3891	.3907	67°
23°	.3907	.3923	.3939	.3955	.3971	.3987	.4003	.4019	.4035	.4051	.4067	66°
24°	.4067	.4083	.4099	.4115	.4131	.4147	.4163	.4179	.4195	.4210	.4226	65°
25°	.4226	.4242	.4258	.4274	.4289	.4305	.4321	.4337	.4352	.4368	.4384	64°
26°	.4384	.4399	.4415	.4431	.4446	.4462	.4478	.4493	.4509	.4524	.4540	63°
27°	.4540	.4555	.4571	.4586	.4602	.4617	.4633	.4648	.4664	.4679	.4695	62°
28°	.4695	.4710	.4726	.4741	.4756	.4772	.4787	.4802	.4818	.4833	.4848	61°
29°	.4848	.4863	.4879	.4894	.4909	.4924	.4939	.4955	.4970	.4985	.5000	60°
30°	.5000	.5015	.5030	.5045	.5060	.5075	.5090	.5105	.5120	.5135	.5150	59°
31°	.5150	.5165	.5180	.5195	.5210	.5225	.5240	.5255	.5270	.5284	.5299	58°
32°	.5299	.5314	.5329	.5344	.5358	.5373	.5388	.5402	.5417	.5432	.5446	57°
33°	.5446	.5461	.5476	.5490	.5505	.5519	.5534	.5548	.5563	.5577	.5592	56°
34°	.5592	.5606	.5621	.5635	.5650	.5664	.5678	.5693	.5707	.5721	.5736	55°
35°	.5736	.5750	.5764	.5779	.5793	.5807	.5821	.5835	.5850	.5864	.5878	54°
36°	.5878	.5892	.5906	.5920	.5934	.5948	.5962	.5976	.5990	.6004	.6018	53°
37°	.6018	.6032	.6046	.6060	.6074	.6088	.6101	.6115	.6129	.6143	.6157	52°
38°	.6157	.6170	.6184	.6198	.6211	.6225	.6239	.6252	.6266	.6280	.6293	51°
39°	.6293	.6307	.6320	.6334	.6347	.6361	.6374	.6388	.6401	.6414	.6428	50°
40°	.6428	.6441	.6455	.6468	.6481	.6494	.6508	.6521	.6534	.6547	.6561	49°
41°	.6561	.6574	.6587	.6600	.6613	.6626	.6639	.6652	.6665	.6678	.6691	48°
42°	.6691	.6704	.6717	.6730	.6743	.6756	.6769	.6782	.6794	.6807	.6820	47°
43°	.6820	.6833	.6845	.6858	.6871	.6884	.6896	.6909	.6921	.6934	.6947	46°
44°	.6947	.6959	.6972	.6984	.6997	.7009	.7022	.7034	.7046	.7059	.7071	45°
	.9	.8	.7	.6	.5	.4	.3	.2	.1	.0		

cos

Table 1. Natural Trigonometric Functions

sin

	.0	.1	.2	.3	.4	.5	.6	.7	.8	.9		
45°	.7071	.7083	.7096	.7108	.7120	.7133	.7145	.7157	.7169	.7181	.7193	44°
46°	.7193	.7206	.7218	.7230	.7242	.7254	.7266	.7278	.7290	.7302	.7314	43°
47°	.7314	.7325	.7337	.7349	.7361	.7373	.7385	.7396	.7408	.7420	.7431	42°
48°	.7431	.7443	.7455	.7466	.7478	.7490	.7501	.7513	.7524	.7536	.7547	41°
49°	.7547	.7559	.7570	.7581	.7593	.7604	.7615	.7627	.7638	.7649	.7660	40°
50°	.7660	.7672	.7683	.7694	.7705	.7716	.7727	.7738	.7749	.7760	.7771	39°
51°	.7771	.7782	.7793	.7804	.7815	.7826	.7837	.7848	.7859	.7869	.7880	38°
52°	.7880	.7891	.7902	.7912	.7923	.7934	.7944	.7955	.7965	.7976	.7986	37°
53°	.7986	.7997	.8007	.8018	.8028	.8039	.8049	.8059	.8070	.8080	.8090	36°
54°	.8090	.8100	.8111	.8121	.8131	.8141	.8151	.8161	.8171	.8181	.8192	35°
55°	.8192	.8202	.8211	.8221	.8231	.8241	.8251	.8261	.8271	.8281	.8290	34°
56°	.8290	.8300	.8310	.8320	.8329	.8339	.8348	.8358	.8368	.8377	.8387	33°
57°	.8387	.8396	.8406	.8415	.8425	.8434	.8443	.8453	.8462	.8471	.8480	32°
58°	.8480	.8490	.8499	.8508	.8517	.8526	.8536	.8545	.8554	.8563	.8572	31°
59°	.8572	.8581	.8590	.8599	.8607	.8616	.8625	.8634	.8643	.8652	.8660	30°
60°	.8660	.8669	.8678	.8686	.8695	.8704	.8712	.8721	.8729	.8738	.8746	29°
61°	.8746	.8755	.8763	.8771	.8780	.8788	.8796	.8805	.8813	.8821	.8829	28°
62°	.8829	.8838	.8846	.8854	.8862	.8870	.8878	.8886	.8894	.8902	.8910	27°
63°	.8910	.8918	.8926	.8934	.8942	.8949	.8957	.8965	.8973	.8980	.8988	26°
64°	.8988	.8996	.9003	.9011	.9018	.9026	.9033	.9041	.9048	.9056	.9063	25°
65°	.9063	.9070	.9078	.9085	.9092	.9100	.9107	.9114	.9121	.9128	.9135	24°
66°	.9135	.9143	.9150	.9157	.9164	.9171	.9178	.9184	.9191	.9198	.9205	23°
67°	.9205	.9212	.9219	.9225	.9232	.9239	.9245	.9252	.9259	.9265	.9272	22°
68°	.9272	.9278	.9285	.9291	.9298	.9304	.9311	.9317	.9323	.9330	.9336	21°
69°	.9336	.9342	.9348	.9354	.9361	.9367	.9373	.9379	.9385	.9391	.9397	20°
70°	.9397	.9403	.9409	.9415	.9421	.9426	.9432	.9438	.9444	.9449	.9455	19°
71°	.9455	.9461	.9466	.9472	.9478	.9483	.9489	.9494	.9500	.9505	.9511	18°
72°	.9511	.9516	.9521	.9527	.9532	.9537	.9542	.9548	.9553	.9558	.9563	17°
73°	.9563	.9568	.9573	.9578	.9583	.9588	.9593	.9598	.9603	.9608	.9613	16°
74°	.9613	.9617	.9622	.9627	.9632	.9636	.9641	.9646	.9650	.9655	.9659	15°
75°	.9659	.9664	.9668	.9673	.9677	.9681	.9686	.9690	.9694	.9699	.9703	14°
76°	.9703	.9707	.9711	.9715	.9720	.9724	.9728	.9732	.9736	.9740	.9744	13°
77°	.9744	.9748	.9751	.9755	.9759	.9763	.9767	.9770	.9774	.9778	.9781	12°
78°	.9781	.9785	.9789	.9792	.9796	.9799	.9803	.9806	.9810	.9813	.9816	11°
79°	.9816	.9820	.9823	.9826	.9829	.9833	.9836	.9839	.9842	.9845	.9848	10°
80°	.9848	.9851	.9854	.9857	.9860	.9863	.9866	.9869	.9871	.9874	.9877	9°
81°	.9877	.9880	.9882	.9885	.9888	.9890	.9893	.9895	.9898	.9900	.9903	8°
82°	.9903	.9905	.9907	.9910	.9912	.9914	.9917	.9919	.9921	.9923	.9925	7°
83°	.9925	.9928	.9930	.9932	.9934	.9936	.9938	.9940	.9942	.9943	.9945	6°
84°	.9945	.9947	.9949	.9951	.9952	.9954	.9956	.9957	.9959	.9960	.9962	5°
85°	.9962	.9963	.9965	.9966	.9968	.9969	.9971	.9972	.9973	.9974	.9976	4°
86°	.9976	.9977	.9978	.9979	.9980	.9981	.9982	.9983	.9984	.9985	.9986	3°
87°	.9986	.9987	.9988	.9989	.9990	.9990	.9991	.9992	.9993	.9993	.9994	2°
88°	.9994	.9995	.9995	.9996	.9996	.9997	.9997	.9997	.9998	.9998	.9998	1°
89°	.9998	.9999	.9999	.9999	.9999	1.000	1.000	1.000	1.000	1.000	1.000	0°
	.9	.8	.7	.6	.5	.4	.3	.2	.1	.0		

cos

Table 1. Natural Trigonometric Functions

tan

	.0	.1	.2	.3	.4	.5	.6	.7	.8	.9		
0°	.0000	.0017	.0035	.0052	.0070	.0087	.0105	.0122	.0140	.0157	.0175	89°
1°	.0175	.0192	.0209	.0227	.0244	.0262	.0279	.0297	.0314	.0332	.0349	88°
2°	.0349	.0367	.0384	.0402	.0419	.0437	.0454	.0472	.0489	.0507	.0524	87°
3°	.0524	.0542	.0559	.0577	.0594	.0612	.0629	.0647	.0664	.0682	.0699	86°
4°	.0699	.0717	.0734	.0752	.0769	.0787	.0805	.0822	.0840	.0857	.0875	85°
5°	.0875	.0892	.0910	.0928	.0945	.0963	.0981	.0998	.1016	.1033	.1051	84°
6°	.1051	.1069	.1086	.1104	.1122	.1139	.1157	.1175	.1192	.1210	.1228	83°
7°	.1228	.1246	.1263	.1281	.1299	.1317	.1334	.1352	.1370	.1388	.1405	82°
8°	.1405	.1423	.1441	.1459	.1477	.1495	.1512	.1530	.1548	.1566	.1584	81°
9°	.1584	.1602	.1620	.1638	.1655	.1673	.1691	.1709	.1727	.1745	.1763	80°
10°	.1763	.1781	.1799	.1817	.1835	.1853	.1871	.1890	.1908	.1926	.1944	79°
11°	.1944	.1962	.1980	.1998	.2016	.2035	.2053	.2071	.2089	.2107	.2126	78°
12°	.2126	.2144	.2162	.2180	.2199	.2217	.2235	.2254	.2272	.2290	.2309	77°
13°	.2309	.2327	.2345	.2364	.2382	.2401	.2419	.2438	.2456	.2475	.2493	76°
14°	.2493	.2512	.2530	.2549	.2568	.2586	.2605	.2623	.2642	.2661	.2679	75°
15°	.2679	.2698	.2717	.2736	.2754	.2773	.2792	.2811	.2830	.2849	.2867	74°
16°	.2867	.2886	.2905	.2924	.2943	.2962	.2981	.3000	.3019	.3038	.3057	73°
17°	.3057	.3076	.3096	.3115	.3134	.3153	.3172	.3191	.3211	.3230	.3249	72°
18°	.3249	.3269	.3288	.3307	.3327	.3346	.3365	.3385	.3404	.3424	.3443	71°
19°	.3443	.3463	.3482	.3502	.3522	.3541	.3561	.3581	.3600	.3620	.3640	70°
20°	.3640	.3659	.3679	.3699	.3719	.3739	.3759	.3779	.3799	.3819	.3839	69°
21°	.3839	.3859	.3879	.3899	.3919	.3939	.3959	.3979	.4000	.4020	.4040	68°
22°	.4040	.4061	.4081	.4101	.4122	.4142	.4163	.4183	.4204	.4224	.4245	67°
23°	.4245	.4265	.4286	.4307	.4327	.4348	.4369	.4390	.4411	.4431	.4452	66°
24°	.4452	.4473	.4494	.4515	.4536	.4557	.4578	.4599	.4621	.4642	.4663	65°
25°	.4663	.4684	.4706	.4727	.4748	.4770	.4791	.4813	.4834	.4856	.4877	64°
26°	.4877	.4899	.4921	.4942	.4964	.4986	.5008	.5029	.5051	.5073	.5095	63°
27°	.5095	.5117	.5139	.5161	.5184	.5206	.5228	.5250	.5272	.5295	.5317	62°
28°	.5317	.5340	.5362	.5384	.5407	.5430	.5452	.5475	.5498	.5520	.5543	61°
29°	.5543	.5566	.5589	.5612	.5635	.5658	.5681	.5704	.5727	.5750	.5774	60°
30°	.5774	.5797	.5820	.5844	.5867	.5890	.5914	.5938	.5961	.5985	.6009	59°
31°	.6009	.6032	.6056	.6080	.6104	.6128	.6152	.6176	.6200	.6224	.6249	58°
32°	.6249	.6273	.6297	.6322	.6346	.6371	.6395	.6420	.6445	.6469	.6494	57°
33°	.6494	.6519	.6544	.6569	.6594	.6619	.6644	.6669	.6694	.6720	.6745	56°
34°	.6745	.6771	.6796	.6822	.6847	.6873	.6899	.6924	.6950	.6976	.7002	55°
35°	.7002	.7028	.7054	.7080	.7107	.7133	.7159	.7186	.7212	.7239	.7265	54°
36°	.7265	.7292	.7319	.7346	.7373	.7400	.7427	.7454	.7481	.7508	.7536	53°
37°	.7536	.7563	.7590	.7618	.7646	.7673	.7701	.7729	.7757	.7785	.7813	52°
38°	.7813	.7841	.7869	.7898	.7926	.7954	.7983	.8012	.8040	.8069	.8098	51°
39°	.8098	.8127	.8156	.8185	.8214	.8243	.8273	.8302	.8332	.8361	.8391	50°
40°	.8391	.8421	.8451	.8481	.8511	.8541	.8571	.8601	.8632	.8662	.8693	49°
41°	.8693	.8724	.8754	.8785	.8816	.8847	.8878	.8910	.8941	.8972	.9004	48°
42°	.9004	.9036	.9067	.9099	.9131	.9163	.9195	.9228	.9260	.9293	.9325	47°
43°	.9325	.9358	.9391	.9424	.9457	.9490	.9523	.9556	.9590	.9623	.9657	46°
44°	.9657	.9691	.9725	.9759	.9793	.9827	.9861	.9896	.9930	.9965	1.000	45°
		.9	.8	.7	.6	.5	.4	.3	.2	.1	.0	

cot

322

Table 1. Natural Trigonometric Functions

tan

	.0	.1	.2	.3	.4	.5	.6	.7	.8	.9	
45°	1.000	1.003	1.007	1.011	1.014	1.018	1.021	1.025	1.028	1.032	1.036	44°
46°	1.036	1.039	1.043	1.046	1.050	1.054	1.057	1.061	1.065	1.069	1.072	43°
47°	1.072	1.076	1.080	1.084	1.087	1.091	1.095	1.099	1.103	1.107	1.111	42°
48°	1.111	1.115	1.118	1.122	1.126	1.130	1.134	1.138	1.142	1.146	1.150	41°
49°	1.150	1.154	1.159	1.163	1.167	1.171	1.175	1.179	1.183	1.188	1.192	40°
50°	1.192	1.196	1.200	1.205	1.209	1.213	1.217	1.222	1.226	1.230	1.235	39°
51°	1.235	1.239	1.244	1.248	1.253	1.257	1.262	1.266	1.271	1.275	1.280	38°
52°	1.280	1.285	1.289	1.294	1.299	1.303	1.308	1.313	1.317	1.322	1.327	37°
53°	1.327	1.332	1.337	1.342	1.347	1.351	1.356	1.361	1.366	1.371	1.376	36°
54°	1.376	1.381	1.387	1.392	1.397	1.402	1.407	1.412	1.418	1.423	1.428	35°
55°	1.428	1.433	1.439	1.444	1.450	1.455	1.460	1.466	1.471	1.477	1.483	34°
56°	1.483	1.488	1.494	1.499	1.505	1.511	1.517	1.522	1.528	1.534	1.540	33°
57°	1.540	1.546	1.552	1.558	1.564	1.570	1.576	1.582	1.588	1.594	1.600	32°
58°	1.600	1.607	1.613	1.619	1.625	1.632	1.638	1.645	1.651	1.658	1.664	31°
59°	1.664	1.671	1.678	1.684	1.691	1.698	1.704	1.711	1.718	1.725	1.732	30°
60°	1.732	1.739	1.746	1.753	1.760	1.767	1.775	1.782	1.789	1.797	1.804	29°
61°	1.804	1.811	1.819	1.827	1.834	1.842	1.849	1.857	1.865	1.873	1.881	28°
62°	1.881	1.889	1.897	1.905	1.913	1.921	1.929	1.937	1.946	1.954	1.963	27°
63°	1.963	1.971	1.980	1.988	1.997	2.006	2.014	2.023	2.032	2.041	2.050	26°
64°	2.050	2.059	2.069	2.078	2.087	2.097	2.106	2.116	2.125	2.135	2.145	25°
65°	2.145	2.154	2.164	2.174	2.184	2.194	2.204	2.215	2.225	2.236	2.246	24°
66°	2.246	2.257	2.267	2.278	2.289	2.300	2.311	2.322	2.333	2.344	2.356	23°
67°	2.356	2.367	2.379	2.391	2.402	2.414	2.426	2.438	2.450	2.463	2.475	22°
68°	2.475	2.488	2.500	2.513	2.526	2.539	2.552	2.565	2.578	2.592	2.605	21°
69°	2.605	2.619	2.633	2.646	2.660	2.675	2.689	2.703	2.718	2.733	2.747	20°
70°	2.747	2.762	2.778	2.793	2.808	2.824	2.840	2.856	2.872	2.888	2.904	19°
71°	2.904	2.921	2.937	2.954	2.971	2.989	3.006	3.024	3.042	3.060	3.078	18°
72°	3.078	3.096	3.115	3.133	3.152	3.172	3.191	3.211	3.230	3.251	3.271	17°
73°	3.271	3.291	3.312	3.333	3.354	3.376	3.398	3.420	3.442	3.465	3.487	16°
74°	3.487	3.511	3.534	3.558	3.582	3.606	3.630	3.655	3.681	3.706	3.732	15°
75°	3.732	3.758	3.785	3.812	3.839	3.867	3.895	3.923	3.952	3.981	4.011	14°
76°	4.011	4.041	4.071	4.102	4.134	4.165	4.198	4.230	4.264	4.297	4.331	13°
77°	4.331	4.366	4.402	4.437	4.474	4.511	4.548	4.586	4.625	4.665	4.705	12°
78°	4.705	4.745	4.787	4.829	4.872	4.915	4.959	5.005	5.050	5.097	5.145	11°
79°	5.145	5.193	5.242	5.292	5.343	5.396	5.449	5.503	5.558	5.614	5.671	10°
80°	5.671	5.730	5.789	5.850	5.912	5.976	6.041	6.107	6.174	6.243	6.314	9°
81°	6.314	6.386	6.460	6.535	6.612	6.691	6.772	6.855	6.940	7.026	7.115	8°
82°	7.115	7.207	7.300	7.396	7.495	7.596	7.700	7.806	7.916	8.028	8.144	7°
83°	8.144	8.264	8.386	8.513	8.643	8.777	8.915	9.058	9.205	9.357	9.514	6°
84°	9.514	9.677	9.845	10.02	10.20	10.39	10.58	10.78	10.99	11.20	11.43	5°
85°	11.43	11.66	11.91	12.16	12.43	12.71	13.00	13.30	13.62	13.95	14.30	4°
86°	14.30	14.67	15.06	15.46	15.89	16.35	16.83	17.34	17.89	18.46	19.08	3°
87°	19.08	19.74	20.45	21.20	22.02	22.90	23.86	24.90	26.03	27.27	28.64	2°
88°	28.64	30.14	31.82	33.69	35.80	38.19	40.92	44.07	47.74	52.08	57.29	1°
89°	57.29	63.66	71.62	81.85	95.49	114.6	143.2	191.0	286.5	573.0		0°
	.9	.8	.7	.6	.5	.4	.3	.2	.1	.0		

cot

323

APPENDIX

Table 2. Exponentials

x	e^x	x	e^x	x	e^x	x	e^x	x	e^x
0.00	1.000	1.00	2.718	2.00	7.389	3.00	20.086	4.00	54.598
0.05	1.051	1.05	2.858	2.05	7.768	3.05	21.115	40.5	57.397
0.10	1.105	1.10	3.004	2.10	8.166	3.10	22.198	4.10	60.340
0.15	1.162	1.15	3.158	2.15	8.585	3.15	23.336	4.15	63.434
0.20	1.221	1.20	3.320	2.20	9.025	3.20	24.533	4.20	66.686
0.25	1.284	1.25	3.490	2.25	9.488	3.25	25.790	4.25	70.105
0.30	1.350	1.30	3.669	2.30	9.974	3.30	27.113	4.30	73.700
0.35	1.419	1.35	3.857	2.35	10.486	3.35	28.503	4.35	77.487
0.40	1.492	1.40	4.005	2.40	11.023	3.40	29.964	4.40	81.451
0.45	1.568	1.45	4.263	2.45	11.588	3.45	31.500	4.45	85.627
0.50	1.649	1.50	4.482	2.50	12.182	3.50	33.115	4.50	90.017
0.55	1.733	1.55	4.712	2.55	12.807	3.55	34.813	4.55	94.632
0.60	1.822	1.60	4.953	2.60	13.464	3.60	36.598	4.60	99.484
0.65	1.916	1.65	5.207	2.65	14.154	3.65	38.475	4.65	104.58
0.70	2.014	1.70	5.474	2.70	14.880	3.70	40.447	4.70	109.95
0.75	2.117	1.75	5.755	2.75	15.643	3.75	42.521	4.75	115.58
0.80	2.226	1.80	6.050	2.80	16.445	3.80	44.701	4.80	121.51
0.85	2.340	1.85	6.360	2.85	17.288	3.85	46.993	4.85	127.74
0.90	2.460	1.90	6.686	2.90	18.174	3.90	49.902	4.90	134.29
0.95	2.586	1.95	7.029	2.95	19.106	3.95	51.935	4.95	141.17
1.00	2.718	2.00	7.389	3.00	20.086	4.00	54.598	5.00	148.41

ANSWERS
TO PROBLEMS

CHAPTER 1

1-1. 17.3 in.; 10 in.
1-2. 56.3°
1-3. 17.0 in.
1-4. 24.6 ft
1-5. 142 mi
1-6. 140°
1-7. 71.6°; 63.4°
1-8. 700 ft; 66.7°
1-9. 38.1 in.; 66.8°
1-10. 20.6 in.; 76.0°
1-11. 1.25 in.
1-12. 381 ft
1-13. 31,100 sq yds
1-16. (a) 6.2 in.; (b) 2.09 in.; (c) 13.3 ft; (d) 5.29 in.; (e) 37.3 in.; (f) 15 in.
1-17. 8.5 in.; 18.5 in.
1-18. 15.9 ft; 9.17 ft
1-19. 13.7 in.; 7.82 in.
1-20. 405 ft; 36,900 sq ft
1-21. 54.9 yds
1-22. (a) $\alpha = 110°$; $b = 6.89$ in.; $c = 5.36$ in.
 (b) $\alpha = 23.2°$; $\beta = 104.8°$; $b = 14.7$ in.
 (c) $\alpha = 141.7°$; $\beta = 9.3°$; $a = 19.2$ in.
 (d) $\alpha = 52.7°$; $\beta = 95.3°$; $c = 15$ ft
 (e) $\theta = 89.3°$; $\beta = 54.2°$; $a = 7.55$ in.

(f) $\alpha = 29.7°$; $\beta = 52.4°$; $\theta = 97.9°$
1-23. 82.1 yds
1-24. 95.4°
1-25. 4.11 ft; 46.9°
1-26. 0.738 in.
1-27. 3188 lb per cu yd
1-28. 0.223 cu ft per sec
1-29. 750 mi per hr; 22,000 yd per min
1-30. 0.491 oz
1-31. 543,000 gal

CHAPTER 2

2-2. 6.67 ft
2-3. 13.3 ft
2-4. 8 ft
2-5. 3.00 in.
2-6. 73.3°; 55°
2-7. 510 lb; 101.3° ∡
2-8. 101 lb; 46.4° ∡
2-9. 5.85 k; 57.8° ∡
2-10. 548 lb; 98.6° ∡
2-11. 1310 lb; 107° ∡
2-12. 316 lb; 74.9° ∡
2-13. 757 lb; 152.1° ∡
2-14. 329 lb; 91° ∡
2-15. 74.7 lb; 105.5° ∡
2-16. 675 lb; 104° ∡
2-17. 375 lb; 310.4° ∡
2-18. 3.61 k; 11.3° cw from vertical
2-19. 1200 lb
2-20. 12,700 lb
2-21. 11.5 tons
2-22. 1.73 tons
2-23. 8.66 k; 5.00 k
2-24. 4.70 tons; 1.71 tons
2-25. 718 lb; 1970 lb
2-26. 103 lb; 194 lb
2-27. $A_x = 625 \rightarrow$, $A_y = 125 \downarrow$
$B_x = 105 \leftarrow$, $B_y = 385 \uparrow$
$C_x = 195 \leftarrow$, $C_y = 585 \downarrow$
$D_x = 325 \leftarrow$, $D_y = 325 \uparrow$ all in lb
2-29. 18.2°; 40.5°
2-30. *Hint:* $R_x = 112$ lb $\rightarrow$; $R_y = 412$ lb $\uparrow$
2-31. *Hint:* $R_x = 8.6$ lb $\leftarrow$; $R_y = 20.8$ lb $\uparrow$
2-32. *Hint:* $R_x = 8$ k $\leftarrow$; $R_y = 2$ k $\downarrow$

2-33. *Hint:* $R_x = 90$ lb $\rightarrow$; $R_y = 125$ lb $\uparrow$
2-34. *Hint:* $R_x = 2.57\ F \leftarrow$; $R_y = 4.68\ F \uparrow$
2-35. *Hint:* $R_x = 408$ lb $\leftarrow$
2-36. 230 lb $\leftarrow$
2-37. 2182 lb $\downarrow$
2-38. 153 lb; 67.5° $\nwarrow$
2-39. 14 k, 75.5° $\nwarrow$; 1.3 ft to right of A
2-40. (a) 90.1 lb, 33.7° $\measuredangle$
          (b) 90.1 lb, 33.7° $\searrow$
          (c) 90.1 lb, 33.7° $\nwarrow$
2-41. (a) 380 lb, 31.8° $\measuredangle$
          (b) 23.2 lb, $\leftarrow$
          (c) 323 lb, $\leftarrow$
          (d) 201 lb, 83.4° $\nearrow$
2-44. $\cos \theta_x = 0.324$, $\cos \theta_y = 0.811$, $\cos \theta_z = -0.487$
2-45. $R_x = 90$ lb; $R_y = 252$ lb; $R_z = 88.7$ lb
2-46. 293 lb; $\cos \theta_x = 107/293$, $\cos \theta_y = 103/293$, $\cos \theta_z = -253/293$
2-47. 10 k $\downarrow$, 11.2 ft to right of A
2-48. 400 lb to the right, 23.5 ft above A
2-49. 800 lb to the right, 27.3 ft above A
2-50. (c) 6000 ton ft
2-51. $R_A = 1.1$ ton; $R_B = 0.9$ ton; $M_C = 5$ ton ft
2-52. 33.2 kip ft
2-53. 5 k $\downarrow$; 6 ft to right of A
2-54. 3.5 ton $\downarrow$; 2 ft to right of A
2-55. Resultant force is zero, resultant moment is 600 lb ft
2-56. 6870 lb, 77.1° $\nearrow$; 8.41 ft to right of A
2-57. 10.5 k, 77.3° $\measuredangle$; 9.38 ft to right of A
2-58. 1580 lb, 85.8° $\nwarrow$; 8.11 ft to right of A
2-59. $R_x = 350$ lb $\rightarrow$, $R_y = 100$ lb $\downarrow$; 21 in. to right of A
2-60. $R_x = 180$ lb $\leftarrow$, $R_y = 25$ lb $\uparrow$; 73.9 in. to left of A
2-61. $R_x = 5$ k $\leftarrow$, $R_y = 9.5$ k $\downarrow$; 12.6 in. to right of A
2-62. zero
2-63. 990 lb in. $\circlearrowright$
2-64. 40 lb ft ccw looking downward
2-65. 250 lb ft $\circlearrowleft$
2-66. 1050 lb in. $\circlearrowleft$
2-67. 4800 lb in. cw looking toward the right

CHAPTER 3

3-2. 53.3 in.
3-3. 2.4 ft to left of A and 2.06 ft above base
3-4. 5.25 in. to right of A
3-5. $\bar{x} = 20$ in.
3-6. $\bar{x} = 40/7$ in.; $\bar{z} = 50/7$ in.

3-7. $\bar{x} = 4.95$ in.; $\bar{z} = 4.73$ in.
3-8. $\bar{x} = 70/9$ in.; $\bar{y} = 10/3$ in.; $\bar{z} = 4/3$ in.
3-9. $\bar{x} = 20/7$ in.; $\bar{y} = -10/7$ in.; $\bar{z} = 100/7$ in.
3-10. $\bar{x} = 35/3$ in.; $\bar{y} = 25/6$ in.
3-11. $\bar{x} = 6.33$ in.; $\bar{y} = 10.67$ in.
3-12. $\bar{x} = 3.87$ in.; $\bar{y} = 3.05$ in.
3-13. $\bar{x} = 11.8$ in.; $\bar{y} = 7.12$ in.
3-14. $\bar{y} = 15.3$ in.
3-15. $\bar{y} = 8.64$ in.
3-16. $\bar{y} = 6.99$ in.
3-17. 18.3 in. from free end
3-18. 1.82 ft from light gear
3-19. $\bar{x} = 9.75$ in.; $\bar{y} = 7.24$ in.; $\bar{z} = 5$ in.
3-20. 13.6 in. above base at point of symmetry
3-21. $\bar{x} = 5$ in.; $\bar{y} = 1.79$ in.; $\bar{z} = 8.57$ in.
3-22. $\bar{x} = 9.66$ in.; $\bar{y} = -6.62$ in.; $\bar{z} = 3.62$ in.

CHAPTER 4

4-9. 167 lb; 133 lb
4-10. 173 lb; 100 lb
4-11. 18.2 lb
4-12. $A = 50$ lb; $B = C = 28.9$ lb
4-13. 91.7 lb
4-14. 142 lb
4-15. $A = 222$ lb $\downarrow$; $B = 342$ lb $\uparrow$
4-16. Right: 2510 lb; Left: 1070 lb
4-17. 25.2 lb
4-18. $A = B = 144$ lb
4-19. $W = 50$ lb; $R_A = 149$ lb; $R_B = 164$ lb
4-20. $A_y = 6$ kips $\uparrow$; $A_x = 15$ kips $\leftarrow$; $B = 15$ kips $\rightarrow$
4-21. 402 lb
4-22. 831 lb
4-23. $A = 450$ lb $\uparrow$; $B = 1050$ lb $\uparrow$
4-24. $A_x = 1000$ lb $\leftarrow$; $A_y = 1540$ lb $\uparrow$; $B = 1790$ lb $\uparrow$
4-25. $A = 300$ lb $\downarrow$; $B = 1300$ lb $\uparrow$; $C = 1625$ lb $\uparrow$; $D = 325$ lb $\downarrow$
4-26. $A_x = 173$ lb $\rightarrow$; $A_y = 100$ lb $\uparrow$; $B = 200$ lb; $30°$ $\searrow$
4-27. 10.3 in.
4-28. $A = 0.83$ ton; $B = 4.17$ tons; $C = 2.40$ tons; $D = 2.60$ tons
4-29. 250 lb
4-30. 664 lb ft
4-31. 100 lb
4-32. 300 lb
4-33. $A_x = 3$ kips $\rightarrow$; $A_y = 2.17$ kips $\uparrow$; $B = 3.83$ kips
4-34. 794 lb ft; 6000 lb $\downarrow$
4-35. 11.2 ft ahead of C; 30,000 lb

4-36. $A = 4320$ lb; $B = 6900$ lb; $C = 4780$ lb

4-37. $A_x = 300$ lb $\rightarrow$; $A_y = 200$ lb $\uparrow$; $B = 300$ lb $\leftarrow$

4-38. 680 lb; 460 lb (approximate answers)

4-39. $W = 1400$ lb; $C_x = 1730$ lb $\rightarrow$; $C_y = 2400$ lb $\uparrow$

4-40. $T = 1300$ lb; $A_x = 1130$ lb $\rightarrow$; $A_y = 956$ lb $\downarrow$

4-41. $T = 2500$ lb; $A_x = 4530$ lb $\rightarrow$; $A_y = 1990$ lb $\uparrow$; $F = 5510$ lb

4-42. $W = 90$ lb; $A = B = 270$ lb

4-43. $AD = 123$ lb; $CD = 60.1$ lb; $BD = 40$ lb

4-44. $AD = 1.88$ kips; $BD = 0.314$ kip; $CD = 1.48$ kips

4-45. $T_A = T_B = T_C = 167$ lb

4-46. 17 lb

4-47. $T = 417$ lb; $D_x = 667$ lb; $D_y = 500$ lb

4-48. $T_A = T_C = 469$ lb; $T_D = 750$ lb

4-49. $T_A = 140$ lb; $T_B = 245$ lb; $T_C = 105$ lb

4-50. 566 lb; 267 lb

4-51. $T = 373$ lb; $A_y = -75$ lb; $A_z = -113$ lb; $E_y = 137$ lb; $E_z = -37.5$ lb

4-52. $T = 650$ lb; $A_x = B_x = 0$; $A_y = B_y = 400$ lb; $A_z = 200$ lb; $B_z = 1200$ lb

CHAPTER 5

5-1. $AB = 5200$ lb T; $BC = 4800$ lb C

5-2. $AB = 2$ kips C; $AD = 1.73$ kips T; $BD = 2$ kips T

5-3. Answers in kips: $A = 8/3$; $F = 10/3$; $AB = 10/3$ C; $BC = 0$; $AC = CE = 2$ T; $BE = 5/6$ T; $BD = 5/2$ C; $DE = 2/3$ C; $EF = 5/2$ T; $DF = 25/6$ C

5-4. *Hint:* $DE = 5$ kips C; $EG = 8.66$ kips C

5-5. *Hint:* $BG = DE = EF = 0$

5-6. Answers in kips: $AB = 9.5$ C; $BC = 6.5$ C; $CD = 5$ C; $DE = 2$ T; $EF = 1.5$ T; $FG = 4.5$ T; $GH = 9$ T; $CE = 2.5$ C; $CF = 4$ T; $BF = 5$ C; $BG = 6$ T; $AG = 7.5$ C

5-7. *Hint:* All internal members carry zero load.

5-8. BD

5-9. FH, EH, EI, DI, DJ

5-10. $EG, EH, DH, DI, CI, CJ, BJ$, and BK

5-11. BL, BK, CK, EI, FI, and FH

5-12. BM, CM, CN, DN, FO, and OG

5-13. $EH, EI, DI, DJ, CJ, CK, BK, BL$, and all like members on right-hand side

5-14. $CD = 2.89$ kip C; $DH = 1.44$ kip C; $GH = 3.61$ kip T

5-15. $BC = 1000$ lb T; $BF = 1000$ lb C

5-16. $BC = 1429$ lb T; $BE = 1745$ lb T; $EF = 3485$ lb C

5-17. $BC = 0.845$ kip C; $CG = 5.36$ kip C; $GF = 1.53$ kip T

5-18. 0

5-19. $BC = 33$ kip C; $CK = 9.90$ kip T

5-20. *Hint:* $A_x = 400$ lb $\rightarrow$; $A_y = 950$ lb $\uparrow$ on vertical member

5-21. $A_x = 305$ lb; $A_y = 118$ lb; $B_x = 105$ lb; $B_y = 118$ lb; $C_x = 105$ lb; $C_y = 482$ lb

5-22. *Hint:* $A_x = A_y = B_x = B_y = 125$ lb
5-23. $B_x = 145$ lb $\rightarrow$; $B_y = 500$ lb $\downarrow$; $D_x = 145$ lb $\leftarrow$; $D_y = 1500$ lb $\uparrow$
5-24. $A_x = 150$ lb $\leftarrow$; $A_y = 50$ lb $\uparrow$; $C_x = 150$ lb $\rightarrow$; $C_y = 50$ lb $\uparrow$

CHAPTER 6

6-1. 20 lb in each position
6-2. 25 lb in each case; no
6-4. 0.364
6-5. 1.9°
6-6. Block is moving down
6-7. Yes, in both instances
6-8. 71.6 lb ft
6-9. 150 lb in.
6-10. 200 lb in.
6-11. 67.4°
6-12. 39.5 lb
6-13. 5.71 in.
6-14. 333 lb
6-15. 15 ft
6-16. 8 in.
6-17. 400 lb in.
6-18. $C = rw\mu(1 + \mu)/(1 + \mu^2)^2$
6-19. 1920 lb
6-20. 41.9 lb
6-21. 295 lb
6-22. 100 lb
6-23. 36.5 lb
6-24. 0.16 lb
6-25. 137 lb; 203 lb
6-26. 1.15 turns
6-27. 19.5 lb
6-28. 0.39 D
6-29. 1670 lb
6-30. 0.06 in.
6-31. 200 lb in.
6-32. 0.21
6-33. 175 lb in.
6-34. 490 lb in.

CHAPTER 7

7-1. 100 in.^{4}; 25 in.^{4}; 125 in.^{4}
7-2. 18 in.^{4}; 72 in.^{4}; 90 in.^{4}
7-3. 144 in.^{4}
7-4. 643.5 in.^{4}

7-5. 0.694 per cent
7-6. Exact value is 205.3 in.^{4}
7-10. 665 in.^{4}; 290 in.^{4}
7-11. 90 in.^{4}; 10 in.^{2}
7-12. 3.5 in.^{3}
7-13. 2.83 in.^{3}
7-14. 2560 in.^{4}
7-15. 2 in.
7-16. 6.71 in.
7-17. 10 in.
7-18. 570 in.^{4}
7-19. 2304 in.^{4}
7-20. 216 in.^{4}
7-21. 9760 in.^{4}
7-22. 392 in.^{4}; 1840 in.^{4}
7-23. 3.54 in.
7-24. 315 in.^{4}
7-25. 190.5 in.^{4}
7-26. 118 in.^{4}
7-27. 3.66 in.
7-28. 820 in.^{4}; 340 in.^{4}
7-29. 431 in.^{4}; 159 in.^{4}
7-30. 1400 in.^{4}
7-31. $I_x = 5180$ in.^{4}; $k_x = 8.60$ in.
7-32. $I_x = 775$ in.^{4}; $I_y = 8.73$ in.^{4}
7-33. 713 in.^{4}; 422 in.^{4}; 1135 in.^{4}
7-34. 7.06 in.
7-35. 7840 in.^{4}; 1550 in.^{4}
7-36. 2 ft
7-37. 0.75 slug ft^2
7-38. 0.26 slug ft^2
7-39. 33.7 slug ft^2
7-40. 0.283 slug ft^2
7-41. 0.563 slug ft^2
7-42. 2.33 slug ft^2
7-43. 4.48 in.
7-44. 0.15 slug ft^2; *Hint:* Use a handbook to determine the moment of inertia of the short cylinder.
7-45. 0.22 slug ft^2 *Hint:* Use Table 7-2 and transfer of axis formulas.
7-46. 9.33 slug ft^2

CHAPTER 8

8-1. $R_A = 4500$ lb; $R_B = 1500$ lb
8-2. $R_A = 225$ lb; $R_B = 475$ lb
8-3. $R_A = 750$ lb; $R_B = 1250$ lb
8-4. $R_A = R_B = 1050$ lb

8-5. $R_A = 1650$ lb; $R_B = 1150$ lb

8-6. $R_A = 2W/3$; $R_B = W/3$

8-7. $R_A = 387$ lb; $R_B = 1013$ lb

8-8. $R_A = 1167$ lb; $R_B = 1833$ lb

8-9. $R_A = 80$ lb; $R_B = 1320$ lb

8-10. $R = 0$; $M = 100$ lb ft $\circlearrowright$

8-11. $R = 600$ lb $\uparrow$; $M = 4000$ lb ft $\circlearrowright$

8-12. $R = 1625$ lb $\uparrow$; $M = 6970$ lb ft $\circlearrowright$

8-13. $R = 900$ lb $\uparrow$; $M = 3600$ lb ft $\circlearrowright$

8-14. $R = 600$ lb $\downarrow$; $M = 1200$ lb ft $\circlearrowleft$

8-15. $R = 50$ lb $\uparrow$; $M = 3375$ lb ft $\circlearrowleft$

8-16. $R_{left} = R_{right} = 5.5$ kips; $M_{left} = M_{right} = 19.5$ kip ft

8-17. $R_x = 500$ lb $\leftarrow$; $R_y = 400$ lb $\uparrow$; $M = 2950$ lb ft $\circlearrowright$

8-18. $R = 1500$ lb $\uparrow$; $M = 8000$ lb ft $\circlearrowright$

8-19. 2400 lb ft at 4 ft to the right of A

8-20. 14 kip ft at B

8-21. $AB:$ 2.08 kip ft at E

     $CD:$ 5.6 kip ft at F

     $EF:$ 3.75 kip ft at point of load

8-22. 530 lb ft, 4 ft down from A

8-23. 4.8 kips; 9.6 kip ft

8-24. 7500 lb ft

8-25. 3.78 kips; 9 kip ft

8-26. 24 kip ft

8-27. 1000 lb ft

8-28. 11 kip ft

8-29. $wl^2/8$

8-30. 1410 lb ft at 3.75 ft to right of A

8-31. 2000 lb ft at B

8-32. 10,900 lb ft at 8.8 ft to right of A

8-33. 900 lb ft at B

8-34. 4825 lb ft

8-36. 217 psig; 231.7 psia

8-37. 23.6 psig

8-38. 2808 lb

8-39. 4690 psi

8-40. 7490 lb; 2810 lb; 1120 lb

8-41. 15,900 lb

8-42. 6240 lb

8-43. 9980 lb to right, 4.08 ft up from bottom

8-44. 57,600 lb

8-45. 576

8-46. 5120 lb

8-47. 256

8-48. 56,300 cu ft

8-49. 67.6 lb

8-50. 61.6 lb

8-51. 0.321 cu ft; 156 lb/cu ft
8-52. 0.758 cu ft

CHAPTER 9

9-1. (a) carriage moves 4.33 in. to right
     crossfeed moves 2.50 in. toward center
    (b) carriage moves 5.77 in. to right
     compound rest moves 2.89 in. toward left center
    (c) crossfeed moves 10 in. toward center
     compound rest moves out and to the right 8.66 in.
    (d) variety of answers possible
9-3. 9.43 mi, 32° north of west
9-4. (a) 4.95 ft at 45° ↙
    (b) 7 ft ↓
9-5. 2.55 ft at 11.3°
9-6. 802 yds
9-7. 269 fps
9-8. (a) $S_{a-a} = 8.66$ ft, $S_{b-b} = 5.00$ ft
    (b) $S_{a-a} = S_{b-b} = 5.77$ ft
    (c) $S_{a-a} = 11.54$ ft, $S_{b-b} = 5.77$ ft
9-9. $v_N = 779$ mph; $v_W = 450$ mph
9-10. (a) 0.12; (b) 1.00; (c) 1.36
9-11. (a) 11.5 mph; (b) 16.9 fps; (c) 1013 fpm
9-12. (a) 44 fps; (b) 26.1 knots; (c) 880 yd per min
9-13. 34.1 mph; $V_x = 27.3$ fps; $V_y = 20.5$ fps
9-14. 53.3 mph
9-15. avg speed = 26.7 mph; avg velocity = 0
9-16. graphical solution
9-17. 0.137 hr
9-18. 1.17×10^{19} mi
9-19. 7330 fps; 16 hr
9-20. 2.84 sec
9-21. 5410 fps
9-22. 48 sec
9-23. 2.8° E of S
9-24. (a) 24 mph; (b) 16 mph; (c) 20.4 mph; (d) 17.4 mph
9-25. $V_{A/B} = 1080$ mph at arc tan 2/3 ↙
9-26. 22.4 knots; 77.2 mi
9-27. (a) 20 mph; (b) −20 mph; (c) 1.33 mi
9-28. 5.29 mph
9-29. (a) 3170 ft per min per min
    (b) 52.8 ft per min per sec
    (c) 0.88 ft per sec per sec
9-30. 5.87 ft per sec²
9-31. (a) 4 fps²; (b) 0; (c) −1.33 fps²; (d) 13.3 fps; (e) 400 ft

9-32. (a) 774 ft; (b) 17.6 sec
9-33. 96 sec
9-34. 5.81 ft per sec^2; 30.1 sec
9-35. 3320 ft; 463 fps
9-36. 2.5 ft per sec^2
9-37. 7.04 ft
9-38. 96.6 fps; 403 ft
9-39. (a) 24.9 ft; (b) 1.24 sec; (c) 1210 ft
9-40. (a) 12,600 ft; (b) 87,100 ft; (c) 55.9 sec
9-41. 1930 fps; 100,000 ft
9-42. (a) 4090 ft; (b) 46,200 ft; (c) 1510 fps
9-43. 15°
9-44. 24.9 sec; 1190 fps
9-45. 1050 fps
9-46. 1270 ft
9-47. 19.4 fps^2
9-48. 6.32 fps
9-49. 77.4 mph

CHAPTER 10

10-1. (a) 1800 rad cw
    (b) 2100 rad cw
    (c) 1500 rad cw
10-2. 5.23 rad per sec
10-3. (a) 1.67 rev per sec^2
    (b) 10.5 rad per sec^2
    (c) 3.77 × 10^4 rad per min^2
10-4. 0.471 rad per sec^2; 13.3 sec
10-5. 8.37 rad per sec; zero displacement
10-6. 6.28 rad per sec^2
10-7. (a) 123 rad per sec
    (b) 138 rad per sec
    (c) 26.8 rad per sec
10-8. (a) 175 rad; 30 rad per sec
    (b) 400 rad; 60 rad per sec
10-9. (a) 9 rad per sec^2
    (b) 0
    (c) −2 rad per sec^2
    (d) 1125 rad
10-10. 5.81 × 10^{-5} rad per sec; 1180 fps
10-11. 39,900 fps
10-12. (a) 471 fpm
    (b) 314 fpm
    (c) 235 fpm
10-13. 24 rad; 12 rad per sec^2

10-14. 24 ft per sec^2

10-15. 359 rad; 1.79 rad per sec^2

10-16. 30 rad per sec; 60 rad per sec

10-17. B: 10.4 rad per sec; C: 21.8 rad per sec; D: 14.9 rad per sec, 1440 ft per min

10-18. 2.84 rad per hr

10-19. 5.23 in. downward

10-20. 71.5°

10-21. 4.71 in. per sec

10-22. 500 rpm ↻; 286 rpm ↺

10-23. 989 rad; 824 rad

10-24. 120 rpm; 60 rpm; 30 rpm

10-25. 143 rpm

10-26. 600 rpm; 1800 rpm; 5400 rpm

10-27. (a) 32 rad per sec

(b) 11.6 rad per sec

(c) 13.3 rad per sec

10-28. 5650 ft per min; 2700 rpm

10-29. $a_n = 300$ ft per sec^2; $a_t = 18.8$ ft per sec^2

10-30. 5.48×10^5 ft per sec^2

10-31. $a_{perigee} = 439$ ft per sec^2 (approx)

$a_{apogee} = 27.9$ ft per sec^2 (approx)

10-32. 5 rad per sec; 25 rad per sec^2

10-33. $a_n = 739$ ft per sec^2; $a_t = 2.36$ ft per sec^2

10-34. 11.6 ft per sec^2

10-35. 0.021 ft per sec^2

10-36. (a) 41.9 ft per sec^2 ↓

(b) 83.8 ft per sec^2 ↓

10-37. (a) 41.9 ft per sec^2 ↑

(b) 838 ft per sec^2 ↑

10-38. 1500 ft per sec^2

10-39. $a_c = 600$ ft per sec^2; $a_n = 400$ ft per sec^2

10-40. 793 mph

10-41. 0.0167 ft per sec^2

10-42. 13.4 ft

10-43. $a_{n1} = 5.61 \times 10^{-2}$ ft per sec^2

$a_{n2} = 8.25 \times 10^{-4}$ ft per sec^2

10-44. 1.01×10^{-3} ft per sec^2

10-45. 20 ft per sec ↓

10-46. 22.2 ft per sec at 45° ↘

10-47. 0.834 rad per sec CCW; 7.5 ft per sec ↓

10-48. 6.26 ft per sec

10-49. $v_c = 8.72$ ft per sec ←; $a_{nc} = 76$ fps^2

10-50. $v_B = 13.3$ ft per sec; $v_m = 8.33$ ft per sec

10-51. 10 rad per sec CCW

10-52. 25 rad per sec CW

10-53. 10 in. per sec; 50 in. per sec; 70 in. per sec

10-54. 19.3 ft above A; 5 ft per sec

10-55. 22.5 ft per sec^2
10-56. 45 ft per sec
10-57. (a) 40 ft to right
   (b) 45 ft to right
   (c) 35 ft to right
10-58. 7.5 ft per sec^2 downward
10-59. 16 ft per sec upward

CHAPTER 11

11-1. (a) 1 slug; (b) 40 slugs; (c) 186 slugs
11-2. (a) 96.6 lb; (b) 167 lb; (c) 316 lb
11-3. (a) 34 lb; (b) 540 lb
11-4. (a) 54.7 lb; (b) 129 lb; (c) 868 lb
11-5. $a = 22.4$ ft per sec^2; $\cos \theta_x = 1/\sqrt{5}$
11-6. $a = 200$ ft per sec^2; $\cos \theta_x = -0.707$
11-7. *Hint:* $a_y = 82$ ft per sec^2
11-8. $a = 26.8$ ft per sec^2; $\cos \theta_y = 2/6.7$
11-9. *Hint:* $a = 34.3$ ft per sec^2
11-10. $a = 25$ ft per sec^2; $\cos \theta_x = 3/\sqrt{50}$
11-11. (a) 20 ft per sec^2; (b) 13.6 ft per sec^2; (c) 7.12 ft per sec^2
11-12. 28.1 lb
11-13. 28.5 ft per sec^2; 66.6 lb
11-14. 52.3 ft per sec^2
11-15. (a) 202 lb; (b) 158 lb; (c) and (d) no change
11-16. 7.01 ft per sec^2; 155 lb
11-17. (a) 8.63 ft per sec^2; (b) 15.0 ft per sec^2; (c) 23.4 ft per sec^2
11-18. 1200 lb
11-19. 65.1 lb
11-20. 14.8 lb
11-21. 10.7 ft per sec^2; 133 lb
11-22. 246 lb
11-23. 168 lb
11-24. (a) 58.1 lb; (b) 78.1 lb
11-25. 38.4 rpm
11-26. 18.5°
11-27. 53.2°
11-28. 282 mph
11-29. $R_A = 3.82$ lb; $R_B = 1.28$ lb
11-30. 24 in.
11-31. $R_A = 38.3$ lb; $R_B = 49.0$ lb
11-32. Vertical plane: 3.88 ft from A at 2.3 in.
   Horizontal plane: 8.75 ft from A at 2.4 in.
11-33. $R_A = 0.53$ lb; $R_B = 2.12$ lb

11-34. $R_A = R_B = 35.5$ lb
11-35. 2.74 oz in.; 10.9 in. to right of A
11-36. $R_A = 24.8$ lb; $R_B = 38$ lb
11-37. Tips
11-38. Slips; $a = 6.06$ ft per sec^2
11-39. (a) 13.8 ft per sec^2; (b) 12.2 ft per sec^2
11-40. 84.5 ft
11-41. 5.9°
11-42. 0.103
11-43. $T_A = T_B = 364$ lb
11-44. $T_A = 547$ lb; $T_B = 182$ lb
11-45. 54 ft per sec, slips
11-46. 152 lb
11-47. 58.9 lb ft
11-48. 727 lb ft; 50 rev
11-49. 49.2 rev
11-50. 13.4 rad per sec^2
11-51. 50 lb ft
11-52. 51.5 rev
11-53. 2293 lb ft
11-54. 25.1 lb
11-55. 126 rev
11-56. 813 rad
11-57. (a) 35.6 rad per sec CCW; (b) 21.4 rad per sec CCW; (c) 22 rad per sec
11-58. 4 lb ft CW
11-59. 6 lb ft CW; 12 lb ft CCW
11-60. 7.5 lb ft
11-61. 15 lb ft
11-62. 9.75 lb ft
11-63. 5.33 rad per sec^2
11-64. 9.47 lb ft
11-65. 8.26 ft per sec^2
11-66. 147 lb
11-67. 18.8 lb ft
11-68. 56.3 lb ft
11-69. 510 lb ft
11-70. $C = 60$ lb ft; $(T_1 - T_2) = 48$ lb; $(T_3 - T_2) = 24$ lb
11-71. $2l/3$; $3r/2$; $2r$
11-72. $O_x = 33.3$ lb $\rightarrow$; $O_y = 64.4$ lb $\uparrow$
11-73. $O_x = 66.7$ lb $\leftarrow$; $O_y = 64.4$ lb $\uparrow$
11-74. 0.259
11-75. 0.333
11-76. 18.9 rad per sec^2; 14.2 lb
11-77. 5.77 rad per sec^2; 127 lb
11-78. Disk: 7.34 ft per sec^2; Sphere: 7.87 ft per sec^2; Hoop: 5.51 ft per sec^2
11-79. $3r/2$

CHAPTER 12

12-1. 2000 ft lb

12-2. (a) 100 ft lb; (b) 86.6 ft lb; (c) −86.6 ft lb

12-3. (a) −50 ft lb; (b) −62.5 ft lb; (c) −62.5 ft lb

12-4. −144,000 ft lb

12-5. 76.8 ft lb

12-6. 761 ft lb

12-7. −932 ft lb

12-8. 400 ft lb

12-9. 70 ft lb

12-10. 600 lb in.

12-11. 214 ft lb

12-15. 25 lb per in.

12-16. 25 lb

12-17. 1 in.

12-18. 135 in. lb

12-19. 1080 in. lb

12-20. 720 in. lb

12-21. 1000 in. lb

12-22. 30 lb/in.; 0.667 in.

12-23. 9.42 ft lb

12-24. 1050 ft lb

12-26. 7540 ft lb

12-27. 43,000 ft lb; 387,000 ft lb; 1,076,000 ft lb

12-28. 3.28×10^6 ft lb

12-29. 688,000 ft lb

12-30. 718 ft per sec

12-31. 6240 ft lb

12-32. 33.1 ft per sec

12-33. 6.21 ft lb on earth and on moon

12-34. 0.2 ft

12-35. 23.3 ft per sec

12-36. 1.52 ft

12-37. 11.3 ft per sec

12-38. (a) 21.0 ft per sec; (b) 17.7 ft per sec; (c) block does not move

12-39. 805 ft lb in all four cases

12-40. 1150 ft per sec

12-41. 1150 ft per sec

12-42. (a) 789 ft lb; (b) 3160 ft lb; (c) 78,900 ft lb

12-43. 1750 ft lb

12-44. 20.9 rad per sec

12-45. 29.8 ft per sec

12-46. 3.11 rad per sec

12-47. 7.78 ft per sec

12-48. 15 ft per sec

12-49. 49.3 ft lb
12-50. 36.2 rad per sec
12-51. 48.6 rad per sec
12-52. 112 rad per sec
12-53. 92.8 rad per sec
12-54. 188 ft lb
12-55. 278 ft lb
12-56. 900 ft lb
12-57. 8.15 ft per sec
12-58. 43.2 lb
12-59. 3.22 ft
12-60. (a) 438 ft lb; (b) 219 ft lb; (c) 146 ft lb
12-61. 14.9 KW; 18.7 KW
12-62. 1070 hp
12-63. 77.8 gal per hr
12-64. 6.36×10^7 lb
12-65. 0.2 hp hr
12-66. 3.17

CHAPTER 13

13-1. (a) 20 lb sec; (b) 900 lb sec; (c) 3 lb sec; (d) 10 lb sec
13-2. (a) 6.25 ft per sec to right
    (b) 16.25 ft per sec to right
    (c) 21.25 ft per sec to right
13-3. (a) 41.25 ft per sec to right
    (b) 8.75 ft per sec to left
13-4. 359 mph
13-5. 15.8 lb
13-6. 970 lb
13-7. 56,400 mph
13-8. $V_x = -480$ ft per sec; $V_y = 200$ ft per sec
13-10. 4.67 lb sec
13-11. 19.3 ft per sec
13-12. 2520 lb ft sec
13-13. 4.2 min
13-14. 2.24 ft
13-15. 50 ft per sec to right
13-16. (a) 60 ft per sec to right
13-17. 32.5 ft per sec
13-18. 16.7 ft per sec
13-19. 11.7 ft per sec
13-20. 54.1 lb ft
13-21. 9.36 ft per sec
13-22. 3 ft per sec
13-23. 18.6 ft per sec

13-24. 13.4 ft
13-25. 8.57 ft per sec
13-26. 1.23 ft per sec
13-27. 8270 lb ft
13-28. 3.10 ft per sec
13-29. 46.6 ft per sec
13-30. 112 lb per in.
13-31. 3 rad per sec
13-32. 7.5 rad per sec
13-33. (a) 900 rpm; (b) 17,750 ft lb loss
13-34. 188 lb ft sec
13-35. 9.77 rad per sec
13-36. 29.6 rpm
13-38. (a) 20 ft per sec; (b) 2.72 ft lb
13-39. 0.8
13-40. 0.9 ft lb; Loss in deformation
13-41. 10.2 ft
13-42. 15.4 ft per sec; 28.6 ft per sec
13-43. 44,000 ft lb
13-44. $V_A = 6$ ft per sec to right; $V_B = 38$ ft per sec to right

CHAPTER 14

14-1. 0.00833 sec
14-2. (a) 200 cps; (b) 12,000 cpm; (c) 1256 rad per sec
14-3. 3700 ft per sec^2
14-4. 6.97 cps
14-5. 140 cps
14-6. 19.6 lb per ft
14-7. 1500 lb per in.; 188 cpm
14-8. 7.45 per cent
14-9. 7 cps
14-10. 7 cps
14-11. 2.26 sec
14-12. 0.596 ft per sec; 1.69 ft per sec^2
14-13. 13.1 ft
14-14. 44.2 cpm
14-15. 6.61 cps

INDEX